CURRENT TOPICS IN

DEVELOPMENTAL BIOLOGY

VOLUME 23

RECENT ADVANCES IN
MAMMALIAN DEVELOPMENT

CURRENT TOPICS IN
DEVELOPMENTAL BIOLOGY

EDITED BY

A. A. MOSCONA

CUMMINGS LIFE SCIENCE CENTER
THE UNIVERSITY OF CHICAGO
CHICAGO, ILLINOIS

ALBERTO MONROY

VOLUME 23

RECENT ADVANCES IN
MAMMALIAN DEVELOPMENT

VOLUME EDITORS

ANNE MCLAREN

MEDICAL RESEARCH COUNCIL (MRC)
MAMMALIAN DEVELOPMENT UNIT
WOLFSON HOUSE
UNIVERSITY COLLEGE LONDON
LONDON, ENGLAND

GREGORIO SIRACUSA

DIPARTIMENTO DI SANITÀ PUBBLICA
E BIOLOGIA CELLULARE
II UNIVERSITÀ DI ROMA
ROME, ITALY

ACADEMIC PRESS, INC.
Harcourt Brace Jovanovich, Publishers

San Diego   New York   Berkeley   Boston
London   Sydney   Tokyo   Toronto

ACADEMIC PRESS, INC.
1250 Sixth Avenue
San Diego, California 92101

United Kingdom Edition published by
ACADEMIC PRESS INC. (LONDON) LTD.
24-28 Oval Road, London NW1 7DX

LIBRARY OF CONGRESS CATALOG CARD NUMBER: 66-28604

ISBN 0-12-153123-6   (alk. paper)

PRINTED IN THE UNITED STATES OF AMERICA
87 88 89 90   9 8 7 6 5 4 3 2 1

THIS VOLUME OF *CURRENT TOPICS IN DEVELOPMENTAL BIOLOGY*
IS DEDICATED TO THE MEMORY OF
ALBERTO MONROY

ALBERTO MONROY
1913–1986

CONTENTS

CHAPTER 1.   Mammalian Development Futures, 1987
C. F. GRAHAM

CHAPTER 2.   Cytoskeletal Alterations and Nuclear Architectural Changes
during Mammalian Fertilization
GERALD SCHATTEN AND HEIDE SCHATTEN

CHAPTER 10. Immunological Aspects of Implantation and Fetal Survival: The Central Role of Trophoblast
W. D. BILLINGTON

CHAPTER 11. Homeo Box Genes in Murine Development
ALLEN A. FIENBERG, MANUEL F. UTSET,
LEONARD D. BOGARAD, CHARLES P. HART,
ALEXANDER AWGULEWITSCH,
ANNE FERGUSON-SMITH, ABRAHAM FAINSOD,
MARK RABIN, AND FRANK H. RUDDLE

ALBERTO MONROY

1913–1986

On the 24th of August 1986, in Woods Hole, in the evening of a weekend-day filled with work and meetings, Alberto Monroy suddenly passed away. A remarkable scientist's odyssey abruptly ended; a career that, for half a century, had enriched the science of life was stilled; an inspiring legacy endures.

Twenty years earlier in Woods Hole, on an August evening in 1966, he and I were examining with paternal pride the recently published, first volume of *Current Topics in Developmental Biology*. We had started this series because the then fledgling developmental–molecular biology needed a review platform for current research and concepts. Faced with the first volume, we thought again about the scientific and editorial responsibilities of our commitment, with expectations and apprehensions. Last year, some twenty volumes later, as we recalled that moment, Monroy felt confident that the series had served well the scientific community; the expectations had been met, the effort justified.

It was Monroy's initiative to devote the present volume to mammalian development and to invite Anne McLaren and Gregorio Siracusa to be its editors. The project was important to him; not only was the topic timely and concerned with a major, burgeoning area of developmental biology in which he has been keenly interested, but also this volume was to be a turning point in the evolution of the series. He was enthusiastically engaged in planning it when his life was stayed.

Much has been said and written about Monroy in the past few months. There will be official memoirs. My comments are personal: he was too close a friend for a dispassionate biographical account. That needs more distance in time and relationship.

Alberto Monroy was born on July 26, 1913, in Palermo, Italy. He received the M.D. degree in 1937 from the University of Palermo. Like other biologists of his generation, he studied medicine because he was interested in life sciences, in biological research. By going into an academic profession he broke a family tradition. Few outside his closest circle knew that he was born a Prince, a descendant of Hernan Cortez and of the Viceroy of Sicily. He was not concerned with superficialities of rank and pedigree; what mattered to him were solid accomplishments of lasting value. He stood out by his sincere informality, natural open-mindedness, enthusiasm for science, and eagerness to learn and share his knowledge. He earned his scientific nobility through hard work, unselfish dedication to the pursuit of excellence, and integrity of mind and heart.

His interest in embryology started when he went to work with Otto Mangold and continued when he joined the faculty at the University of Palermo as an assistant professor of anatomy. Soon after World War II, Monroy went to Naples to head the physiological laboratory of the Stazione Zoologica. At a time when classical embryology was losing touch with the mainstream of science, Monroy was among the few to use biochemical approaches in his studies on eggs and embryos. He chose to study the sea urchin and, together with John Runnstrom of Sweden and Albert Tyler of California, helped make it into the effective research system it has since become. Early on he realized the significance of the nascent discipline of molecular biology and embraced it with enthusiasm and characteristic drive. By combining this new science with his knowledge of embryology, he became one of the founders and leaders of developmental biology.

In 1952 he returned to Palermo as professor and head of the Institute of Comparative Anatomy. His laboratory attracted students, young investigators, and a stream of visiting scientists from around the world. It became a mainspring of research and ideas that influenced the course of developmental biology. His work and that of his colleagues focused on the biochemistry of egg maturation, fertilization, and early stages of embryonic development. Monroy had a superb talent for defining the essence of problems, translating ideas into critical tests of reality, and extracting general principles from seemingly modest facts. His book "Chemistry and Physiology of Fertilization" became a cornerstone in this field and a catalyst of research for generations of biologists.

In 1969 he was persuaded by the Italian National Research Council to move back to Naples to establish and direct the Laboratory of Molecular Embryology at Arco Felice. It too became a beehive of research, a magnet for scientists. It was not only Monroy's scientific activities, but also his ability to nurture generations of gifted co-workers and his delight in the achievements of others, that attracted universal respect. He was a rigorous, demanding teacher and an encouraging mentor—an inspiring listener as well as a superb lecturer. Far from being a "dry" scientist, his interests were panoramic; he was at home in literature and history, in music and art.

Monroy was a statesman of science, an ambassador of developmental biology, dedicated to serving the scientific community worldwide. He was a founder of laboratories, head of professional societies, convener of international congresses and symposia. His respect for knowledge had no national boundaries, no political bias, no class limitations. To him, prejudice, dogma, and pretense had no place in science or in human affairs. His wisdom and counsel were in constant demand around the world; he accepted these calls willingly, with a high sense of responsibility and with good cheer. He brought back home the latest ideas and advances in science, planted them in young minds, and saw them grow and flower. The renaissance of modern biology in postwar Italy and the eminence of developmental biology in modern science owe much to Alberto Monroy.

In 1976 Monroy became the director of the Stazione Zoologica, and his career came full cycle. There, some 30 years earlier, he and Anna Monroy-Oddo started the scientific journey that brought him back to head this great institution. The directorship was a labor of dedicated administrative service and leadership, but it was also a time of undiminished scientific activity and output. It was destiny met and mission fulfilled. In the grand halls of the Stazione, among the echoes of Dohrn, Roux, Driesch, Herbst, Boveri, Whitman, Morgan, and Wilson, Monroy's scholarly productivity and spectrum of interests surpassed even those of his earlier years. His legacy is a lasting mainstay in the Stazione's course and tradition.

But there was yet another special station in Monroy's life, with strong historical–scientific links to the one in Naples, though very different in content, rhythm, and scope—the Marine Biological Laboratory in Woods Hole on Cape Cod. There, he migrated every summer and immersed himself in a deluge of scientific activity. He lectured, taught courses, worked in the laboratory and in the library. In this round-the-clock great summerfest of science, among old and new colleagues, he felt supremely in his true element. There, his unique qualities as intellectual catalyst, innovator and synthesizer of ideas, and patron of young talent flowered richest and brightest. There, his international embassy of fellowship in science achieved its greatest fulfillment and acclaim. And there, as if preordained by some supreme logic, peacefully came the end.

Non est mortuus qui scientiam vivificavit.

A. A. Moscona

PREFACE

Alberto Monroy helped plan the present volume. His own special interest in fertilization and early development is well represented and leads naturally on to a consideration of cell lineage in general and the possible role of homeo box genes. The volume includes a closer look at some specific developmental topics: sex determination, the behavior of fetal germ cells, the development of muscle, and trophoblast as an example of an extraembryonic lineage. Chris Graham's conspectus sets the whole in the context of the spectacular rise of mammalian development over the past few decades and of the genetic and molecular developmental avenues that lead us invitingly into the future.

Anne McLaren
Gregorio Siracusa

CHAPTER 1

MAMMALIAN DEVELOPMENT FUTURES, 1987

C. F. Graham

CANCER RESEARCH CAMPAIGN
DEVELOPMENTAL TUMOURS RESEARCH GROUP
DEPARTMENT OF ZOOLOGY
UNIVERSITY OF OXFORD
OXFORD OX1 3PS, ENGLAND

I. Introduction

It is fun to review a particular year's worth of publications about mammalian development; the discoveries in the brief span of 1986 will soon be regarded as archaic, prosaic, prophetic, or classic. Each main section of this chapter ends with a section called "Future"; there are listed crystal ball visions about future progress. In the main, this chapter is concerned with novel techniques or techniques newly applied to mammalian development. Some of these procedures may become as widespread as paraffin embedding in future developmental biology laboratories. This emphasis on novelty and the promise of advance eliminates the discussion of many excellent papers which employ accepted procedures, and which have already increased the understanding of mammalian development. Much of this steady progress is described in other chapters in this volume.

A. SOCIETY'S DEMANDS

More than any other branch of developmental biology, mammalian embryology fits into the society where the work proceeds. This study has rarely been pursued for its own sake, and its progress is swayed and succored by society's demands for practical applications. The field responds with programs of research which would be quite foreign to those investigating the development of nematodes and fruit flies. The following list includes some of these programs (actual or potential).

1. Study of the metabolism of the preimplantation conceptus with the intention either of discovering features that can be blocked by contraception, or of monitoring the human conceptus' vigor in clinical

1

in vitro fertilization procedures to cure infertility. Examples are the study of products secreted by cultured human pre-embryos as a guide to implantation events (Cocchiara *et al.*, 1986), and the development of new methods for monitoring nutrient uptake of single mouse pre-embryos, in the hope that such a noninvasive technique can be used to discriminate between viable and unhealthy human pre-embryos before transfer back to a mother (Gardner and Leese, 1986). There is considerable progress in human *in vitro*-fertilization practice (see V. Bolton and P. Braude, Chapter 5, this volume).

2. Study of genetic and teratogen-induced animal abnormalities, with the aim of avoiding, curing, or alleviating the human version of the same. The frequency and origin of human chromosomal abnormalities is reviewed in Edwards (1986), and the possibility of obtaining minute biopsies of the human pre-embryo for the diagnosis of these abnormalities has been discussed (Penketh and McLaren, 1987). It is probable that very sensitive new methods for detecting known variant forms of genes (Saiki *et al.*, 1986) will be applied to such material if the biopsy procedure does not greatly reduce embryo viability.

3. Genetic manipulation of the genome either to create more productive farm animals or to cure permanently human genetic defects. As a step toward human gene therapy, the following gene defects in mice have either been permanently cured or partially alleviated: β-thalassemia (Costantini *et al.*, 1986), infertility due to lack of a complete gonadotrophin-releasing hormone gene (Mason *et al.*, 1986), and one form of dwarfism (Hammer *et al.*, 1984).

4. The cloning of particularly productive farm animals by nuclear transplantation. This has been achieved for the first time with sheep (Willadsen, 1986).

5. Introduction of genes into the hereditary material of farm animals to mass-produce rare biochemicals of therapeutic value. It would be helpful if such genes were abundantly expressed in the mammary glands of cows, for then the product might be extracted from dairy milk.

6. Study of regulated embryonic stem cell multiplication to shed light on the growth of human tumors. The mirror of this program is the understanding of human embryonic growth which may emerge from the study of human tumors. For instance, we are closer to finding the loci involved in the etiology of retinoblastoma and Wilms' tumor (reviewed by Nyhan, 1987; van Heyningen and Porteous, 1986). In both, normal loci appear to be lost or inactivated in growing tumors, which suggests that these normal loci are involved in the control of growth and differentiation during development.

These practical programs attract extensive research funds, but they also hobble mammalian embryologists as they scale the ivory tower: no general theoretical statements about the organization of developing systems have yet originated from mammalian embryology. Instead, mammalian embryologists have concentrated on analyzing developmental processes in the only vertebrates with a large number of described genes. They have defined the cell and molecular biology underlying events which are common to the development of many other animal phyla: these events include cell polarization (reviewed in Johnson and Maro, 1987), nuclear specialization (J. Aronson and D. Solter, Chapter 3, this volume), and lineage divergence (J. Rossant, Chapter 6, this volume).

B. DISSEMINATION OF TECHNIQUES

It is a remarkable year for quick access to techniques. The publications of *Manipulating the Mouse Embryo* (Hogan *et al.*, 1986), *Teratocarcinomas and Embryonic Stem Cells: A Practical Approach* (Robertson, 1987) and *Experimental Approaches to Mammalian Embryonic Development* (Rossant and Pedersen, 1987) for the first time bring together extensive lists of recipes and reviews for beginners. They partly supersede the more limited range which are fully discussed in *Methods in Mammalian Reproduction* (Daniels, 1978). Further, mammalian developmental techniques are now in the marketplace. Jaenisch and Mintz (1974) achieved somatic integration of SV40 DNA sequences after injection into the blastocyst, Gordon *et al.* (1980) obtained similar results after injection into pronuclei at the one-cell stage, and by 1986 these apparently subtle procedures are "made available to everyone," at a price (genetic engineering company advertisement in *Nature* **324,** 6097). The technique has also started to appear in regular gene-handling manuals (e.g., Davis *et al.,* 1986).

Fortunately, the natural curiosity of scientists about their embryological origins balances the blinkered immediacy of commercial and medical demands, and much recent research has increased or promises to increase our academic knowledge of mammalian development.

II. Cell Lineages

A. PREIMPLANTATION LINEAGE

1. Problems

Embryologists require an exact knowledge of a cell's ancestors and descendants; with a comprehensive description of a mammal's normal cell lineage in hand, they could next ask pertinent questions about the

control of cellular development. Some of the problems of defining preimplantation cell lineages stem from the bland form of the mammalian
conceptus: the cell lineages of eggs with early unequal cell divisions or
with color-coded ends can now be followed for long stretches of development, and the invariance of some invertebrate cell lineages has
speeded progress (see examples in Gardner and Lawrence, 1986). Most
mammalian eggs lack fixed and visually obvious features. The polar
bodies of the mouse egg either lyse or move about during preimplantation development, and they are not a reliable landmark.

The direct method for studying cell lineages is to observe cell divisions continuously through a microscope. This procedure is currently
limited to the first three cleavage divisions in the mouse, for as internal cells are formed at the next cleavage, so it becomes difficult to see
their membranes, even with Nomarksi optics.

2. Short-Term Labeling

As a substitute for direct observation, even more refined short-term
injected lineage markers are used (see J. Rossant, Chapter 6, this
volume). One such study measures the probability of a cell contributing descendants to the inside and outside parts of the pre-embryo (Pedersen *et al.*, 1986). It is found that the daughters of surface cells have
a progressively reduced chance of entering the interior as the blasto-
coel begins to form, while the inside cells seem to stay in place. This is
the best controlled lineage analysis to date, and the results give an
impression of a probabilistic cell lineage. The cell biology of this lineage divergence has been more fully studied than any similar event in
any other animal (see Johnson and Maro, 1987). It is interesting that it
has not been necessary to invent a set of managerial genes involved in
this lineage fork (see Sections III and IV). Rather, the lineage divergence is shown to depend on a host of cellular functions, such as cell
adhesion, cell flattening, cell polarization, the temporal order of cell
division, and the direction of mitosis.

3. Future

In the absence of persistent visible reference points in egg structure
and direct observations, many believe that the mammalian preimplantation lineage is indeed irregular. The future development of improved
image analysis techniques (e.g., Hochstrasser *et al.*, 1986), of confocal
microscopy (e.g., Brakenhoff *et al.*, 1985) and vital stains should solve
the technical problems; then both the internal cell membranes and the
controversy should be resolved. Impressed by the totipotency of blastomeres, it is often thought that the regularity or irregularity of the

lineage is of no consequence: cells can substitute for each other. However, if there are several ways of achieving development, then one will probably be better than another. Detection of the optimal route through the lineage may require study of both embryo viability and adult fitness.

As yet, there are no preliminary descriptions of the human preimplantation cell lineage. This indifference to human origins is bizarre: many societies still permit such studies, and "spare" human pre-embryos are available from clinical *in vitro* fertilization programs.

B. POSTIMPLANTATION LINEAGE

1. Problems

There is substantial progress in following the fate of labeled cells in short-term cultures of the postimplantation rodent embryo; the cells are either injected with label in place, or they are labeled in culture, and then grafted into the conceptus (e.g., Copp *et al.*, 1986; Lawson *et al.*, 1986; Tan and Morriss-Kay, 1986). Despite these short-term successes, it is still of paramount importance to develop new techniques, so that cell behavior can be continuously recorded and the progeny of marked cells followed from the postimplantation conceptus into the mature cell types of particular organs. These techniques will overcome the inherent difficulty of studying cell lineages in organisms developing in an opaque reproductive tract.

2. Short-Term Filming

The direct and arduous method of filming development can now provide detailed information about local cell behavior. Thus, the individual migrations of mesoderm cells away from the mouse primitive streak have been recorded for the first time, providing a moving image of the origin of internal mammalian body structure (Nakatsuji *et al.*, 1986). The technique is currently limited to a 5-hour recording session, for the embryo is held compressed in a drop of culture medium, and it begins to degenerate visibly after 12 hours in this restricted environment. A vast array of cellular events must now be filmed with similar systems. Information from such studies are a necessary complement to the knowledge about the probability of lineage divergence, which is beginning to emerge from DNA lineage marking.

3. Long-Term DNA Markers

Splattering the postimplantation lineage with marked DNA is the vogue procedure for following cell lineages through to complete organs.

The DNA may either be injected into pronuclei, or introduced by viral infection. The markers may be the restriction enzyme length variation around the integration site of the foreign DNA, or enzyme activities which can be detected in histological sections. The principal advantages are that the cells are marked in the intact conceptus, and that the markers are probably stable. The main disadvantages are that there may be damage during marking, and the moment of DNA integration is uncertain, so that the embryological stage of clone marking is unknown. Further, with virus-mediated marking it is not possible to choose the cell which is marked, and it is not known whether integration and expression can occur with equal probability in all cell types.

Some of these difficulties can be illustrated by a pair of studies (Soriano and Jaenisch, 1986; Wilkie et al., 1986). In both, DNA is introduced into the preimplantation mouse conceptus, and the markers are observed in extracts of the placenta and embryo shortly before birth. This is a relatively good test of the techniques, because it is generally assumed that these two lineages do not diverge until some time after the four-cell stage. When DNA is injected into a pronucleus at the one-cell stage, then the embryo and placenta often share common integration sites (9 of 12 cases), and rarely display different integration sites (3 of 12 cases; see Wilkie et al., 1986). When integration sites differ between the lineages, then integration must have occurred after lineage divergence, and at least beyond the S phase of the one-cell stage. Once the conceptus is a mosaic of integration sites, then there is a possibility that cell selection will influence the contribution of marked clones.

The cell-lineage interpretation of such integration mosaics is easiest when the time of marking is varied; if two lineages share progressively fewer integration sites as the stage of marking is advanced, then the lineages must be diverging. Thus the embryo and placenta share common integration sites at a lower frequency when DNA is injected into one nucleus of the two-cell stage (4 of 7 cases; Wilkie et al., 1986), and share even fewer integration sites when four- to eight-cell stages are infected with retroviruses (only 3 of 52 common integration sites observed in 19 conceptuses; see Soriano and Jaenisch, 1986); the frequency of joint lineage marking decreases as the stage of DNA introduction progresses. There is no directly comparable information from short-term injection labeling experiments (Section II,B,1), because the inner cells of the preimplantation mouse form both the embryo and the extraembryonic membranes, and these membranes were not tested for DNA integration in these experiments. However, it is a good guess that integration regularly occurs up to three cell cycles after DNA introduction.

4. Visible Markers of Expressed DNA

The postimplantation stages of mammalian development are obscured by the reproductive tract, and it is a great advance to be able to mark cells in the conceptus at various stages of development. Thus mammalian organogenesis is now open to lineage analysis while the conceptus continues to develop in the uterus. The high French art of lineage splattering is reached with the use of DNA which catalyzes cell coloring; marked cells are painted blue in location (Sanes *et al.*, 1986). Using a replication-defective recombinant retrovirus, bearing the bacterial *lacZ* gene, it is possible to infect the postimplantation conceptus at different stages, and then to detect the progeny of marked cells by staining sections to reveal β-galactosidase activity. In these experiments, there is no independent evidence that a marked group of cells is the product of a single integration event. However, when the marked groups are widely dispersed, then it is likely that each group stems from a single integration event in one cell. Multiple integration events would be detected if the palette of retroviruses could be extended (multicolor lineage painting).

By infecting the postimplantation lineages at different times, it has already been shown that there is coherent clonal growth in the mesoderm of the extraembryonic visceral yolk sac between 7 and 13 days of development. Further, there is preliminary evidence for lineage divergence among these mesoderm cells between day 7 and day 9. This clonal coherence in the mesoderm layer of the visceral yolk sac is mirrored by coherent clonal growth in the endoderm layer of the same organ (injection chimeras). However, clone dispersal is well established in the parietal endoderm, and it is predicted that the embryo precursor cells will also be found to intermix promiscuously (cell injection chimeras, reviewed by Gardner, 1986).

The mosaics produced by DNA introduction can be used to estimate the number of embryo founder cells and the degree of intermingling of their progeny. The calculation of the number of founder cells is confounded both by uncertainty about the time of DNA integration and by the possibility that DNA integration affects the growth of the marked clones (see J. Rossant, Chapter 6, this volume; Rossant, 1986).

The intermingling between the progeny of the embryo founder cells can be studied by measuring mosaicism for different proviral integration sites in different organs. All the studied organs of one mouse contain similar concentrations of each provirus, just as mosaics from pronuclear injections display an even spread of the integrated gene across the body (Wilkie *et al.*, 1986). These observations suggest that the progeny of clones emanating from the embryo founder cells are subsequently blended to an evenly dispersed mix before cells contribute to a particular organ. The alternative view is that around eight precursors grow out as regular files, as if squeezed from a striped-toothpaste tube. If each organ originates from a cross section of all the files, then all the clones would be represented, in the same way that each toothbrush obtains a complete sample of the stripes, which are mixed together as the teeth are brushed (R. L. Gardner, personal communication).

5. *Future*

Clearly, it is next essential to mark the embryo founder cells with DNA markers which can be visualized in the sectioned conceptus, and then to observe the behavior of their descendants over the short term. It is still possible that the postimplantation embryonic cell lineage contains much coherent clonal growth in the medium term, and that the apparent blending indicates that morphogenesis regularly involves the intimate interleaving of different cell types with separate origins: standard histology suggests that this is the case, and circulating blood will certainly smooth out any clonal heterogeneity in organ samples. This cautious view is sustained by the observation that in the one case when a single cell type is assayed from mosaic animals, then the frequency of mosaicism in this cell type (sperm) often diverges from that of homogenized organs (Wilkie *et al.,* 1986).

Thus, many of the tools for describing the cell lineage in the intact conceptus are available. When the information is in, then previous studies on the pattern of colonization of injected cells will become more important. For the first time it will be possible to relate cell behavior on transplantation to normal lineage divergence: cell behavior may alter either before or after a lineage split. If new cell behavior precedes a fork in the lineage, then all sorts of manipulations might be imposed on transplanted cells to change their colonization behavior and eventual fate. One example of this tactic does not work: inner cell mass cells and embryonal carcinoma (EC) cells, when treated with retinoic acid before transplantation to host blastocysts, did not change their pattern of colonization (Waters and Rossant, 1986): perhaps they quickly cease division, so that their contribution to the conceptus cannot be detected. This important approach should be extended, with further types of treatment before transplantation.

III. Developmental Genetics

Developmental genetics is only one branch of developmental biology, but its concerns are increasingly central to the whole enterprise. The implicit goals of animal developmental genetics are to elucidate the principles of genetic control that operate in particular animal systems and to establish the elements of universality in genetic control between different systems. Much of the agenda of molecular biology is also devoted to these programmatic goals, but the approach is very different. Eukaryotic molecular biologists tend to focus on the molecular machinery that physically controls gene expression. Geneticists, on the other hand, are more concerned with the regulatory logic that governs the process. (Wilkins, 1986)

A. PROBLEMS

Mammalian embryologists would like to know the logic of gene interactions during the flow of developmental sequences. Many believe that there is a hierarchy of genetic regulation, with a few managerial genes acting to control lineage divergence and to oversee the gene expression which is characteristic of particular cell types. Such managerial genes are often believed to act directly on the cis-regulatory elements around subservient genes, and the latter are thought to realize the decisions of the managers. Such hierarchical theories have the virtue of restricting the number of genes which are thought to be important in development and which require study. A contrary view is that many genes act in concert, and that a balance of their activity leads to decisive developmental events; this is a theory of a workers' cooperative of genes, and they could interact at the level of multiple cis-regulatory elements near a gene or by the collaboration of their protein products in composing the phenotype of cells. Others wish to view development as a sequence of gene expression, with the expression of each gene dependent on the activity of its predecessor. These and other views are discussed in Wilkins (1986).

The principles of genetic developmental regulation will emerge when mammalian genetic control can be described in greater detail. Many of the advances in fruit fly and nematode embryology stem directly from the ability to identify nearly all the genes which regulate the organization of early development (e.g., Anderson and Nusslein-Volhard, 1984; Nusslein-Volhard and Weischaus, 1980; Isenghi *et al.,* 1983).

Mammalian developmental genetics seeks to emulate these achievements, but it is handicapped by a vast genome and a diploid karyotype. Further, developmental mutations are rarely discovered by direct observation, but rather show up as increased embryonic death. Nobody has yet succeeded in deliberately selecting a developmental mutation. Recent progress suggests that many of these difficulties can be overcome, and that it will be possible to saturate the genome with mutations which act on the early events of development.

The mouse remains the paramount genetic mammal: it has about

1160 named genes, and 903 of these have been assigned to particular chromosomes (Peters, 1986). Such numbers still fall far short of fulfilling the need to give a complete description of the gene expression which is directly involved in the major events of development. In the absence of the short life cycles of fruit flies and nematodes, a battery of new ideas and techniques must be deployed to gain this information in a reasonable time.

B. ANALYSIS OF LARGE GENOMES

The extent and complexity of the mammalian genome makes it difficult to find genes. One procedure is to litter the mouse genome with retroviral integration sites, and fill in the gaps between recognized loci with novel signs; retroviral litter marking is an inevitable by-product of insertional mutagenesis (see Section III,D). The filling in of the genetic map can be made more selective by cloning dissected parts of chromosomes (recently exploited by Herrmann *et al.*, 1986), or by isolating parts of chromosomes in cells of another species and then identifying the expressed products or functions of the fragment (chromosome-mediated gene transfer, e.g., van Heyningen and Porteous, 1986). These techniques allow a closer approach to loci of interest, and there are new methods for efficiently ordering overlapping cosmid clones (Coulson *et al.*, 1986), and for quickly jumping along contiguous stretches of the genome (discussed by Poustka and Lehrach, 1986; Little, 1986). The remaining need is for cloning methods that include very long stretches of DNA within a single construct.

It is also probable that the massive task of isolating the human genome in overlapping cosmid clones will soon begin. The case for such a directory of the human genome has been well made (Scriver, 1985). If this resource of ordered cosmids does become available, then the genetic material of humans will be more accessible than that of any other mammal, and the case for studying human developmental genetics is apparent.

C. ONE SET OF GENES

Yeast and cellular slime molds are superb genetic organisms, partly because they contain only one copy of each gene for most of their life cycle. The X chromosome of male mammals presents a similar opportunity to observe and select mutants quickly. These genetic advantages lead to persistent attempts to expose the action of every mammalian gene, by constructing haploid mammals or by developing haploid embryonic stem (ES) cells. The enemies of promise are the developmental need for a pair of pronuclei from heterosexual gametes, and the tendency of haploid mouse nuclei to double the chromosome set. These two problems are clear from recent work.

There is increasing evidence that the sexual origin of chromosomes regulates their performance during early mouse development (most recently, Surani *et al.*, 1986; see J. Aronson and D. Solter, Chapter 3, this volume). The impress of their parental origin is heritable: haploid nuclei retain a memory of their origins through three cleavage divisions in cytoplasm activated by fertilization, and normal development only occurs if they are complemented by a haploid pronucleus derived from a parent of the opposite sex. Pronuclear unisex limits mouse development to the first 10 days: all-egg origins lead to 25-somite embryos with diminutive extraembryonic membranes, while all-sperm origins lead to retarded 6- to 8-somite embryos with disproportionately large membranes. Consequently, it currently seems that the haploid conceptus can only be used as an expression vector for new mutations during the early part of development.

Although a unisexual origin disrupts development in the uterus, it does not impede the development of mature cell types which usually appear later in embryogenesis. These cell types are observed when the cells are carried through development in association with normal embryos, and when the cells differentiate in extrauterine sites. Thus, a number of developmental events could be studied with this material.

The problem of the instability of haploid cells in culture is nearing solution. By careful nursing, it is now possible to grow cells from haploid blastocysts, and these cultures retain a high proportion of haploid mitotic cells for at least 3 days (Schnebelen and Kaufman, 1986). This is a marked improvement in maintaining haploidy, and it is now necessary to develop permanent cell lines with stable haploid karyotypes.

D. MUTATION AND SELECTION

1. Insertional Mutagenesis

The advantage of causing developmental mutations with marked DNA is that the marker guides the search for the altered gene. Insertional mutagenesis in transgenic mice has already been very productive: the role of the $\alpha 1(I)$ collagen gene has been defined in mouse development (most recently, Kratochwil *et al.*, 1986), and a limb deformity locus has been isolated (Woychik *et al.*, 1985). The technique is only limited by the probability of disrupting interesting genes, and by the necessity to breed homozygotes and reveal recessive mutations.

Ideally one would wish to mutate haploid multipotential cell lines which can recapitulate most of the events of development in cell cul-

ture: then any visible disruption of development could be conveniently
scored after insertional mutagenesis. The closest approach to this ideal
are the diploid ES cells, grown out from normal mouse blastocysts. It is
encouraging that these cells have passed the test of forming germ cells
in chimeras, after the introduction in culture of retroviral vectors bearing selectable markers (Robertson *et al.*, 1986; Gossler *et al.*, 1986).
Male diploid ES cells could immediately be used to select mutants on
the X chromosome which alter their limited differentiation in culture.

2. Selecting Developmental Mutants

Haploid ES cells could provide the material for observing and selecting developmental mutations across the genome. ES cells form extraembryonic endoderm-like cells as a rind around developing cultured
aggregates, and mutations blocking this process could be picked by
observation. It might also be possible to select mutations which lead to
the overproduction of this endoderm. In the conceptus, this endoderm
layer sustains the growth and the survival of the embryo precursor
cells (Gardner, 1985). If the same support is provided by the equivalent
layer in cultured aggregates, then it is a good guess that this is partly
achieved by the synthesis of transferrin and lipoproteins by this layer
(e.g., Meehan *et al.*, 1984; Shi and Heath, 1984). If these components
were omitted from serum-free culture medium, it should be possible to
select for endoderm overproducers. If this dream of haploid ES cell
genetics is realized, then it will be possible to describe the organization
of the genes controlling one early event in mammalian development. A
detailed study of at least one system would discriminate among a
horde of hypotheses.

3. Revealing Tissue-Specific Promoters

There are various strategies for detecting tissue-specific promoters,
and all involve intricate genetic manipulation (see Section IV). Recent
studies with totipotent plant cell cultures suggest a shortcut (Teeri *et
al.*, 1986), which might be used with ES cells. Undifferentiated plant
cells are treated with a transposition fusion vector containing an un-
transcribed kanamycin resistance gene: when the DNA integrates
downstream of a promoter, then the drug resistance is expressed. Resistance is only weakly expressed in the undifferentiated cells, but this
low-level expression allows the selection of transformants. When the
independent transformants are regenerated into plants, then the enzyme responsible for resistance has abundant activity in different combinations of the leaf, root, and stem: the pattern of abundance varies
from one transformant to another. If enzyme abundance reflects close

proximity to tissue-specific promoters, then this might be a method for quickly isolating a range of such promoters, and the method could be applied to diploid ES cells. It would be a particularly powerful approach if the vector also carried an enzyme activity which could be revealed by color in fixed material, after its expression had been elevated by an endogenous promoter. The limitations of using this technique for finding tissue-specific promoters are the disruption of essential genes by insertional mutagenesis, and the long-distance action of some promoters.

E. ANALOGY GENETICS AND HOMEOBOXES

Mammalian embryologists often hope to borrow gene sequences from those studying nematode and fruit fly development, and then to use these sequences to discover analogous genes in mammals. Sequence begging has been rife in the hunt for genes which control the body plan of mammals (see A. A. Fienberg *et al.*, Chapter 11, this volume).

It is hard to guess if analogy genetics will ever be a quick method for studying mammalian development. Mammalian genes with homeoboxes are fascinating because their pattern of expression fits no theory of morphogenesis: they have a tendency to express in limited regions of the hindbrain and the spinal cord, in the kidney, and in the testis. The interpretation of transcript distribution awaits further knowledge of the developmental events which coincide with the abundance of transcripts containing homeoboxes; currently there is no direct evidence for regarding these genes as managers of mammalian morphogenesis.

Nor is there a simple way of discovering if partial sequence conservation is ever likely to be a good guide to similar developmental function. Many genes seem to be cobbled together from bits and pieces borrowed from other genes: the functions of the low-density lipoprotein (LDL) receptor would not be confused with those of the epidermal growth factor precursor, and yet parts of both genes share a common genomic organization and express similar amino acid sequences (Sudhof *et al.*, 1985).

F. FUTURE

It would be fascinating to conduct a full mutational analysis of the cis-regulatory sequences around any single gene which begins to be abundantly expressed as ES cells differentiate in culture. It is possible to target mutations into chromosomal genes at increasing frequency (Thomas *et al.*, 1986), but more cis-regulatory elements will probably be discovered by the extensive selection of mutants from haploid cells. Detection of the site of mutation might be speeded by further developing methods for detecting sequence changes (Saiki *et al.*, 1986).

It would also be advantageous to increase the range of "frozen states" of development which are represented in permanent cell lines. A greater variety of these states may be propagated in the future, either by infecting cultures of early embryos and embryonal carcinoma cells with "immortalizing" viral fragments (Evrard *et al.*, 1986; Kellermann and Kelly, 1986), or by starting with embryos containing overexpressed *c-myc*; the latter embryos develop tumors in a variety of sites (e.g., Leder *et al.*, 1986). Additional "frozen states" of development will allow further study of the genetics of development by induced mutation, and these cell lines should bridge the gap between the stage of development represented by ES cells and that represented by committed cell lines, such as erythroleukemia cells and myoblasts.

The bias of this section on developmental genetics is toward reducing the complexity of mammalian development to single events, and then studying those events in great detail. There is also an emphasis on culture systems where development can be readily observed, and mutants selected. One reason for preferring culture systems is that society will probably allow the study of human ES cells in culture. Then it will be possible to marry together the predicted resource of overlapping cosmid libraries of the human genome with a genetic analysis of early human development.

There is slow progress in deriving a multipotential human stem cell which would be suitable for such a study. No ES cells have been derived from the human blastocyst, and chromosomally abnormal teratoma cells have been used as a poor substitute. One undifferentiated cell line from human teratoma will differentiate into cells with the characteristics of trophoblast, but this line fails to form any other identified cell type (Izhar *et al.*, 1986). Other undifferentiated cell lines fail to form cells with the features of trophoblast or secondary yolk sac endoderm, and their only routine differentiation is into neurons and a wide variety of other different cell morphologies (recently, Andrews *et al.*, 1986; Lee and Andrews, 1986; Webb *et al.*, 1986). This limited differentiation restricts their use as guides to early human development, and human ES cells are required for this purpose.

Multipotential cell lines can never substitute for the study of the conceptus: they simply provide a tool for identifying and isolating interesting genes. The action of these genes in embryogenesis must finally be followed in the complete conceptus.

IV. Gene Expression

A. PROBLEMS

Another method for studying the management of gene expression in development is to analyze the molecular machinery of transcription in stem cells and their differentiated derivatives. Work is concentrated on those genes which are expressed in particular organs at distinct periods of development. In early developing systems, such tissue-specific gene expression is often confined to small cell populations, and new methods for making cDNA libraries from rare cells have had to be developed (McConnell and Watson, 1986). However, the supply of early embryonic tissue is likely to be rate-limiting because female mammals produce relatively few eggs.

Currently it is assumed that mRNA abundance is primarily controlled by the rate of transcription, and two methods are widely used in the analysis of tissue-specific gene expression in early mammalian developrrent. The complexity of cis-regulatory elements around structural genes is assayed by introducing manipulated genes into mouse zygotes, while mouse EC stem cells are used as a bulk source of the trans-acting factors which may address these regulatory elements.

It is not known whether most mammalian genes are regulated by a variety of cis elements. The cis-regulatory elements around and in the SV40 early genes and the yeast HO mating-type switching locus are impressively complicated, and there is certainly a variety of trans-acting factors which bind to these elements in the SV40 genome (reviewed by McKnight and Tjian, 1986; Nasmyth, 1985a,b). In the case of SV40, it seems that the trans-acting factors must both bind and line up with each other, for the extent of transcription depends on the number of DNA-helix half-turns between the cis-regulatory sequences and the site of transcription initiation (Takahashi et al., 1986). Further, there appears to be regular repeating structural complementarity between the trans-acting factors and the DNA within a cis-regulatory sequence; this is best defined in the interaction between transcription factor IIIA and the Xenopus 5 S genes (Rhodes and Klug, 1986). This newly discovered interplay between the geometry and sequence requirements of transcription makes it particularly difficult to interpret the results of gross deletions around and in cis-regulatory elements.

The genomes of both animal viruses and yeast must regulate their expression in a single cytoplasm, and it is inevitable that precision is achieved by reacting differentially with the variety of trans-acting factors in their environment. Multicellularity and the sophistication of mammalian differentiation might reduce the number of cis-acting elements required around a gene: if a gene is only expressed in one cell type, then it need only respond to one trans-acting factor which is peculiar to that cell type. Thus the complexity of cis-regulatory elements might be replaced by the complexity of development, which includes the diversification of trans-acting factors in different cell types. Unfortunately, many mammalian genes are expressed both at different times in development and in a variety of cell types. Such genes are likely to have long and diverse cis-regulatory sequences. The variety of these elements and the number of different trans-acting factors need not be great: if all such factors could interact in any combination with any gene, then 10 complementary factor–element pairs would be sufficient to pick out the individual expression of any mammalian gene (Voss *et al.*, 1986). Of course, the problem of orchestrating the differential expression of genes within a single cell nucleus would still persist with this limited number of trans-factor/cis-element complementary pairs.

Recent information suggests that it is simplistic to think only about complementary pairs of interactions between trans factors and cis elements. Different steroid hormone-binding proteins interact with overlapping regions of the same 5′-DNA sequences, and these proteins probably bind to the DNA with fingerlike projections (von der Ahe *et al.*, 1985; Krust *et al.*, 1986; Green and Chambon, 1987). Thus, one single cis-regulatory sequence may be addressed in slightly different ways by several trans factors; if this method of interacting with cis-regulatory sequences is a general method for controlling transcription in mammals, then there will be extensive diversity of trans-acting factors and a relative uniformity in the cis-regulatory sequences.

B. cis SEQUENCES IN TRANSGENIC MICE

The complexity of cis-regulatory elements can be assessed by injecting manipulated genes into the pronuclei of one-cell mouse eggs, and then studying the sequence requirements for tissue-specific expression of the integrated gene (reviewed by Palmiter and Brinster, 1986). The procedure has been very successful in identifying short sequences which are necessary and sufficient for expression in a single cell type: a 133-base pair sequence 5′ to the elastase-I gene confers appropriate pancreatic expression on both this gene and other genes attached to this sequence (Ornitz *et al.*, 1985).

The most fascinating studies follow the expression of genes with more complicated patterns of expression in development. In general, these studies show that the cis-regulatory elements are contained in much longer stretches of DNA. There are several transgenic experiments which illustrate the diversity of cis elements.

1. β-Globin Gene Family

When introduced into mice, human γ^A-globin genes are only expressed in the yolk sac erythrocytes, while human β-globin genes are expressed as liver hemopoiesis begins in the transgenic mice, and they continue to be transcribed in adult blood (Magram et al., 1985; Chada et al., 1986; Kollias et al., 1986). These distinct times and places of expression must be regulated by different cis-regulatory elements, for when the 5' end of the γ^A-globin gene is attached to the 3' end of the β-globin gene, then the introduced hybrid is expressed in the yolk sac, but also maintains its expression in adult erythrocytes (Kollias et al., 1986). It appears that the γ^A-globin half-gene and its 5'-, 1300-bp flanking sequence contain the address for transcription in the yolk sac, while the β-globin half-gene and its 2500 3'-flanking sequences maintain the expression of the hybrid gene in adult erythrocytes. The normal regulated expression of each gene must depend on at least two cis elements with different functions.

2. α-Fetoprotein Gene

The α-fetoprotein gene, like many other genes that code for serum proteins, is transcribed in a variety of cell types during mouse and human development (discussed in Hopkins et al., 1986). Mouse α-fetoprotein gene transcripts are abundant in the yolk sac, the fetal liver, and the fetal gut, but they are also found in the brain, the kidney, and the heart. The tissue-specific expression of a mouse α-fetoprotein minigene has been assayed after 5' deletions and introduction into mouse eggs. Deletions over a region up to 5000 bp 5' to the mRNA cap site alter the relative abundance of the introduced gene transcripts in the yolk sac, liver, and gut (Krumlauf et al., 1985; Hammer et al., 1987), and it is likely that each organ addresses different parts of the 5'-flanking sequence.

More detailed information about the complexity of 5' cis-regulatory elements emerges from the performance of mouse and rat α-fetoprotein genes, after their introduction into cultured cells (Godbout et al., 1986; Muglia and Rothman-Denes, 1986; Widen and Papaconstantinou, 1986).

These studies with cultured cells suggest that at least three kinds of 5' cis-regulatory elements are involved in the tissue-specific expression of the α-fetoprotein gene; these are distant enhancers, distant inhibitors, and close promoters. It is now necessary to discover if all these effects operate in transgenic mice.

3. Aberrant Expression

An introduced gene can express in unusual tissues, presumably because its activity is regulated by its chromosomal environment. However, if a particular gene consistently behaves in this way in transgenic mice, then it is likely that it does not contain the requisite number of cis-regulatory elements. For instance, when gonadotrophin-releasing hormone genes are introduced into mice that lack a normal version of this gene, then the introduced genes are expressed both in the distinct set of neurons that usually express the endogenous gene, and in additional new sites, such as an extra set of neurons and the liver. Such observations provide additional evidence for multiple regulatory elements.

C. trans-ACTING FACTORS

Any cell line which represents a frozen stage of development can provide a bulk source of trans-acting factors. The credentials of mouse EC cells and mouse ES cells are particularly impressive, because both can "thaw" and reveal their multipotentiality either in cell culture or in chimeras.

The major problem in identifying and isolating relevant trans-acting factors is to design protein–DNA binding assays which pick out those interactions which can account for the tissue specificity of gene expression. It is essential to have a source of DNA templates that are differentially expressed in the EC cells and their differentiated derivatives, and it is particularly helpful when mutants can be selected which alter this pattern of expression: these can be used to identify relevant DNA–protein interactions. One powerful method for obtaining mutant DNA templates is to select viruses which can replicate and express in inappropriate cells. Thus a subset of viruses that grow in differentiated mouse cell lines are unable to replicate and express in EC cells, but they are able to initiate these functions after these stem cells have differentiated. This subset of viruses behaves in the same way in the intact mouse conceptus. It is possible to select and grow up rare variants of polyoma, SV40, and M-Mulv viruses which can express in the undifferentiated cells, and these mutants may provide discriminatory DNA sequences in assays of trans-factor binding (recently reviewed by Sleigh, 1985; recent papers by Gorman et al., 1985; Barklis et al., 1986).

Undifferentiated cell lines from human teratomas are also nonpermissive for the replication of some viruses. Human cytomegalovirus will not grow in the undifferentiated cells, but it replicates and expresses in the differentiated progeny produced by retinoic acid treatment (Gonczol *et al.*, 1984; Andrews *et al.*, 1986). This opens up the possibility of selecting mutants of tissue-specific viral expression in these multipotential human cells.

The availability of mutant DNA templates now allows a detailed analysis of trans-acting factor function in undifferentiated teratoma cells and their differentiated derivatives. This powerful approach only awaits fulfillment in the biochemical purification of the factors which both bind differentially to the wild-type and mutant templates and which are present in different amounts in the undifferentiated and the differentiated cells.

D. FUTURE

The predicted advances in developmental genetics (Section III) and the knowledge of gene expression control (Section IV) should provide a whole set of reagents for describing gene and protein expression in the intact conceptus. It will also be possible to test detailed hypotheses about embryo development by introducing tailored genes both into the one-cell egg and into various stages of the pre- and postimplantation lineage using viral vectors (Section II). These tools will allow mammalian embryology to become as sophisticated as the study of fruit fly and nematode development. The cell lineages of early mouse development (Section II) already suggest that it will be a different kind of embryology, and that its study will provide the paradigm developmental analysis of animals with both a "regulative" embryology and a well-defined genome. The continuing difficulties of operating on the postimplantation mammalian embryo emphasize the need to supplement mammalian work with studies in other vertebrates, such as amphibians, birds, and fish.

ACKNOWLEDGMENTS

The following persons kindly assisted in writing this review: R. Beddington, R. L. Gardner, B. L. M. Hogan, S. Kearsey, A. McLaren, P. Schofield, and V. Tate. The author's work is supported by the Cancer Research Campaign.

The review is dedicated to Alberto Monroy, whose enthusiasm for all parts of developmental biology sustained many young embryologists.

REFERENCES

Anderson, K., and Nusslein-Volhard, C. (1984). *Nature (London)* **311**, 223–227.
Andrews, P. W., Gonczol, E., Plotkin, S. A., Dignuzio, M., and Oosterhuis, J. W. (1986). *Differentiation* **31**, 119–126.
Barklis, E., Mulligan, R. C., and Jaenisch, R. (1986). *Cell* **47**, 391–399.

Brakenhoff, G. J., van der Voort, H. T. M., van Spronsen, E. A., Linnemans, W. A. M., and Nanninga, N. (1985). *Nature (London)* **317,** 748–749.

Chada, K., Magram, J., and Costantini, F. (1986). *Nature (London)* **319,** 685–689.

Cocchiara, R., Trapani, G., Azzolina, A., Albeggiani, G., and Geraci, D. (1986). *Hum. Reprod.* **1,** 445–447.

Copp, A. J., Roberts, H. M., and Polani, P. E. (1986). *J. Embryol. Exp. Morphol.* **95,** 95–115.

Costantini, F., Chada, K., and Magram, J. (1986). *Science* **233,** 1192–1194.

Coulson, A., Sulston, J., Brenner, S., and Karn, J. (1986). *Proc. Natl. Acad. Sci. U.S.A.* **83,** 7821–7825.

Daniels, J. C., ed. (1978). "Methods in Mammalian Reproduction." Academic Press, New York.

Davis, L. G., Dibner, L. G., and Battey, J. F. (1986). "Basic Methods in Molecular Biology." Elsevier, Amsterdam.

Edwards, R. G. (1986). *Hum. Reprod.* **1,** 185–198.

Evrard, C., Galiana, E., and Rouget, P. (1986). *EMBO J.* **5,** 3157–3162.

Gardner, D. K., and Leese, H. J. (1986). *Hum. Reprod.* **1,** 25–27.

Gardner, R. L. (1985). *J. Embryol. Exp. Morphol.* **88,** 303–326.

Gardner, R. L. (1986). *J. Cell Sci. (Suppl.)* **4,** 337–356.

Gardner, R. L., and Lawrence, P. A., eds. (1986). "Single Cell Marking and Cell Lineage in Animal Development." *Philos. Trans. R. Soc. London Ser. B* **312,** 3–187.

Godbout, R., Ingram, R., and Tilghman, S. M. (1986). *Mol. Cell. Biol.* **6,** 477–487.

Gonczol, E., Andrews, P. W., and Plotkin, S. A. (1984). *Science* **224,** 159–161.

Gordon, J. W., Scangos, G. A., Plotkin, D. J., Barbosa, J. A., and Ruddle, F. H. (1980). *Proc. Natl. Acad. Sci. U.S.A.* **77,** 7380–7384.

Gorman, C. M., Rigby, P. W. J., and Lane, D. P. (1985). *Cell* **42,** 519–526.

Gossler, A., Doetschman, T., Korn, R., Serfling, E., and Kemler, R. (1986). *Proc. Natl. Acad. Sci. U.S.A.* **83,** 9065–9069.

Green, S., and Chambon, P. (1987). *Nature (London)* **325,** 75–78.

Grosschedl, R., Weaver, D., Baltimore, D., and Costantini, F. (1984). *Cell* **38,** 647–658.

Hammer, R. E., Palmiter, R. D., and Brinster, R. L. (1984). *Nature (London)* **311,** 65–67.

Hammer, R. E., Krumlauf, R., Camper, S. A., Brinster, R. L., and Tilghman, S. M. (1987). *Science* **235,** 53–58.

Herrmann, B., Bucan, M., Mains, P. E., Frischauf, A.-M., Silver, L. M., and Lehrach, H. (1986). *Cell* **44,** 469–476.

Hochstrasser, M., Mathog, D., Gruenbaum, Y., Saumweber, H., and Sedat, J. W. (1986). *J. Cell Biol.* **102,** 112–123.

Hogan, B., Costantini, F., and Lacy, E. (1986). "Manipulating the Mouse Embryo: A Laboratory Manual." Cold Spring Harbor Laboratory, Cold Spring Harbor, New York.

Hopkins, B., Sharpe, C. R., Baralle, F. E., and Graham, C. F. (1986). *J. Embryol. Exp. Morphol.* **97,** 177–187.

Isnenghi, E., Cassada, R., Smith, K., Denich, K., Radnia, K., and von Ehrenstein, G. (1983). *Dev. Biol.* **98,** 465–480.

Izhar, M., Siebert, P. D., Oshima, R. G., deWolf, W. C., and Fukuda, M. N. (1986). *Dev. Biol.* **116,** 510–518.

Jaenisch, R., and Mintz, B. (1974). *Proc. Natl. Acad. Sci. U.S.A.* **71,** 1250–1254.

Johnson, M. H., and Maro, B. (1987). *In* "Experimental Approaches to Mammalian Embryonic Development" (J. Rossant and R. Pedersen, eds.), pp. 35–65. Cambridge Univ. Press, London and New York.

Kellermann, D., and Kelly, F. (1986). *Differentiation* **32,** 74–81.

Kollias, G., Wrighton, N., Hurst, J., and Grosveld, F. (1986). *Cell* **46,** 89–94.

Kratochwil, K., Dziadek, M., Lohler, J., Harbers, K., and Jaenisch, R. (1986). *Dev. Biol.* **117,** 596–606.

Krumlauf, R., Hammer, R. E., Tilghman, S. M., and Brinster, R. L. (1985). *Mol. Cell. Biol.* **5,** 1639–1648.

Krust, A., Green, S., Argos, P., Kumar, V., Walters, P., Bornert, J.-M., and Chambon, P. (1986). *EMBO J.* **5,** 891–897.

Lawson, K. A., Meneses, J. J., and Pedersen, R. A. (1986). *Dev. Biol.* **115,** 325–339.

Leder, A., Pattengale, P. K., Kuo, A., Stewart, T. A., and Leder, P. (1986). *Cell* **45,** 485–495.

Lee, V. M.-Y., and Andrews, P. W. (1986). *J. Neurosci.* **6,** 514–521.

Little, P. (1986). *Nature (London)* **321,** 558–559.

McConnell, J., and Watson, C. J. (1986). *FEBS Lett.* **195,** 199–202.

McKnight, S., and Tjian, R. (1986). *Cell* **46,** 795–805.

Magram, J., Chada, K., and Costantini, F. (1985). *Nature (London)* **315,** 338–320.

Mason, A. J., Pitts, S. L., Nikolics, K., Szonyi, E., Wilcox, J. N., Seeburg, P. H., and Stewart, T. A. (1986). *Science* **234,** 1372–1378.

Meehan, R. R., Barlow, D. P., Hill, R. E., Hogan, B. L. M., and Hastie, N. D. (1984). *EMBO J.* **3,** 1881–1885.

Muglia, L., and Rothman-Denes, L. B. (1986). *Proc. Natl. Acad. Sci. U.S.A.* **83,** 7653–7657.

Nakatsuji, N., Snow, M. H. L., and Wylie, C. C. (1986). *J. Embryol. Exp. Morphol.* **96,** 99–109.

Nasmyth, K. (1985a). *Cell* **42,** 213–223.

Nasmyth, K. (1985b). *Cell* **42,** 225–235.

Nusslein-Volhard, C., and Weischaus, E. (1980). *Nature (London)* **287,** 795–801.

Nyhan, W. L. (1987). *BioEssays* **6,** 5–8.

Ornitz, D. M., Palmiter, R. D., Hammer, R. E., Brinster, R. L., Swift, G. H., and MacDonald, R. J. (1985). *Nature (London)* **313,** 600–602.

Palmiter, R. D., and Brinster, R. L. (1986). *Annu. Rev. Genet.* **20,** 465–499.

Pedersen, R. A., Wu, K., and Balakier, H. (1986). *Dev. Biol.* **117,** 581–595.

Penketh, R., and McLaren, A. (1987). *In* "Fetal Diagnosis of Genetic Defects" (C. Rodeck, ed.). Saunders, Philadelphia, Pennsylvania.

Peters, J., ed. (1986). *Mouse News Lett.* **74,** 5–68.

Poustka, A., and Lehrach, H. (1986). *Trends Genet.* **2,** 174–179.

Rhodes, D., and Klug, A. (1986). *Cell* **46,** 123–132.

Robertson, E., ed. (1987). "Teratocarcinomas and Embryonic Stem Cells: A Practical Approach." IRL Press, Oxford.

Robertson, E., Bradley, A., Kuehn, M., and Evans, M. (1986). *Nature (London)* **323,** 445–448.

Rossant, J. (1986). *Trends Genet.* **2,** 302–303.

Rossant, J., and Pedersen, R. A., eds. (1987). "Experimental Approaches to Mammalian Embryonic Development." Cambridge Univ. Press, London and New York.

Saiki, R. K., Bugawan, T. L., Horn, G. T., Mullis, K. B., and Erlich, H. A. (1986). *Nature (London)* **324,** 163–166.

Sanes, J. R., Rubenstein, J. L. R., and Nicolas, J.-F. (1986). *EMBO J.* **5,** 3133–3142.

Schnebelen, M. T., and Kaufman, M. H. (1986). *J. Embryol. Exp. Morphol.* **98,** 167–174.

Scriver, C. S. (1985). *Trends Genet.* **1,** 315–316.

Shi, W.-K., and Heath, J. K. (1984). *J. Embryol. Exp. Morphol.* **81,** 143–152.

Sleigh, M. J. (1985). *Trends Genet.* **1,** 17–21.

Soriano, P., and Jaenisch, R. (1986). *Cell* **46,** 19–29.

Sudhof, T. C., Goldstein, J. L., Brown, M. S., and Russell, D. W. (1985). *Science* **228,** 815–822.

Surani, M. A. H., Barton, S. C., and Norris, M. L. (1986). *Cell* **45,** 127–136.

Takahashi, K., Vigneron, M., Matthes, A., Wildeman, A., Zenke, M., and Chambon, P. (1986). *Nature (London)* **319,** 121–126.

Tan, S. S., and Morriss-Kay, G. M. (1986). *J. Embryol. Exp. Morphol.* **98,** 21–58.

Teeri, T. H., Herrera-Estrella, l., Depicker, A., van Montagu, M., and Palva, E. T. (1986). *EMBO J.* **5,** 1755–1760.

Thomas, H. R., Folger, K. R., and Capecchi, M. R. (1986). *Cell* **44,** 419–428.

van Heyningen, V., and Porteous, D. J. (1986). *Trends Genet.* **2,** 4–5.

von der Ahe, D., Janich, S., Scheidereit, C., Renkawitz, R., Schutz, G., and Beato, M. (1985). *Nature (London)* **313,** 706–709.

Voss, S. D., Schlokat, U., and Gruss, P. (1986). *Trends Biochem. Sci.* **11,** 287–289.

Waters, B. K., and Rossant, J. (1986). *J. Embryol. Exp. Morphol.* **98,** 99–110.

Webb, M., Graham, C. F., and Walsh, F. S. (1986). *J. Neuroimmunol.* **11,** 67–86.

Widen, S. G., and Papaconstantinou, J. (1986). *Proc. Natl. Acad. Sci. U.S.A.* **83,** 8196–8200.

Wilkie, T. M., Brinster, R. L., and Palmiter, R. D. (1986). *Dev. Biol.* **118,** 9–18.

Wilkins, A. S. (1986). "Genetic Analysis of Animal Development." Wiley, New York.

Willadsen, S. M. (1986). *Nature (London)* **320,** 63–65.

Woychik, R. P., Stewart, T. A., Davis, L. G., D'Eustachio, P., and Leder, P. (1985). *Nature (London)* **318,** 36–40.

CHAPTER 2

CYTOSKELETAL ALTERATIONS AND NUCLEAR ARCHITECTURAL CHANGES DURING MAMMALIAN FERTILIZATION

Gerald Schatten and Heide Schatten

INTEGRATED MICROSCOPY RESOURCE FOR BIOMEDICAL RESEARCH
ZOOLOGY RESEARCH BUILDING
UNIVERSITY OF WISCONSIN
MADISON, WISCONSIN 53706

I. Introduction

Fertilization bridges the discontinuity in generations and is considered successful if one, and only one, sperm nucleus unites with the egg nucleus within an activated egg cytoplasm. In addition the fertilized egg must also be primed to prepare for its next challenges: the cell divisions leading to embryogenesis.

For fertilization to be accomplished, several architectural changes in the nuclei and cytoplasm must occur, and several movements must take place. Sperm are typically motile, and their swimming movement is usually required for the sperm to traverse the fluid medium to the egg surface. In some, but certainly not all, sperm, the acrosome reaction involves a reorganization of the sperm's cytoskeleton. In many sperm from marine invertebrates, an explosive burst of actin assembly produces a bundle of microfilaments forming the elongated acrosomal process. It is this extension from the sperm's cytoskeleton that establishes the initial contact between the sperm and the egg surfaces.

The egg also effects several motions as well as numerous alterations in cytoplasmic and nuclear structure. The physical incorporation of the sperm, the elicitation of polar bodies in systems inseminated as oocytes, and the formation of the fertilization or incorporation cone are changes in cell shape mediated by the egg cortex. Once discharged into the cytoplasm, the sperm and egg nuclei (male and female pronuclei, respectively) must unite or become apposed, typically at the egg center, and these nuclear migrations are the result of the elaboration of the egg cytoskeleton. While these events have direct implications in

23

joining the parental genomes, there are also likely to be several structural alterations required for egg activation and the progression through the first cell cycle. These sorts of changes include microvillar formation and elongations as well as the assembly and disassembly of cytoplasmic asters in preparation for mitosis.

Evidence is accumulating that the architecture of the sperm and egg nuclei is quite modified and perhaps considerably reduced. Because a goal of fertilization is syngamy, the sperm and egg nuclei must be structurally primed to permit pronuclear fusion or chromosome intermixing readily at mitosis. This process will first require male pronucleus formation from the sperm nucleus. In those systems inseminated as oocytes in which pronuclear fusion does not occur, as in many mammals, the formal process of fertilization will overlap with both meiosis and mitosis. Therefore, the changes in chromatin structure permitting the maternal meiotic chromosomes to decondense into the female pronucleus and the second polar body nucleus, as well as the later condensation of the male and female pronuclei into the mitotic chromosomes, will also be considered.

The aim of this review chapter is to consider the structural organization of the egg cytoskeletal and nuclear architectural changes during mammalian, especially mouse, fertilization. Because much of the evidence regarding fertilization has been derived from investigations on invertebrate and lower vertebrate systems, this information will also be considered as the paradigm against which the mammalian work is compared. Then the state of the knowledge regarding mammalian fertilization will be considered, with the inclusion of some of the remaining questions. The aim of this chapter is 2-fold: to kindle further interest in the application of cellular and molecular structural investigations for solving fundamental problems in developmental biology, and to highlight the importance of studying cells during development in order to generate a fuller appreciation for cell and molecular biology.

II. The Question of Actin Polymerization during the Acrosome Reaction

The first morphologically apparent event during fertilization is the acrosome reaction of the sperm, and the first response of the egg occurs during sperm incorporation. In many marine invertebrates, sperm dramatically assemble or unwind a microfilament-containing process during the acrosome reaction. In some systems, such as that of the sea cucumber *Thyone*, the acrosomal process can be as long as the sperm tail, and it can extend to this length within 30 seconds (Tilney and

Inoue, 1981). The formation of the acrosomal process has become a model in which to explore actin assembly and its ionic regulation (reviewed by Tilney and Tilney, 1984; Schackman *et al.*, 1978). In sperm of other marine organisms, such as the horseshoe crab *Limulus,* the microfilaments of the acrosomal process are already assembled in the mature sperm. The acrosome reaction then involves the unwinding of the previously assembled process rather than the *de novo* assembly of the acrosomal actin. Because the actin isolated from the periacrosomal cap of the sperm head is held in a nonfilamentous state, and because it will not spontaneously assemble *in vitro,* this sort of actin has been referred to as "profilamentous actin" or "profilactin" (reviewed by Tilney and Tilney, 1984).

Although the dramatic assembly of actin in marine invertebrate sperm undergoing the acrosome reaction is serving as a model for the exploration of the actin behavior, questions remain about the acrosome reaction in mammalian sperm. The acrosome reaction in mammalian sperm does not involve the formation of any similarly dramatic process. In addition, the site at which the sperm fuses its plasma membrane with the egg's differs from that in most fertilization systems in which fertilization is external.

Because mammalian sperm fuse with the egg along the equatorial region of the sperm head, investigations to detect and localize actin in this area have been performed. The rationale for these studies includes the question of whether actin need be present along the cortical plasma membrane faces of both the sperm and the egg surface to permit these membranous regions to be fusigenic. Some, but not all, mammalian sperm (Clarke and Yanagimachi, 1978; Clarke *et al.*, 1982; Flaherty *et al.*, 1983; Halenda *et al.*, 1984) have been reported to contain actin, and questions remain about the requirements for microfilaments during the acrosome reaction.

Because these experiments seem to indicate that some, but not all, mammalian sperm may contain polymerized actin at the fusigenic site, we have posed the question of whether actin assembly in the sperm is required for sperm incorporation. Recently Kashman *et al.* (1980) have isolated and characterized latrunculins, novel marine toxins from the Red Sea sponge *Latrunculia magnifica,* and Spector *et al.* (1983) have demonstrated that latrunculins will disrupt microfilament organization in cultured cells at concentrations that do not affect the rate of actin polymerization *in vitro,* suggesting that latrunculins may represent a new experimental drug with which to investigate microfilament organization and behavior.

To demonstrate that sea urchin sperm require the assembled microfilaments found after the acrosome reaction for sperm incorporation, insemination was performed with varying concentrations of sea urchin sperm induced to undergo the acrosome reaction in the presence of 2.6 μM latrunculin A. As shown in Table I, latrunculin dramatically affects the sea urchin sperm's ability to fertilize sea urchin eggs.

Mammalian sperm, however, may not require actin assembly for successful sperm incorporation. As also demonstrated in Table I, mouse sperm treated with an identical concentration of latrunculin are relatively unaffected in their ability to be incorporated into mouse oocytes during fertilization *in vitro*. This result appears to indicate that microfilaments in the mouse sperm may not be required for sperm incorporation and raises questions about the universality of actin assembly during the acrosome reaction.

III. Absence of a Requirement for Microfilament Assembly during Sperm Incorporation

Microfilaments assemble at the site of sperm–egg fusion in many invertebrate systems, and this dramatic eruption of the fertilization cone provides the rationale for questioning whether a similar process

TABLE I

EFFECTS OF LATRUNCULIN ON THE ABILITY OF SPERM TO FERTILIZE SEA URCHIN AND MOUSE EGGS[a]

Species	Fertilization (%)	
	Control	Latrunculin
Sea urchin[b]		
Low sperm concentration		
(~3 sperm per egg)		
5 minutes postinsemination	58.0 ± 16.4	11.9 ± 1.5
10 minutes postinsemination	80.2 ± 8.9	18.6 ± 2.8
High sperm concentration		
(~50 sperm per egg)		
5 minutes postinsemination	98.0 ± 0.2	28.7 ± 6.4
10 minutes postinsemination	98.7 ± 0.5	35.3 ± 2.8
Mouse fertilization[c]		
10^5 sperm per oocyte	67.8 ± 26.4	58.4 ± 15.9

[a] From Schatten *et al.* (1986a).

[b] Successful fertilization is assayed in sea urchin eggs by the elevation of the fertilization envelope and the centering of both pronuclei.

[c] Successful fertilization in mouse oocytes is determined by the introduction of the sperm tail into the egg and the decondensation of a male pronucleus.

occurs during mammalian fertilization. However during mammalian fertilization, microfilaments may not be active during sperm incorporation and may only be required for events different from those requiring microfilaments during sea urchin fertilization. Careful studies of the surface events during sperm incorporation have questioned whether microvilli on the mammalian oocyte actively engulf the successful sperm (Shalgi *et al.*, 1978), as appears to be the case in most lower systems. However, it is curious that the oocyte surface has specialized regions for sperm–oocyte fusion and for second polar body formation and that the region for sperm–egg fusion is characterized by the presence of microvilli (Nicosia *et al.*, 1977). In Fig. 1, a mouse oocyte during sperm incorporation depicts the specialized surface regions including the absence of microvilli by the forming second polar body and over the incorporation cone; the site of sperm tail incorporation is somewhat displaced from the incorporation cone.

Microfilament activity in oocytes has been implicated during the formation of the second polar body and the incorporation cone in mammals, and during pronuclear apposition at fertilization (Longo, 1978; Shalgi *et al.*, 1978; Maro *et al.*, 1984; Battaglia and Gaddum-Rose,

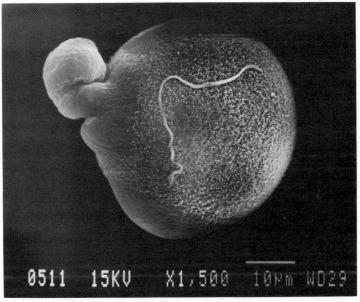

Fɪɢ. 1. Scanning electron micrograph of sperm incorporation during mouse fertilization. Sperm incorporation in mice occurs with the sperm positioned tangential to the egg surface. The incorporation cone may form at a region distal from the site of sperm entry and is denoted by its absence of microvilli. Bar, 10 μm.

1985). Neither cytochalasins (Longo, 1978; Maro *et al.*, 1984) nor latrunculin (Schatten *et al.*, 1986a) prevent sperm incorporation in mice, indicating that sperm entry may occur independent of both sperm and egg microfilaments in mammals.

The effects of the new microfilament inhibitor latrunculin on mouse fertilization is shown in Fig. 2 and Table I. The second polar body does not form after sperm incorporation (Fig. 2A), although meiosis is completed as assessed by the appearance of the two maternal pronuclei (F in Fig. 2C) corresponding to a female pronucleus and a second polar body nucleus. Sperm incorporation (Fig. 2A–C) and pronuclear formation (Fig. 2B,C) appear to occur normally, but the sperm and egg nuclei are unable to move into apposition at the egg center (Fig. 2C,D). Pseudocleavage is noted at ~8 hours postinsemination (Fig. 2D–F). In addition, cortical microfilaments are detected in the

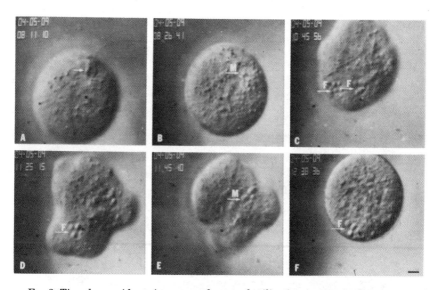

Fɪɢ. 2. Time-lapse video microscopy of mouse fertilization *in vitro* in the presence of the microfilament inhibitor latrunculin A. The incorporation of the sperm head (A) occurs in the presence of 2.6 μM latrunculin, though the incorporation cone does not enlarge normally at 4 hours postinsemination (B). The male pronucleus (M) develops (B). Since the formation of the second polar body is inhibited (B, C), two maternal pronuclei develop, corresponding to a female pronucleus and the second polar body nucleus. The egg becomes unusually active in the pronucleate stage (D–F), but the pronuclei are not moved from the egg cortex and further development is arrested. M, Male pronucleus; F, maternal pronuclei. Bar, 10 μm. (Reprinted with permission from Schatten *et al.*, 1986a.)

pseudocleaving mouse eggs with rhodamine–phalloidin. This observation is similar to that shown with cytochalasin B (Wassarman et al., 1977), which has also been shown to induce pseudocleavage, but in that case in preovulatory oocytes. Bundles of cortical actin are found along the egg cortex and in the pseudocleavage furrow, but the pronuclei, unlike the meiotic chromosomes, are unable to induce a regional accumulation of microfilaments.

Sperm incorporation during mouse fertilization *in vitro* is unaffected by treatment of either the sperm or the oocyte with latrunculin, suggesting that microfilament activity is not required in either gamete during this initial phase of mammalian fertilization, as it is for sperm incorporation in sea urchins. However, latrunculin will prevent the apposition of the pronuclei during mouse fertilization, as does cytochalasin (Maro et al., 1984). This finding indicates that, also unlike that during sea urchin fertilization, pronuclear apposition in this mammal requires microfilament function.

A way in which assembling actin may assist sperm incorporation in some systems involves nonerythrocyte spectrin, and the absence of this protein at the site of sperm–oocyte fusion in mice (Fig. 3) supports conclusions that actin may not be involved in mammalian sperm incorporation. Spectrin, thus called because it is isolated from plasma membrane "ghosts" prepared by removing the hemoglobulin from red blood cells, has recently been isolated from a variety of nonerythrocyte cells (reviewed by Glenney and Glenney, 1983). The spectrinesque protein from brain has been well studied by Willard and colleagues (Cheney et al., 1983; Hirokawa et al., 1983; Levine and Willard, 1981, 1983), and is referred to as fodrin. In sea urchins, fodrin can be detected in the sperm acrosome and at the egg surface, with a marked accumulation in the fertilization cone (Schatten et al., 1986b). Because a role of spectrin is to create a viscous gel with actin oligomers, a model for sperm incorporation in lower animals may be that spectrin creates a region of increased viscosity anchoring the successful sperm to the egg plasma membrane.

Nonerythrocyte spectrin has been found by several investigators in mammalian gametes, zygotes, and embryos (Sobel, 1983; Sobel and Alliegro, 1985; Sobel et al., 1985; Damjanov et al., 1986; Reima and Lehtonen, 1985; Schatten et al., 1986b). Although it appears that different types of spectrinlike proteins are found in different regions at various developmental stages, the precise role and even distribution of this spectrin are not precisely clear. It may, for example, interact with actin at the plasma membrane to provide gelated cortices, as it does at the red cell membrane.

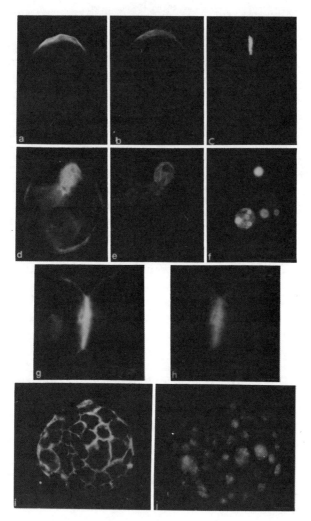

FIG. 3. Actin and fodrin in mouse oocytes, zygotes, and embryos. (a–c) Unfertilized mouse oocyte. In unfertilized oocytes, actin (a) and fodrin (b) are colocalized at the oocyte cortex with a pronounced concentration adjacent to the meiotic spindle. (c) DNA of the maternal meiotic chromosomes is detected by use of a fluorescent marker at the spindle equator. (d–f) Pronucleate mouse egg. After insemination fodrin (e) remains colocalized with cortical actin (d). The intensity of the fluorescence throughout the cortex appears to have increased and there is a concentration of both stains on the cortex of the second polar body. Cytoplasmic actin fluorescence (d) also is apparent. (f) Pronuclei and polar body nucleus detected with Hoechst DNA fluorescence. (g, h) First cleavage. There is a marked accumulation of both actin (g) and fodrin (h) at the cleavage furrow during first division. (i, j) Fodrin in mouse blastocyst. (i) In blastocysts, fodrin is found at each cell border. (j) DNA fluorescence. (a–c and d–f) Triple labeling for actin (a, d), fodrin (b, e), and DNA (c, f). (g, h) Double labeling for actin (g) and fodrin (h) at first cleavage. (i, j) Double labeling for fodrin (i) and DNA (j) in a blastocyst. Bars, 10 μm. (Reprinted with permission from Schatten et al., 1986b.)

Sperm incorporation in lower systems typically results in the regional eruption of the egg surface around the successful sperm. The resulting structure is referred to as the "fertilization cone" in invertebrate systems and the "incorporation cone" in mammals. Although the two terms could be thought of as more or less synonymous because they are both microfilament-containing swellings near or at the site of sperm–egg fusion, they probably have different roles and are triggered to form by different means. Invertebrate sperm approach the egg in a perpendicular fashion and initially penetrate vertically through the fusion site. The fertilization cone, perhaps initiated by the regional increase in calcium ion concentration and elevated pH that the sperm introduces, forms precisely around the sperm–egg fusion site and is probably crucial for sperm incorporation. In contrast, the incorporation cone in mammals seems to be the result, not the cause, of sperm incorporation. The mammalian sperm fuses laterally or tangentially with the oocyte plasma membrane. There may not be one small region of membrane fusion; rather the sperm and oocyte may fuse membranes along their whole contact regions: an analogy might be that of a zipper which starts at the equatorial region of the sperm head. The formation of the incorporation cone, which is sensitive to microfilament inhibitors (Shalgi et al., 1978), is not required for sperm incorporation. It might even be the result of a regional interaction between the sperm chromatin and the oocyte cortex. As will be described later, the maternal meiotic chromosomes induce regional accumulations of oocyte cortical actin (Longo and Chen, 1985; Maro et al., 1986; Schatten et al., 1986a), and perhaps the sperm chromatin has a similar effect. If so it would result in the formation of a microfilament-containing surface protrusion, the mammalian incorporation cone.

Details of the precise mechanisms of sperm incorporation in mammals are still unclear. The presence of assembled actin in the acrosome-reacted sperm is still controversial, and it appears that sperm incorporation can occur in the absence of microfilament assembly in both gametes. The sperm binds and fuses with the oocyte while oriented tangentially, and fusion might even occur all along the sperm's entire length, rather than through a small region. The sperm might be thought of as slowly sinking into the egg laterally rather than as actively drawn in through a small aperture. The incorporation cone forms after sperm incorporation and is probably not required for sperm incorporation.

IV. Cytoskeletal Dynamics in the Unfertilized Oocyte

The microfilament inhibitors cytochalasin (Maro et al., 1984) and latrunculin (Schatten et al., 1986a) have remarkable effects on unfer-

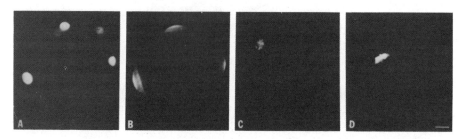

FIG. 4. Latrunculin inhibits Colcemid-induced chromosome dispersion and blocks the cortical accumulations of actin adjacent to the dispersed meiotic chromosomes. The meiotic chromosomes of unfertilized mouse oocytes treated with 50 μM Colcemid disperse along the egg cortex (A: Hoechst DNA fluorescence), and the dispersed chromosomes induce regional accumulations of cortical actin (B: rhodaminyl–phalloidin microfilament fluorescence). This dispersion is prevented by 2.6 μM latrunculin (C: Hoechst DNA fluorescence). Latrunculin alone does not affect chromosome distribution (D: Hoechst DNA fluorescence). All cells processed at 14 hours postinsemination. Bar, 10 μm. (Reprinted with permission from Schatten *et al.*, 1986a.)

tilized mouse oocytes. When the microtubules of the meiotic spindle in the unfertilized oocyte are disrupted with microtubule inhibitors, the meiotic chromosomes are dispersed along the oocyte cortex (Longo and Chen, 1985; Schatten *et al.*, 1985b). Longo and Chen (1985), Maro *et al.* (1986), and Schatten *et al.* (1986a) have noted regional accumulations of cortical actin adjacent to each dispersed chromosome mass.

In Fig. 4 the regional accumulations of cortical actin (Fig. 4B) are depicted adjacent to each mass of dispersed chromosomes (Fig. 4A) in Colcemid-treated unfertilized oocytes. Latrunculin interferes with this dispersion of the chromosomes (Fig. 4C), and cortical microfilaments are restricted to the region that would have formed the second polar body constriction. This experiment indicates that microtubules normally hold the meiotic chromosomes together in the unfertilized oocyte and that a counterforce of cortical microfilaments pulls the chromosomes apart.

The meiotic chromosomes of unfertilized mouse oocytes scatter along the egg cortex when the spindle is disrupted with 50 μM Colcemid, and cortical actin accumulates regionally by the scattered chromosomes. Latrunculin, 2.6 μM, inhibits chromosome dispersion induced by Colcemid, similar to the effects of cytochalasin reported by Maro *et al.* (1986); 2.6 μM latrunculin alone does not affect chromosome distribution. Recovery from the Colcemid effects in these unfertilized oocytes results in the formation of miniature meiotic spindles adjacent to the scattered chromosomes (Maro *et al.*, 1986). In Fig. 5,

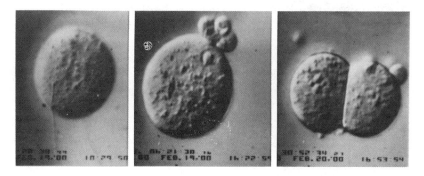

Fig. 5. Time-lapse video of recovery from Colcemid in a mouse oocyte. Although multiple second polar bodies are apparent, development occurs normally through first cleavage.

fertilization of an oocyte undergoing recovery from Colcemid is depicted from still frames of a time-lapse video sequence. Although multiple polar bodies form in Fig. 5B, sperm incorporation, pronuclear apposition, and the events through first cleavage are normal. Figure 6 summarizes the effects of microfilament inhibitors during mouse fertilization.

An interesting facet of this observation is its temporal nature. It appears that, once the chromosomes decondense into nuclei with annulated nuclear envelopes, they no longer induce this regional assembly of cortical actin. Perhaps the exposed chromatin itself or a peripheral

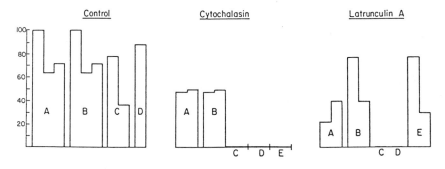

Fig. 6. Effects of microfilament inhibitors during mouse fertilization. A, Sperm incorporation; B, pronuclear formation; C, pronuclear centration; D, cleavage; E, pseudocleavage. Microfilament inhibitors do not completely arrest the incorporation of the sperm head, but prevent pronuclear apposition. Ordinate is percentage of cells examined. (Reprinted with permission from Schatten and Schatten, 1986a.)

nuclear protein like P_1 can trigger microfilament assembly if located near the cortex. However, perhaps the nuclear envelope or lamins interfere with this induction.

This possible scenario could explain the formation of the incorporation cone. Perhaps the sperm chromatin can induce a cortical microfilament assembly over a small region. This assembly would be reflected in the formation of a surface bleb until such time as the male pronucleus developed with a lamin-containing nuclear envelope. At that time the cone might be expected to be resorbed, as is observed during mammalian fertilization.

V. Mechanisms Accounting for Pronuclear Migrations

A. CYTOPLASMIC MICROTUBULES DURING THE PRONUCLEAR MIGRATIONS

The classic depiction of the migrations of the sperm and egg nuclei leading to syngamy derives from the earliest studies nearly a century ago. It was recognized that the sperm in most animals introduces a focal point onto which "the sperm aster" assembles. We now know that the sperm aster is composed of radially arrayed microtubules that extend from the centrosome, a structure of critical importance discussed later.

As with sperm incorporation, the movements and responsible machinery leading to pronuclear union differ between mammals and most other systems. The organization of the sperm aster and role of microtubules will first be considered in invertebrate and lower vertebrate systems, and then the state of knowledge during mammalian fertilization will be addressed.

The microtubules of the sperm aster, organized by centrosomes which surround the sperm centriole, are responsible for first moving the male pronucleus (incorporated sperm nucleus) from the inner face of the egg cortex into the egg cytoplasm. Later, as the sperm aster increases in size, some of the microtubule ends will contact the female pronucleus. Regardless of the relative positions of the male and female pronucleus, as the microtubules of the sperm aster increase in size they will, sooner or later, contact the female pronuclear surface. At that moment, the female pronucleus, by a still elusive mechanism requiring microtubule disassembly, rapidly translocates along these microtubules to their source, the spot where the male pronucleus resides. Once the male and female pronuclei are adjacent, the remaining sperm astral microtubules continue to assemble, moving the adjacent pronuclei to the center of the egg cytoplasm. Typically these microtubules disassemble prior to pronuclear fusion.

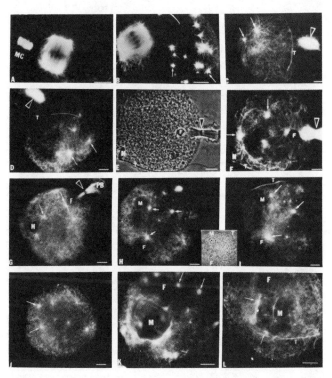

FIG. 7. Microtubules during sperm incorporation and in pronucleate eggs. (A) Unfertilized oocyte. The meiotic spindle is the dominant microtubule-containing structure in the unfertilized oocyte; it is barrel shaped and anastral, with broad meiotic poles, and anchored parallel to the oocyte cortex. Inset: Meiotic chromosomes detected with DNA fluorescence. (B) Cytoplasmic asters in unfertilized oocyte. Several hours after ovulation, about a dozen cytoplasmic asters (arrows) assemble throughout the cytoplasm. (C, D) Sperm incorporation. At sperm incorporation, the microtubules of the axoneme (T), the meiotic midbody (triangle), and the cytoplasmic asters are apparent. (E, F) Early pronucleate eggs, 6 hours postovulation. Microtubules are found in the incorporated axoneme (T), in the midbody of the rotated meiotic spindle (triangle), and ramifying throughout the cytoplasm as a latticework extending from asters (arrows), some of which are in association with each pronucleus. The asters are not organized by the base of the incorporated sperm axoneme (T). (G–J) Pronucleate eggs, 12 hours postovulation. As the male and female pronuclei form, the cytoplasmic asters enlarge, and a pair associate with the pronuclei (arrows). (K, L) Late pronucleate eggs, 18 hours postovulation. As the pronuclei are moved together to the egg center, a dense array of microtubules forms. This array has focal sites with the pronuclei embedded within its center. Insets: M, male pronucleus; F, female pronucleus; PB, polar body nucleus; MC, meiotic chromosomes; T, sperm axoneme; arrows, cytoplasmic asters; triangle, meiotic midbody. Bars, 10 μm. (Reprinted with permission from Schatten *et al.*, 1985a.)

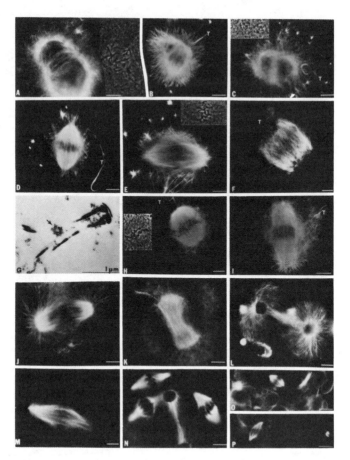

Fig. 8. Mitosis and early development: first division to blastocyst. (A) At the end of first interphase the cytoplasmic microtubules disassemble from the interior and are replaced by sheaths of microtubules surrounding the adjacent, but still separate, pronuclei (16 hours postovulation). Inset: Chromosomes condensing within the adjacent pronuclei. (B, C) Prophase. The paternal and maternal chromosome sets are still separated by the perinuclear microtubules within a monaster. (C) A spindle begins to emerge as the parental chromosomes meet. The sperm axoneme is apparent. (D–G) Metaphase, 18 hours postovulation. The metaphase spindle is typically barrel shaped and anastral, with relatively broad mitotic poles. It sometimes has focused poles, as in (D), which appear to broaden during mitosis. (G) Sperm axoneme and centriole complex in a metaphase egg. Although numerous parallel microtubules are found in the spindle region, microtubules are not observed near the incorporated sperm axoneme, with its centriole (arrow) and implantation fossa. (H, I) Anaphase. The spindle lengthens, and sparse microtubules extend from the broad poles toward the cell surface. (J) Telophase. Interzonal microtubules develop, and a few microtubules extend from the wide poles toward the cell surface. (K) Cleavage. The interzonal microtubules bundle into a midbody. (L) Second interphase. The daughter nuclei are positioned at the blastomere cell centers within monasters extending from the nuclear surfaces. A midbody persists, and the second polar body remains attached at the left. (M) Second mitosis, 26 hours postovula-

The pattern of microtubules found during mammalian fertilization differs considerably from that described above and raises a number of questions concerning the inheritance of microtubule-organizing centers. These implications will be considered in the section on the centrosome.

Mammalian oocytes, like most eggs, are fertilized as oocytes. Sperm incorporation and the final stages of meiotic maturation occur together. In most mammals, the oocyte at the time of fertilization is arrested at second meiotic metaphase. As seen in Fig. 7, the unfertilized oocyte already has a microtubule array: the second meiotic spindle.

Unexpectedly, after incorporation the sperm does not play any major role in organizing microtubules. As shown in Fig. 7B, over a dozen cytoplasmic foci derived from the oocyte serve as the centers of small asters. During pronuclear development, these microtubule-containing asters increase in size as the cytoplasm becomes filled with a microtubule matrix. The pronuclei are embedded within this matrix, and by a process involving both assembly and disassembly the male and female pronuclei are moved into apposition at the cell center.

Time-lapse studies demonstrate that the pronuclei move in a seemingly random jostling fashion to reach the egg center, and they do not follow particular paths at specific times as in other systems. However, it must be remembered that the fertilization process in mammals, which concludes when the parental genomes intermix at first mitosis (Fig. 8), can take as long as a day, whereas in other systems, like sea urchins, syngamy is achieved within 15 minutes! This rate places severe constraints on the activity of the egg cytoskeleton. Figure 9 summarizes the effects of microtubule inhibitors during mouse fertilization.

Although the pattern of microtubule configurations during mammalian fertilization is atypical, studies with microtubule inhibitors demonstrate that microtubular activity is required to achieve pronuclear union. As is shown in Table II and Fig. 9, both microtubule assembly and disassembly inhibitors arrest fertilization, and if pronuclear development occurs, the pronuclei cannot be moved to the egg center.

---

tion. At metaphase the spindle still has broad mitotic poles. (N) Third mitosis, 32 hours postovulation. Fusiform spindles with well-focused mitotic poles are observed at third division. (O) Morula, 64 hours postovulation. (P) Blastocyst, 80 hours postovulation. Typical fusiform mitotic spindles are detected at fourth (O) and fifth (P) divisions. Bars, 10 μm, except G. (Reprinted with permission from Schatten et al., 1985a.)

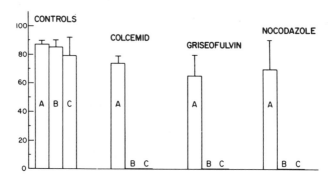

Fɪɢ. 9. Effects of microtubule inhibitors during mouse fertilization. Colcemid, gris-
eofulvin, and nocodazole prevent pronuclear formation (B bars) and the movements
leading to pronuclear centration (C bars). Sperm incorporation (A bars) is not significantly inhibited. Ordinate is percentage of cells examined; bars are mean +SD for the
indicated processes. (Reprinted with permission from Schatten et al., 1985a.)

B. Microfilament Activity

Microfilaments are active during mouse fertilization at an unusual
site. Though not required for sperm incorporation (Table II), pronuclear apposition is inhibited by microfilament inhibitors. As shown by
Maro et al. (1984) with cytochalasin D and by Schatten et al. (1986a)
with latrunculin, microfilament inhibitors will prevent pronuclear apposition but not pronuclear development. Microfilaments can be local-

TABLE II
Motility during Mouse and Sea Urchin Fertilization

	Type of activity[a]	
	Sea urchin	Mouse
Sperm motility	MT	MT
Sperm acrosome reaction	MF	None
Sperm incorporation	Egg MF	None
Completion of meiosis	NA	Egg MT
Second polar body formation	NA	Egg MF
Pronuclear formation	None	MT
Pronuclear migrations	MT	MT and MF
First spindle	Fusiform, with asters	Barrel, anastral
Centrosome source	Paternal	Maternal

[a] MT, Microtubule activity; MF, microfilament activity; NA, not applicable.

ized in mouse eggs during fertilization and first cleavage with rho-damine–phalloidin and are found at two sites. In addition to cortical microfilaments, a perinuclear array of microfilaments is found diffusely throughout the cytoplasm. This perinuclear microfilament array appears to be required, in addition to the cytoplasmic microtubule matrix, for the movements leading to pronuclear apposition during mammalian fertilization.

VI. Pronuclear Development and Nuclear Architecture

Fertilization and the onset of development requires several dramatic changes in nuclear organization (reviewed by Krohne and Benavente, 1986). The architecture of the nuclear surface (reviewed by Franke *et al.*, 1981; Maul, 1982; Berezney, 1979; Gerace and Blobel, 1980) involves the nuclear lamins, typically three proteins subjacent to the inner nuclear membrane (Fawcett, 1966; Gerace *et al.*, 1978), and nuclear peripheral proteins, referred to as "P_1" (Chaly *et al.*, 1984) and "perichromin" (McKeon *et al.*, 1984), which reside between the chromatin and the nuclear lamins. During mitosis in somatic cells, the lamins dissociate from the nuclear envelope at prophase and reappear with the reconstituting envelope at telophase (Gerace and Blobel, 1980). Unlike the behavior of the lamins at mitosis, the peripheral antigens separate from the nuclear periphery and ensheath the condensing chromosomes before nuclear envelope breakdown and dissolution of the lamins during mitosis (Chaly *et al.*, 1984; McKeon *et al.*, 1984). During spermatogenesis, the nuclear lamins are lost or vastly reduced (Stick and Schwarz, 1982; Moss *et al.*, 1984; Maul *et al.*, 1986a; Benavente and Krohne, 1985), whereas during oogenesis the lamina may be composed of only a single lamin (Stick and Schwarz, 1983; Stick and Krohne, 1982; Maul and Avdalovic, 1980; Maul *et al.*, 1984, 1986b), which differs from somatic lamins (Krohne *et al.*, 1984; Stick and Hausen, 1985; Benavente *et al.*, 1985).

Because nuclear architecture is modified during gametogenesis, and because fertilization presents the special demand of uniting the parental genomes, the behavior and appearance of nuclear lamins and other peripheral nuclear antigens is of considerable interest. In addition, alterations in nuclear structure, which might be maintained following determinative cell divisions, have been proposed to play an important role in cell differentiation, particularly during embryogenesis (Blobel, 1985).

Changes in nuclear lamins during fertilization have been studied in the amphibian *Xenopus* (Benavente *et al.*, 1985; Stick and Hausen, 1985), in sea urchins, and in mice (Schatten *et al.*, 1985b). These systems represent extremes in fertilization mechanisms. For example, the sea urchin egg is spawned as a mature egg with a female pronucleus, and pronuclear fusion or syngamy occurs shortly after sperm incorporation. The ovulated mouse oocyte is arrested at second meiotic metaphase and, because pronuclear fusion does not occur, fertilization is only completed at first mitosis when the parental chromosomes align at metaphase.

Fertilization involves the appearance of nuclear lamins and rearrangements of the peripheral nuclear antigens. Detectable lamins are vastly reduced in sperm, and the formation of the male pronucleus in both systems, involving dramatic biochemical (reviewed in Zirkin *et al.*, 1982; Poccia, 1982; Longo, 1978) and ultrastructural rearrangements (Anderson *et al.*, 1975; Longo and Anderson, 1968), is coupled with the appearance of lamins associated with the male pronuclear envelope. In mouse oocytes, lamins appear on the female pronucleus as it develops after the completion of meiosis. The polar body nucleus has a reduced lamin complement, as judged by fluorescence intensity, perhaps as a result of its restricted access to the cytoplasmic pool of lamins; this circumstance suggests a possible pathway leading to its ultimate degeneration.

Fertilization in the mouse is only formally completed at first division when the parental chromosomes intermix. At prophase, the lamins dissociate from the pronuclei, and the peripherals ensheath each chromosome, in a pattern typical for somatic cells (Chaly *et al.*, 1984; McKeon *et al.*, 1984; Gerace and Blobel, 1980). After telophase, when diploid nuclei first form, the lamins and peripheral antigens redistribute to the nuclear surface.

In the unfertilized mouse oocyte, peripheral antigens ensheath each meiotic chromosome (MC in Fig. 10A) and the lamins are not detected (lamins AC: Fig. 10B; see Table III for results with other tested antibodies). Hoechst DNA fluorescence of the chromosomes is shown in Fig. 10C.

During fertilization, the developing male and female pronuclei acquire lamins (lamins AC: Fig. 10E) and the peripheral antigens redistribute to the nuclear periphery (Fig. 10D). The polar body nucleus (Pb in Fig. 10E) is only dimly labeled with lamin antibody.

At mitosis the peripheral antigens condense around each chromosome (Fig. 10G), as the lamins dissociate from the chromosome mass (Fig. 10H). Following first division, the peripheral antigens again redistribute to the periphery of each nucleus (Fig. 10J) and the lamins reappear on the reconstituted blastomere nuclei (Fig. 10K). Table III summarizes these localizations.

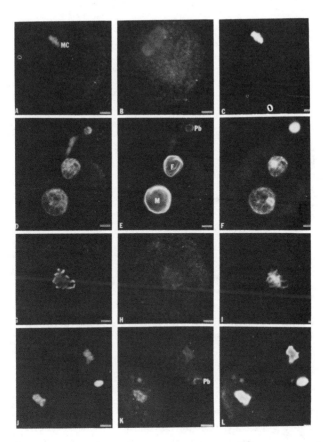

FIG. 10. Nuclear lamins and peripheral nuclear antigens during mouse fertilization and early development. (A) Unfertilized oocyte. The P₁ peripheral antigens ensheath the surface of each meiotic chromosome (MC). Lamin staining is lost in the ovulated oocyte, which is arrested at second meiotic metaphase (B: lamins AC). (C) Hoechst DNA fluorescence. (D) Pronucleate egg. The peripheral antigens are associated with the rims of the male (M) and female (F) pronuclei and with the polar body nucleus (Pb). The lamins reassociate with the nuclear surface (E: lamins AC), and characteristically the polar body nucleus stains only weakly. (F) Hoechst DNA fluorescence. (G) Mitotic egg. At prophase, the P₁ antibody against the peripheral antigens is redistributed from the pronuclear surfaces to cover each chromosome. The lamins dissociate from the mitotic chromosomes. (I) Hoechst DNA fluorescence. (J) Cleavage. As the daughter nuclei reform after first division, the peripheral antigens dissociate from the decondensing chromosomes and reassociate with the nuclear periphery (J: P₁). The lamins associate with the re-formed nuclear envelope (K). (L) Hoechst DNA fluorescence. Bars, 10 μm. (Reprinted with permission from Schatten et al., 1985b.)

TABLE III

DISTRIBUTION OF NUCLEAR LAMINS AND PERIPHERAL NUCLEAR ANTIGENS IN MOUSE
OOCYTES AND EMBRYOS DURING FERTILIZATION AND EMBRYOGENESIS[a,b]

	Lamins			Peripherals
	B pAb	A mAb	& C pAb	P_1 mAb
Mouse				
Sperm	+/−	§	−/[c]	−
Oocytes, germinal vesicles	+	+	+	+
Meiotic chromosomes, unfertilized	−	−	−	+
Male pronucleus	+	+	+	+
Female pronucleus	+	+	+	+
Polar body nucleus	−	−	−	+
Mitotic chromosomes	−	−	−	+
Blastomere nuclei	+	+	+	+
Morula nuclei	+	−	−	+
Blastocyst nuclei	+	−	−	+
Adult somatic cells (3T3)	+	+	+	+

[a] Reprinted with permission from Schatten et al. (1985b).
[b] pAb, Polyclonal antibodies; mAb, monoclonal antibodies; §, at acrosomal and centrosomal fossae.
[c] Apparent only after extraction with DNase and 2 M NaCl.

During embryogenesis, specific lamins may be replaced. Lamins A and C, closely related proteins (Gerace and Blobel, 1980; Kaufman et al., 1983), are apparently absent in mouse morulae and blastocysts but reappear later in somatic cells. In sea urchin embryos both lamins A and C and lamin B, as detected with polyclonal antibodies, are lost after the blastula stage, although a different lamin AC epitope emerges as recognized by a monoclonal antibody. The differential disappearance of the lamins during embryogenesis occurs after the first divisions in the mouse and only at the blastula stage in sea urchins.

Mouse and sea urchin embryos display an unexpected appearance and disappearance of lamin epitopes (Table III). In the mouse, staining of lamins A and C with either monoclonal or polyclonal antibody has become unrecognizable at the morula and blastocyst stages, although lamin B staining is retained. Sea urchin embryogenesis displays a similar phenomenon, with the loss of lamin recognition by human autoimmune antibodies in blastula, gastrula, and plutei and the recognition of a new monoclonal lamin antibody at these stages, which does not bind to egg or morula nuclei (Table III).

The nuclear lamins lost during spermatogenesis are restored at fertilization, probably from maternal sources, although the new exposure of paternal proteins cannot yet be excluded. The peripheral antigens associate with the surface of chromosomes during meiosis and mitosis, and with the periphery of pronuclei and nuclei during interphase; sea urchin sperm nuclei also have a coating of the peripheral antigens, although it appears to be absent in mature mouse sperm nuclei. In the mammalian system, the nuclear lamins behave during mitosis as observed in somatic cells: they undergo dissolution at late prophase and reassemble at telophase. In contrast, nuclear lamins are retained on the chromosomes during mitosis in sea urchin eggs. During embryogenesis, specific lamins are differentially expressed or exposed in both systems studied. These changes in the architecture of the nuclei, which participate in fertilization and embryogenesis, may prove crucial for later events leading to development and differentiation.

During mouse fertilization, microtubule assembly appears to be a prerequisite in the cascade of events leading to pronuclear development, nuclear lamina acquisition, and DNA synthesis. It does not appear to be required for the acquisition of the peripheral P_1 antigens. Because the mouse egg is fertilized as an oocyte, the requirement for microtubule activity in the meiotic spindle may be coupled with the associated karyoskeletal events. Indeed, lamin distribution in pronucleate mouse eggs is unaffected by Colcemid application.

Oocytes fertilized *in vitro* in the presence of Colcemid permit sperm incorporation (Fig. 11A). The sperm nucleus (SN) is outlined with the P_1 antigen (Fig. 11A). However, neither the scattered meiotic chromosomes (MC) nor the incorporated sperm nucleus acquires the expected nuclear lamins (Fig. 11B), and they appear to remain in a condensed state, as judged by DNA fluorescence microscopy at 12 hours postinsemination (Fig. 11C).

Fig. 11. Microtubule inhibitors prevent nuclear lamina acquisition during mouse fertilization. In the presence of Colcemid, the peripheral nuclear antigen appears (A), but nuclear lamins do not appear on the condensed chromatin found at 12 hours postinsemination (C).

However, when Colcemid is added 4 hours after insemination, before the full development of the cytoplasmic microtubule array and the appearance of the pronuclei, and the eggs cultured to 12 hours postinsemination, the pronuclei develop normally and acquire the nuclear lamins and P_1 peripheral antigens.

Fertilization is only formally completed when the parental genomes merge. This step can occur during interphase when the male and female pronuclear envelopes fuse to form a complete diploid zygote nucleus, as in sea urchins. In mammals, however, pronuclear fusion does not occur. Instead the male and female pronuclei remain intact during the first cell cycle and are held in close apposition at the egg center. At first mitosis, the chromosomes condense within each pronucleus and the genomes only intermix at mitotic metaphase when the chromosomes align along the mitotic spindle equator.

VII. Centrosomes during Mammalian Fertilization

Centrosomes specify the configurations of microtubules, which in turn direct mitosis (Mazia, 1984), the orientation of cellular movements (Albrecht-Buehler, 1985), the organization of the interphase cytoskeleton (Brinkley et al., 1981), nuclear migrations at fertilization (Schatten, 1984), and a variety of other intracellular processes, including the maintenance of cell shape and structure (reviewed by Wheatley, 1982; McIntosh, 1983). While the molecular composition of centrosomes is not understood, classical cytologists such as Boveri (1904; reviewed by Wilson, 1925; Mazia, 1984) recognized their critical importance. Laser oblation experiments by Berns and co-workers (Berns et al., 1977; Peterson and Berns, 1978; Koonce et al., 1984) have demonstrated the importance of the centrosomal region in directing mitotic spindle formation and cellular migrations. Ultrastructural analyses have resolved clouds of osmiophilic material surrounding centrioles, termed "pericentriolar material" (PCM) or "microtubule-organizing centers" (MTOCs), in a variety of animal cells (Gould and Borisy, 1977; Rieder and Borisy, 1982; Paweletz et al., 1984). Indeed, similar osmiophilic material is observed at expected organizing centers in plant cells (Pickett-Heaps, 1969; Wick et al., 1981; Bajer and Mole-Bajer, 1982). Autoimmune antibodies have been shown to be reliable markers for centrosomal detection (Calarco-Gillam et al., 1983), providing a new avenue for their exploration and characterization.

During fertilization, centrosomes are thought to be paternally inherited, along with the incorporated sperm centriole. Indeed, Boveri's theory of fertilization postulated that the centrosome was the "fertilizing element" that, once imported into the egg by the sperm, established the future mitotic poles (reviewed by Wilson, 1925). This scheme mandates extranuclear contributions by both parents. Because centrosomes establish the precise configurations of assembling microtubules, they define mitotic axes, unequal cell divisions, and cytoskeletal patterns for development, differentiation, and direction. During the cell cycle, centrosomes must reproduce and subsequently separate so that each sibling cell receives a full complement. This investigation provides experimental evidence that centrosomes are indeed flexible structures, as proposed by Mazia (1984), who directly predicts the observed microtubule configurations. They reproduce during interphase and aggregate and separate during mitosis. Sea urchins and probably most animals obey Boveri's rules, with the centrioles and centrosomes paternally inherited. Surprisingly, mouse centrosomes appear to be of maternal origin.

Since the configurations of microtubules observed during mouse fertilization (Schatten et al., 1985a) indicate an unusual organization, the further exploration of the behavior and inheritance of centrosomes in this mammal was extremely exciting. Schatten et al. (1986c) have traced centrosomal antigen throughout the entire course of fertilization and first division. Centrosomal material is found at the spindle poles in unfertilized oocytes (Fig. 12), as reported by Calarco-Gillam et al. (1983), and as multiple punctate concentrations scattered throughout the cytoplasm (Fig. 12; Maro et al., 1985).

At sperm incorporation when the meiotic spindle rotates, centrosomal material is found throughout the egg cytoplasm (Schatten et al., 1986b). As the pronuclei develop, centrosomal foci and asters begin to associate with the peripheries of both pronuclei. Later numerous foci are found adjacent to the apposed pronuclei, which are embedded within an array of microtubules (Fig. 12).

Toward the end of first interphase, the number of detectable foci increases and they all migrate toward the pronuclear surfaces, with several between the pronuclei. At the completion of first interphase, at the first signs of chromosome condensation within the intact pronuclear envelopes, the centrosomal antigen aggregates centrally, forming bright foci that circumscribe each pronucleus.

The centrosomal foci move as two broad clusters to opposing cytoplasmic regions at prophase (Fig. 13) as an array of microtubules extends from the centrosomes toward the chromosomes. The chromosomes align between the centrosomes at prometaphase as the mitotic spindle becomes apparent. At metaphase (Fig. 13) the centrosomes condense and the spindle is well defined. During anaphase and telophase (Fig. 13) the centrosomes remain closely associated as a band or

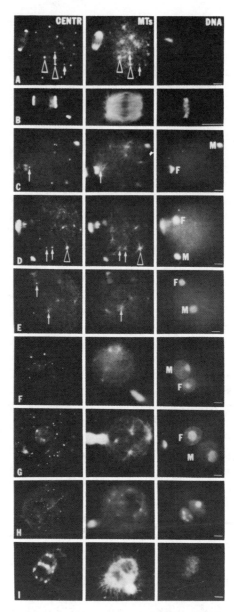

FIG. 12. Centrosomes during mouse fertilization. Centrosomes (CENTR: left panels) are found as cytoplasmic foci (A) and at the meiotic spindle poles (A, B) in unfertilized oocytes. Microtubules (MTs: middle panels) extend from the centrosomal material forming the meiotic spindle and cytoplasmic asters; each focus organizes an aster (arrows), with brighter ones associated with larger asters (triangles). Centrosomes are not detected in mouse sperm or with the entering sperm during incorporation (C, D). They associate with the developing pronuclei (C–G) as microtubules fill the cytoplasm. The foci aggregate (H) and condense (I) around the apposed pronuclei at the completion of first interphase as the cytoplasmic microtubules disassemble, leaving perinuclear

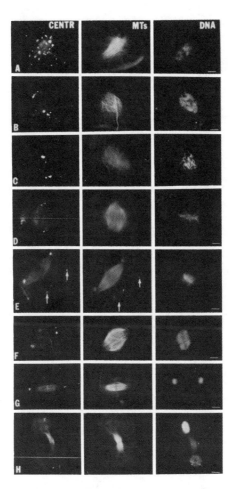

Fɪɢ. 13. Centrosomes during first division in mouse eggs. Centrosomes (CENTR: left panels) move as two clusters into the cytoplasm at prophase (A, B), as an irregular mass of microtubules (MTs: middle panels) forms around the aligning mitotic chromosomes (DNA: right panels). At prometaphase (C) the centrosomes appear as broad clusters on opposing sides of the chromosome mass as a barrel-shaped anastral spindle becomes apparent. At metaphase the centrosomes aggregate into either loose irregular bands (D) or more tightly focused sites (E). Centrosomal foci not associated with spindle poles organize microtubules (arrows: E). During anaphase (F) the centrosomes continue their separation. At cleavage (G, H) the centrosomes are found along the poleward surfaces of the blastomere nuclei and the midbody becomes apparent. All images are triple-labeled for centrosomes, microtubules, and DNA. Bar, 10 μm. (Reprinted with permission from Schatten *et al.*, 1986c.)

---

sheaths. (A–E) Triple labeled for centrosomes, microtubules, and DNA. (F–I) Double labeled for centrosomes and DNA with antitubulin images at the same stage. MC, Meiotic chromosomes; M, male pronucleus; F, female pronucleus; arrows, centrosomal foci and small asters; triangles, corresponding bright centrosomal foci and larger asters. Bars, 10 μm. (Reprinted with permission from Schatten *et al.*, 1986c.)

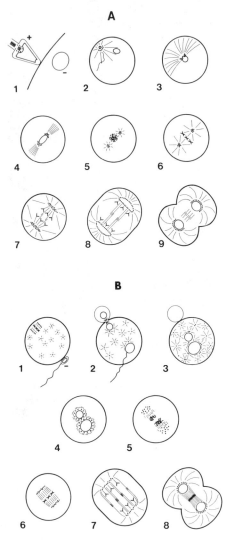

FIG. 14. Centrosomes during fertilization and cell division. (A) Centrosomes in sea urchin eggs. The unfertilized egg lacks centrosomes, and they are introduced along with the sperm centriole during incorporation (1). As the microtubules of the sperm aster assemble, the centrosomes spread around the male pronucleus (2). Following the migration of the female pronucleus, they reside at the junction between the pronuclei (3), and separate at about the time of syngamy. The centrosomes have increased in intensity and are found at opposing poles of the zygote nucleus at the streak stage (4). At prophase, when the nuclear envelope has disintegrated, they are displaced into the cytoplasm and nucleate the formation of the bipolar mitotic apparatus (5). They enlarge by metaphase but retain their spherical configurations (6), and at anaphase they begin to flatten and

plate composed of several foci from which microtubules extend. The arrangements of the microtubules at the various stages conforms well to the shapes of the centrosomes. As cleavage starts the centrosomes decondense and multiple foci are observed. After cleavage they are found as crescents associated with the poleward faces of the blastomere nuclei. The interzonal microtubules are prominent, and typically, a partial monaster of microtubules extends from the nuclei.

The organization and arrangement of centrosomes in sea urchins and mice during fertilization, the first cell cycle, and mitosis, diagramed in Fig. 14, solve some essential problems in cell biology but raise a number of questions. The appearance of centrosomes in sea urchin sperm but not eggs and in mouse eggs but not sperm predicts centrosomal retention during oogenesis in the mouse rather than the typical pattern of centrosome fidelity during spermatogenesis. Typically the mitotic centrosomes appear organized perpendicular to one another in the third dimension. Although this organization does not affect the next mitotic axis, it may have important consequences during the following division. This shifting in centrosomal axes may prove critical to the embryo's ability to organize future division axes and unequal cleavage planes that may generate pattern.

Comparisons of these fertilization systems provide insights into the interactions between centrosomes and nuclei or chromosomes. Nuclei attract and associate with centrosomes. This behavior is observed in the mouse after sperm incorporation when both pronuclei acquire centrosomes. The mature sea urchin sperm has a tightly affixed centriole

---

spread with axes perpendicular to the mitotic axis (7). At telophase the centrosomes have expanded into hemispheres as the astral microtubules disassemble within the asters and continue to elongate at the astral peripheries. Centrosomes are found on the poleward faces of the blastomere nuclei in cleaving eggs (8). (B) Centrosomes in mouse eggs. Mouse sperm lack centrosomes and the unfertilized oocyte has multiple cytoplasmic aggregates of centrosomal antigen as well as centrosomal bands at the meiotic spindle poles (1). Each centrosomal focus organizes an aster, and, following sperm incorporation, some foci along with their asters begin to associate with the developing male and female pronuclei (2). When the pronuclei are closely apposed at the egg center, several foci are found in contact with the pronuclei, and typically a pair resides between the adjacent pronuclei (3). Toward the latter half of the first cell cycle the number of foci increases. At the end of interphase all the foci condense on the pronuclear surfaces, and sheaths of microtubules circumscribe the adjacent pronuclei (4). At prophase the centrosomes detach from the nuclear regions, appearing as two broad clusters (5) which aggregate into irregular bands at metaphase (6); the first mitotic spindle is typically barrel shaped, anastral, and organized in the absence of centrioles. At anaphase and telophase the centrosomes widen somewhat (7), and at cleavage the centrosomes appear on the poleward nuclear faces (8). Triangles, Centrosomal foci; lines, microtubules. (Reprinted with permission from Schatten et al., 1986c.)

and centrosomes, which after incorporation spread around the decondensing male pronucleus but always remain associated with it. In the absence of centrosomes in the unfertilized sea urchin egg, the female pronucleus can only associate with them after contact with the male pronucleus and from that point on is always found in association with centrosomes. It is of interest that centrosomes always reside between the tightly apposed male and female pronuclei. After first cleavage in both systems each blastomere nucleus is associated with centrosomes.

Chromosomes appear to repel centrosomes. Centrosomes remain associated with the nuclear regions until the breakdown of the nuclear envelopes, when they are displaced into the cytoplasm. In sea urchin eggs the centrosomal particles remain tightly packed around the centrioles, whereas in mouse eggs they are only loosely associated. This repulsion of centrosomes from chromosomes may explain the requirement for kinetochores to anchor the opposing microtubule ends. Microtubules organized by centrosomes as asters at interphase may be organized into spindles at meiosis or mitosis by the bundling together of opposing microtubule ends. The stringent requirement for microtubule assembly in meiotic or mitotic cytoplasm and the regional influence of chromosomes in promoting localized microtubule assembly from centrosomes (Karsenti et al., 1984) explain the loss of cytoplasmic microtubules and the appearance of spindles. The absence of functional kinetochores during interphase is not surprising, since centrosomes will interact with the nuclear surface. The loss of kinetochores during mammalian spermatogenesis (Brenner and Brinkley, 1982) is particularly noteworthy, since if the entering sperm had functional kinetochores, like the second meiotic chromosomes, it too might induce the formation of a meiotic spindle and the ejection of some of its chromatin.

Centrosomes mirror chromatin during the cell cycle. At interphase they are dispersed and duplicated. At prophase both the chromatin and the centrosomes condense and lose their associations with the nuclear envelope. At metaphase, chromosomes and centrosomes are in their most compact state. During anaphase and telophase both separate, but in different directions; the chromosomes move to the centrosomes while the centrosomes flatten into plates with their axes predicting the next mitotic planes. As the cells enter the next interphase, both the chromosomes and centrosomes decondense and again resume their association with the reconstituted nuclear envelope. Phosphorylation of both nuclear lamins (Gerace and Blobel, 1980) and centrosomes (Vandré et al., 1984) at prophase, dephosphorylation of both at telophase, and the association of a cyclic AMP-dependent protein kinase with centrosomes (Nigg et al., 1985) may provide clues to the modifications necessary for these interconversions from interphase structure during mitosis.

VIII. Conclusions

Several conclusions are emerging about the role of the cytoskeleton during mammalian fertilization. These conclusions are rather unexpected and raise numerous questions central to our understanding of the ways in which animal cells direct their shapes and motions. It appears likely that the acrosome reaction may not involve microfilament assembly and that sperm incorporation may occur independent of either microtubules or microfilaments in either gamete. The organization of the meiotic chromosomes is maintained by the seemingly complicated arrangement of the meiotic spindle microtubules aligning the chromosomes at the metaphase plate, with cortical microfilaments positioning the spindle at the cell surface. Pronuclear formation with the acquisition of nuclear lamins requires microtubule assembly, and pronuclear apposition requires the concerted effort of both cytoplasmic microtubules and microfilaments. The microtubule-organizing centers active during mouse fertilization do not appear to be paternally derived; instead the centrosome seems to be maternally inherited. This is unlike the situation in most animals. Furthermore, the first mitotic spindles in mouse zygotes and embryos appear reminiscent of plant cell spindles with barrel shapes, blunt poles, and an absence of asters. In addition, they seem to be organized in the absence of functional centrioles. The time when centrioles appear during mammalian embryogenesis is still unknown, and the function of these elaborate structures remains unclear.

ACKNOWLEDGMENTS

It is our pleasure to acknowledge our many wonderful collaborators, and the support we have received from the National Institutes of Health and the National Science Foundation.

REFERENCES

Albrecht-Buehler, G. (1985). *In* "Gene Expression in Muscle" (R. C. Strohman and S. Wolf, eds.), pp. 1–21. Plenum, New York.

Anderson, E., Hoppe, P. C., Whitten, W. K., and Lee, G. S. (1975). *J. Ultrastruct. Res.* **50**, 231–252.

Austin, C. R. (1968). "Ultrastructure of Fertilization." Holt, New York.

Bajer, A. S., and Mole-Bajer, J. (1982). *Cold Spring Harbor Symp. Quant. Biol.* **46**, 263–283.

Balakier, H., and Tarkowski, A. (1976). *J. Embryol. Exp. Morphol.* **35**, 25–39.

Balczon, R., and Schatten, G. (1983). *Cell Motil.* **3**, 213–226.

Battaglia, D. E., and Gaddum-Rose, P. (1985). *J. Exp. Zool.* **237**, 97–105.

Bavister, B. D., Leibfried, M. L., and Lieberman, G. (1983). *Biol. Reprod.* **28**, 235–247.
Benavente, R., and Krohne, G. (1985). *Proc. Natl. Acad. Sci. U.S.A.* **82**, 6176–6180.
Benavente, R., Krohne, G., and Franke, W. (1985). *Cell* **41**, 177–190.
Berezney, R. (1979). *In* "The Cell Nucleus" (H. Busch, ed.), Vol. 7, pp. 413–456. Academic Press, New York.
Berns, M. W., Rattner, J. B., Brenner, S., and Meredith, S. (1977). *J. Cell Biol.* **72**, 351–367.
Bestor, T. H., and Schatten, G. (1981). *Dev. Biol.* **88**, 80–91.
Bestor, T. H., and Schatten, G. (1982). *Exp. Cell Res.* **141**, 171–178.
Blobel, G. G. (1985). *Proc. Natl. Acad. Sci. U.S.A.* **82**, 8527–8529.
Borisy, G. G., and Olmsted, J. B. (1972). *Science* **177**, 1196–1197.
Boveri, Th. (1904). "Zellen-Studien IV. Ueber die Natur der Centrosomen." Fischer, Jena.
Branton, D., Cohen, C., and Tyler, J. (1981). *Cell* **24**, 24–32.
Brenner, S. L., and Brinkley, B. R. (1982). *Cold Spring Harbor Symp. Quant. Biol.* **46**, 241–254.
Brinkley, B., Fistel, R., Marcum, J., and Pardue, R. (1980). *Int. Rev. Cytol.* **63**, 59–95.
Brinkley, B. R., Cox, S. M., Pepper, D. A., Wible, L., Brenner, S. C., and Pardue, R. L. (1981). *J. Cell Biol.* **90**, 554–562.
Burke, B., and Gerace, L. (1986). *Cell* **44**, 639–652.
Burridge, K., Kelly, T., and Mangeat, P. (1982). *J. Cell Biol.* **95**, 478–486.
Calarco-Gillam, P. D., Siebert, M. C., Hubble, R., Mitchison, T., and Kirschner, M. (1983). *Cell* **35**, 621–629.
Chaly, N., Bladon, T., Setterfield, G., Little, J. E., Kaplan, J. G., and Brown, D. L. (1984). *J. Cell Biol.* **99**, 661–671.
Cheney, R., Hirokawa, N., Levine, J., and Willard, M. (1983). *Cell Motil.* **3**, 649–655.
Clarke, G. N., and Yanagimachi, R. (1978). *J. Exp. Zool.* **205**, 125–132.
Clarke, G. N., Clarke, F., and Wilson, S. (1982). *Biol. Reprod.* **26**, 319–327.
Cline, C., and Schatten, G. (1986). *Gamete Res.* **14**, 277–291.
Damjanov, I., Damjanov, A., Lehto, V.-P., and Virtanen, I. (1986). *Dev. Biol.* **114**, 132–140.
Donovan, M. J., Mayhew, P. L., and Bellvé, A. R. (1984). *J. Cell Biol.* **99**, 127a.
Eager, D., Johnson, M. H., and Thurley, K. W. (1975). *J. Cell Sci.* **22**, 345–353.
Epel, D. (1978). *Curr. Top. Dev. Biol.* **12**, 186–246.
Fawcett, D. W. (1966). *Am. J. Anat.* **119**, 129–146.
Flaherty, S. P., Breed, W. G., and Sarafis, V. (1983). *J. Exp. Zool.* **225**, 497–500.
Franke, W. W., Scheer, U., Korhne, G., and Jarasch, E.-D. (1981). *J. Cell Biol.* **91**, 39s–50s.
Gerace, G., and Blobel, G. (1980). *Cell* **19**, 277–287.
Gerace, G., Glum, A., and Blobel, G. (1978). *J. Cell Biol.* **79**, 546–566.
Glenney, J., Jr., and Glenney, P. (1983). *Cell* **34**, 503–512.
Goldman, R., Goldman, A. E., and Yang, H.-Y. (1985). *J. Cell Biol.* **99**, 332a.
Gould, R. R., and Borisy, G. G. (1977). *J. Cell Biol.* **73**, 601–615.
Halenda, R. M., Primakoff, P., and Myles, D. G. (1984). *J. Cell Biol.* **99**, 394a.
Hirokawa, N., Cheney, R., and Willard, M. (1983). *Cell* **32**, 953–965.
Howlett, S. K., and Bolton, V. N. (1985). *J. Embryol. Exp. Morphol.* **87**, 175–206.
Karsenti, E., Newport, J., Hubble, R., and Kirschner, M. (1984). *J. Cell Biol.* **98**, 1730–1745.
Kashman, Y., Groweiss, A., and Shmueli, U. (1980). *Tetrahedron Lett.* **21**, 3629–3636.
Kaufmann, S. H., Gibson, W., and Shaper, J. H. (1983). *J. Biol. Chem.* **258**, 2710–2719.
Koonce, M. P., Cloney, R. A., and Berns, M. W. (1984). *J. Cell Biol.* **98**, 1999–2010.
Krohne, G., and Benavente, R. (1986). *Exp. Cell Res.* **162**, 1–10.

Krohne, G., Debus, E., Osborn, M., Weber, K., and Franke, W. W. (1984). *Exp. Cell Res.* **150,** 47–59.
Levine, J., and Willard, M. (1981). *J. Cell Biol.* **90,** 631–643.
Levine, J., and Willard, M. (1983). *Proc. Natl. Acad. Sci. U.S.A.* **80,** 191–195.
Lohka, M., and Maller, J. (1985). *J. Cell Biol.* **101,** 518–523.
Longo, F. J. (1978). *Dev. Biol.* **67,** 249–265.
Longo, F. J., and Anderson, E. (1968). *J. Cell Biol.* **39,** 339–368.
Longo, F. J., and Chen, D.-Y. (1985). *Dev. Biol.* **107,** 382–394.
McIntosh, J. R. (1983). *Mod. Cell Biol.* **2,** 115–142.
McGrath, J., and Solter, D. (1985). *Science* **226,** 1317–1319.
McKeon, F. D., Tuffanelli, D. L., Fukuyama, K., and Kirschner, M. W. (1983). *Proc. Natl. Acad. Sci. U.S.A.* **80,** 4374–4378.
McKeon, F. D., Tuffanelli, D. L., Kobayashi, S., and Kirschner, M. W. (1984). *Cell* **36,** 83–92.
Maro, B., Johnson, M., Pickering, S., and Flach, G. (1984). *J. Embryol. Exp. Morphol.* **81,** 211–237.
Maro, B., Howlett, S. K., and Webb, M. (1985). *J. Cell Biol.* **101,** 1665–1672.
Maro, B., Johnson, M. H., Webb, M., and Flach, G. (1986). *J. Embryol. Exp. Morphol.* **92,** 11–32.
Maul, G. G. (1982). "The Nuclear Envelope and the Nuclear Matrix." Liss, New York.
Maul, G. G., and Avdalovic, N. (1980). *Exp. Cell Res.* **130,** 229–240.
Maul, G., and Schatten, G. (1986). *In* "Nuclear Architecture" (W. W. Franke, ed.). Springer-Verlag, Berlin and New York, in press.
Maul, G. G., Baglia, F. A., Newmeyer, D. D., and Ohlsson-Wilhem, B. M. (1984). *J. Cell Sci.* **67,** 69–85.
Maul, G. G., French, B. T., and Bechtol, K. B. (1986a). *Dev. Biol.* **115,** 68–77.
Maul, G., Schatten, G., French, B., Lee, W., Pinkus, T., Jimenez, S., and Carrera, A. (1986b). *Dev. Biol.,* in press.
Mazia, D. (1984). *Exp. Cell Res.* **153,** 1–15.
Miake-Lye, R., and Kirschner, M. W. (1985). *Cell* **41,** 165–176.
Moss, S. B., Burnham, B. L., and Bellvé, A. R. (1984). *J. Cell Biol.* **99,** 126a.
Nash, M., Angerer, L., Angerer, R., Schatten, H., Schatten, G., and Marzluff, W. (1987). *J. Cell Biol.* **104,** 1133–1142.
Nicosia, S. V., Wolf, D. P., and Inoue, M. (1977). *Dev. Biol.* **57,** 56–74.
Nigg, E. A., Schäfer, G., Hilz, H., and Eppenberger, H. M. (1985). *Cell* **41,** 1039–1051.
Paweletz, N. (1981). *Cell Biol. Int. Rep.* **5,** 323–336.
Paweletz, N., and Mazia, D. (1979). *Eur. J. Cell Biol.* **20,** 37–44.
Paweletz, N., Mazia, D., and Finze, E.-M. (1984). *Exp. Cell Res.* **152,** 47–65.
Peterson, S. P., and Berns, M. W. (1978). *J. Cell Sci.* **34,** 289–301.
Petzelt, C. (1972). *Exp. Cell Res.* **70,** 333–339.
Petzelt, C., and Hafner, M. (1986). *Proc. Natl. Acad. Sci. U.S.A.* **83,** 1719–1722.
Pickett-Heaps, J. D. (1969). *Cytobios* **3,** 257–280.
Poccia, D. (1982). *Proc. Wash. Acad. Sci.* **72,** 24–33.
Reparsky, E. A., Granger, B. L., and Lazarides, E. (1982). *Cell* **29,** 821–833.
Reima, I., and Lehtonen, E. (1985). *Differentiation* **30,** 68–75.
Rieder, C. L., and Borisy, G. G. (1982). *Biol. Cell.* **44,** 117–132.
Sanger, J., and Sanger, J. (1975). *J. Exp. Zool.* **193,** 441–447.
Schackman, R. W., Eddy, E. M., and Shapiro, B. M. (1978). *Dev. Biol.* **65,** 483–495.
Schatten, G. (1981). *Dev. Biol.* **86,** 426–437.
Schatten, G. (1984). *Subcell. Biochem.* **10,** 357–451.
Schatten, G., and Schatten, H. (1981). *Exp. Cell Res.* **135,** 311–330.
Schatten, G., Schatten, H., Bestor, T., and Balczon, R. (1982). *J. Cell Biol.* **94,** 455–465.

Schatten, G., Simerly, C., and Schatten, H. (1985a). *Proc. Natl. Acad. Sci. U.S.A.* **82,** 4152–4156.
Schatten, G., Maul, G., Schatten, H., Chaly, N., Balczon, R., and Simerly, C. (1985b). *Proc. Natl. Acad. Sci. U.S.A.* **82,** 4727–4731.
Schatten, G., Schatten, H., Spector, I., Cline, C., Paweletz, N., Simerly, C., and Petzelt, C. (1986a). *Exp. Cell Res.* **166,** 191–208.
Schatten, H., and Schatten, G. (1980). *Dev. Biol.* **78,** 435–449.
Schatten, H., and Schatten, G. (1986a). *Cell Motil. Cytoskeleton* **6,** 163–175.
Schatten, H., Cheney, R., Balczon, R., Willard, M., Cline, C., Simerly, C., and Schatten, G. (1986b). *Dev. Biol.* **118,** 457–466.
Schatten, H., Schatten, G., Mazia, D., Balczon, R., and Simerly, C. (1986c). *Proc. Natl. Acad. Sci. U.S.A.* **83,** 105–109.
Scholey, J. M., Porter, M. E., Grissom, P. M., and McIntosh, J. R. (1985). *Nature (London)* **318,** 483–486.
Shalgi, R., Phillips, D. M., and Kraicer, P. F. (1978). *Gamete Res.* **1,** 27–37.
Shapiro, B. M., and Eddy, E. M. (1980). *Int. Rev. Cytol.* **66,** 257–302.
Sluder, G., and Begg, D. (1985). *J. Cell Biol.* **100,** 897–903.
Sobel, J. S. (1983). *Dev. Biol.* **100,** 207–213.
Sobel, J. S., and Alliegro, M. A. (1985). *J. Cell Biol.* **100,** 333–336.
Sobel, J. S., Opas, M., and Kalnins, V. I. (1985). *J. Cell Biol.* **101,** 1766a.
Spector, I., Shochet, N., Kashman, Y., and Groweiss, A. (1983). *Science* **183,** 493–495.
Stick, R., and Hausen, P. (1985). *Cell* **41,** 191–200.
Stick, R., and Krohne, G. (1982). *Exp. Cell Res.* **138,** 319–330.
Stick, R., and Schwarz, H. (1982). *Cell Differ.* **11,** 235–243.
Stick, R., and Schwarz, H. (1983). *Cell* **33,** 949–958.
Surani, M. A. H., Barton, S. C., and Norris, M. L. (1986). *Cell* **45,** 127–136.
Szöllösi, D., Calarco, P., and Donahue, R. P. (1972). *J. Cell Sci.* **11,** 521–541.
Tilney, L. (1976). *J. Cell Biol.* **69,** 51–72.
Tilney, L. G., and Inoue, I. (1981). *J. Cell Biol.* **91,** 298a.
Tilney, L. G., and Jaffe, L. A. (1980). *J. Cell Biol.* **87,** 771–782.
Tilney, L. G., and Tilney, M. S. (1984). *J. Cell Biol.* **99,** 765–825.
Tilney, L., Hatano, S., Ishikawa, H., and Mooseker, M. (1973). *J. Cell Biol.* **59,** 109–126.
Vacquier, V. D. (1981). *Dev. Biol.* **84,** 1–26.
Van Blerkom, J., and Bell, H. (1986). *J. Embryol. Exp. Morphol.* **93,** 213–238.
Vandré, D. D., Davis, F. M., Rao, P. N., and Borisy, G. G. (1984). *Proc. Natl. Acad. Sci. U.S.A.* **81,** 4439–4443.
Virtanen, I., Badley, R., Paasivuo, R., and Lehto, V.-P. (1984). *J. Cell Biol.* **99,** 1083–1091.
Wasserman, P. M., and Fujiwara, K. (1978). *J. Cell Sci.* **29,** 171–188.
Wasserman, P., Ukena, T., Josefowicz, W., and Karnovsky, M. (1977). *Nature (London)* **265,** 742–744.
Webb, M., Howlett, S. K., and Maro, B. (1986). *J. Embryol. Exp. Morphol.* **95,** 131–145.
Wheatley, D. N. (1982). "The Centriole: A Central Enigma of Cell Biology." Elsevier, Amsterdam.
Whittingham, D. G. (1968). *Nature (London)* **220,** 592–593.
Wick, S. M., Seagull, R. W., Osborn, M., Weber, K., and Gunning, B. E. S. (1981). *J. Cell Biol.* **89,** 685–690.
Wilson, E. B. (1925). "The Cell in Development and Heredity." Macmillan, New York.
Yanagimachi, R., and Noda, Y. D. (1976). *J. Ultrastruct. Res.* **31,** 465–485.
Zirkin, B. R., Soncek, D. A., and Chang, T. S. K. (1982). *Johns Hopkins Med. J.* **151,** 102–112.

CHAPTER 3

DEVELOPMENTAL POTENCY OF GAMETIC AND EMBRYONIC GENOMES REVEALED BY NUCLEAR TRANSFER

John Aronson and Davor Solter

THE WISTAR INSTITUTE
PHILADELPHIA, PENNSYLVANIA 19104

I. Introduction

The encounter of gametes, each the terminally differentiated product of a distinct cell lineage, initiates profound alterations in their genomic functions. These alterations render the fertilized egg totipotent.

Boveri was the first to question the differential contribution of each gamete in development by comparing the fate of normally fertilized sea urchin eggs with that of artificially activated eggs (gynogenones) or of nonnucleated egg fragments that were then fertilized (androgenones). This problem was subsequently approached in vertebrates through the study of parthenogenesis. The essential contribution of both the male and female genome to mammalian development was shown using the nuclear transfer method (McGrath and Solter, 1983, 1986a) and genetic analysis (Searle and Beechey, 1978). Nuclear transfer allowed the dissection of the role of the functionally unique components of the zygote (the maternal and paternal genomes, and the maternal and paternal cytoplasm), and also made possible analysis of the ability of the blastomere nuclei to support normal development after transfer into the zygote.

II. Role of Maternal and Paternal Genomes in Mammalian Development

A. PARTHENOGENESIS

Parthenogenesis is the derivation of live progeny without genetic contribution from the paternal genome. Naturally occurring parthenogenetic vertebrate species have been described among fish, amphib-

55

TABLE I
PARTHENOGENESIS IN VERTEBRATES

Class	Total number of species[a]	Parthenogenetic species[b]	Number of eggs per reproductive period[a]
Pisces	23,000	+ (3)	150–1,000,000
Amphibia	2,000	+ (3)	18–1,000
Reptilia	5,000	+ (19)	1–120
Aves	8,590	± (1, turkey)	2–14
Mammalia	4,500	− (0)	1–9

[a] Altman and Dittmer (1972).
[b] Bell (1982).

ians, reptiles, and birds but not among mammals (Table I). Since the parthenogenetic mode of reproduction is evident only in specific ecological situations (Cuellar, 1977), the absence of parthenogenesis does not necessarily imply its biological impossibility. Spontaneous parthenogenesis does suggest that the maternally derived genome is generally totipotent in vertebrates, but does not address the potency of the paternally derived genome.

The possibility of spontaneous parthenogenesis in mammals was never seriously investigated, but following the development of experimental procedures to induce activation of the egg *in vitro* and to return it to the reproductive tract (Pincus, 1939a,b), numerous attempts were made to produce parthenogenetic mammals experimentally. Despite early claims of success (Pincus, 1939a,b), the consensus is that complete parthenogenetic development in mammals cannot occur (Beatty, 1957; Graham, 1974; Kaufman, 1983), although development to midgestation is possible (Kaufman *et al.*, 1977).

The developmental failure of experimentally generated parthenotes was explained by excessive homozygosity for lethal genes in the parthenotes (Markert, 1982), or by the absence of a physical or functional extragenomic contribution of the sperm (Graham, 1974). This second possibility was strongly supported by the observations reported by Hoppe and Illmensee (1977) that uniparental (both maternal and paternal) diploid embryos could develop. In these experiments either the male or the female pronucleus was removed from normally fertilized zygotes and the remaining pronucleus was diploidized by blocking the first cleavage division with cytochalasin B. Following the return of such embryos to pseudopregnant females, androgenetic and gynogenetic progeny with appropriate genetic markers were born (Table II). However, numerous attempts to repeat these experiments failed

TABLE II

Normal Developmental Requirement for Both Maternally and Paternally Derived Genomes

Category	Number of parents[a]	Ploidy	Cytoplasmic host[b]	N[c]	Preimplantation development	Advanced normal embryo or progeny	References
Androgenetic and gynogenetic	1	2n	Z	135	93[d]	5 Female, 2 male	Hoppe and Illmensee (1977)
Parthenogenetic	1	2n (ICM)	Z	28	7[d]	4	Hoppe and Illmensee (1982)
Gynogenetic	1	2n	Z	402	ND[e]	0	Surani and Barton (1983)
	2	2n	Z	339	ND[e]	0	McGrath and Solter (1984a)
	2	2n	AO	110	ND[e]	0	Surani et al. (1984)
Parthenogenetic	1	1n	AO	165	5	ND[e]	Surani et al. (1986a)
	1	2n	AO	500	ND[e]	0	Markert (1982)
	1	2n	AO	81	ND[e]	0	Modlinski (1980)
	1	2n	Z	34	ND[e]	0	Mann and Lovell-Badge (1984)
Androgenetic	1	1n	Z	575	0	ND[e]	Surani et al. (1986a)
	1	2n	Z	89	ND[e]	0	Surani and Barton (1983)
	2	2n	Z	176	39	ND[e]	Surani et al. (1986a)
	2	2n	Z	208	ND[e]	0	Barton et al. (1984)
	2	2n	Z	328	ND[e]	0	McGrath and Solter (1984a)
Maternal plus paternal	2	2n	Z	30	ND[e]	9	Surani et al. (1984)
	2	2n	Z	348	ND[e]	16	McGrath and Solter (1984a)
	2	2n	Z	194	ND[e]	62	Barton et al. (1984)
	2	2n	AO	32	ND[e]	22	Mann and Lovell-Badge (1984)

[a] 1, Uniparental; or 2, biparental, depending on whether diploidy was restored by endoreduplication of a single pronucleus or by transfer of a pronucleus from another zygote.

[b] AO, Activated oocyte; Z, zygote.

[c] N, Number of embryos surviving surgery and either cultured or reimplanted.

[d] Number of preimplantation embryos reimplanted.

[e] ND, Not determined.

(Modlinski, 1980; Markert, 1982; Surani and Barton, 1983), in that following preimplantation development, the manipulated embryos started to die and none survived beyond the stages when death was observed in parthenogenetically developing embryos (Table II) (Markert, 1982; Surani and Barton, 1983). Therefore, no firm experimental evidence could be found to support the notion that failure of parthenotes is due to the absence of extragenomic contribution of the sperm. In fact evidence to the contrary comes from experiments in which pronuclei from zygotes are transferred to chemically activated oocytes. When a female pronucleus was introduced the egg failed to develop, but when a male pronucleus was transferred, viable offspring were produced (Surani et al., 1984). In addition, embryos produced by transfer of pronuclei from diploid parthenogenetically activated eggs into enucleated zygotes failed to develop beyond the postimplantation stages, whereas transfer of the zygote pronuclei into enucleated parthenogenetic eggs resulted in normal development and live birth (Mann and Lovell-Badge, 1984). These experiments indicated that cytoplasm of parthenogenetically activated eggs supports normal development as long as both a male and a female genome are present and argues against the role of an extragenomic sperm contribution to development (Table II). However, these experiments did not entirely eliminate the possibility that transfer of the male pronucleus as a karyoplast might include the additional transfer of nonchromosomal material derived from sperm and associated uniquely with the male pronucleus, so that they did not address the developmental potential of the paternal genome alone. Further experiments dealt with these questions and firmly established the functional uniqueness of each parental genome.

B. Paternal and Maternal Genomes in Development

Nuclear transfer techniques have provided experimental evidence that the paternal and maternal genomes are fundamentally different and that the presence of both is essential for normal development. Embryos containing either two male pronuclei (biparental androgenones) or two female pronuclei (biparental gynogenones) do not complete normal development (McGrath and Solter, 1984a; Barton et al., 1984). In contrast, control embryos, which contained both a maternal and a paternal pronucleus but not necessarily the original ones, showed a high frequency of normal development, giving rise to live progeny (Table II).

Morphological analysis of the androgenetic and gynogenetic embryos suggested that each genome played an important but slightly different role in the development of certain tissues (Surani *et al.*, 1984, 1986b; Barton *et al.*, 1984; Surani, 1985). Preimplantation development in each case appears identical, since both classes of embryos can reach the blastocyst stage (McGrath and Solter, 1984a, 1985, 1986b; Surani, 1985). However, even discounting loss due to the absence of the X chromosome in YY embryos, which only divide a few times, the rate of cleavage of androgenones is slower, particularly as haploids (Surani *et al.*, 1986a), than that of gynogenones or normal embryos. Following implantation the developmental differences between androgenetic and gynogenetic embryos become more marked. Those gynogenetic embryos that implant fail to develop normal extraembryonic membranes, so that the ectoplacental cone, trophoblast, and yolk sac are greatly reduced. This in turn might affect the growth of the embryo proper, resulting in morphologically normal but small embryos which abort. This view is supported by the finding that gynogenetic or parthenogenetic inner cell masses (ICM) placed within normal trophectoderm develop much further, though not to term (Barton *et al.*, 1985). Androgenetic embryos can also implant and, while the development of the extraembryonic membranes appears comparable to normal embryos, the embryonic part is greatly reduced (Surani, 1985). These results argue that the cause of developmental failure of androgenones and of gynogenones resides solely in a functional inequality of the male and female genomes during early development and that these inequalities are mutually compensated during normal development. They also indicate that the paternally derived genome is active during early development, as is the maternally derived genome, and that neither is totipotent.

The absence of one of the two parental genomes is lethal to the embryo but not to individual cells within the diploid embryo. This point has been experimentally demonstrated for the maternal genome using chimeric embryos, obtained by combining blastomeres from normal embryos with blastomeres from parthenogenetic embryos (Stevens *et al.*, 1977; Stevens, 1978; Kaufman *et al.*, 1977). Cell lines have also been produced from parthenogenetic (Kaufman *et al.*, 1983; Robertson *et al.*, 1983) and gynogenetic (G. R. Martin, J. Aronson, and D. Solter, unpublished results) embryos. The ability of androgenetic embryos to participate in viable chimeras or to serve as a starting point for derivation of cell lines has not yet been demonstrated, although attempts have been made (Surani *et al.*, 1986b; J. McGrath and D. Solter, unpublished results). Even though parthenogenetic or gynogenetic embryos can in effect be rescued by normal embryos, the incidence of viable chimeras is much reduced (Stevens *et al.*, 1977; Anderegg and Markert, 1986). One possible explanation to account for the low number of viable chimeras containing parthenogenetic cells is that those cells containing the maternal genome alone do not interact properly with cells from normal embryos, thus causing collapse of embryonic structures. Alternatively, parthenogenetically derived cells may be unable to perform certain tissue-specific functions. In this case tissues containing a high proportion of these cells may be unable to survive. In either case, the development of some viable gynogenetic ↔ normal chimeras could be explained by a fortuitous distribution of gynogenetic cells in a manner compatible with normal development. Whatever the deficiency in gynogenetic cells, it is not heritable because the progeny of chimeras containing germ cells derived from parthenogenetic or gynogenetic components are completely normal (Stevens, 1978; Evans et al., 1985).

The failure of gynogenetic and androgenetic embryos to develop could conceivably be explained in nongenetic terms by postulating that developmentally essential factors exist uniquely bound to male and to female pronuclei. Within the limits of current technology (i.e., it is not yet possible to separate genomic and extragenomic nuclear components), this cannot be disproved experimentally. There are, however, genetic experiments which indicate that at least some parts of the male and female genome are functionally different during normal early development. Mice heterozygous for complete or partial chromosomal translocations produce a certain percentage of gametes in which specific chromosomal segments are duplicated or absent due to meiotic nondisjunction. Mating of these mice results in a small number of progeny which are diploid at all loci and in addition possess maternal disomy/paternal nullisomy, or vice versa, for specific chromosomes or chromosomal segments. When appropriate genetic markers are included, the presence or absence of each progeny class can be reliably detected. The absence of a specific progeny class can be used as evidence that parental disomy or nullisomy for a particular autosomal region is not compatible with normal development. Studies of this kind indicate that regions of chromosomes 2, 6, 7, 8, 11, and 17 lead to anomalies in development many of which are lethal when both copies are derived from a single parent (Searle and Beechey, 1978, 1985; Cattanach and Kirk, 1985; Cattanach, 1986). Paternal duplication–maternal absence for specific region(s) of chromosome 17 and paternal absence–maternal duplication for chromosome 6 are lethal, while the reciprocal patterns have no effect on development. However, duplication of chromosomes 2 and 11 from either parent shows an effect (Cattanach and Kirk, 1985). Major regions of chromosomes 1, 3–5, 9, and 13–15 do not show detectable effects due to parental disomy (Cattanach and Kirk, 1985; Cattanach, 1986).

Two developmental effects associated with the parental derivation of a defined genetic element have recently been experimentally analyzed. Deletion of the proximal part of chromosome 17 is lethal when inherited from the mother, but when inherited from the father viable progeny with a tail malformation (T^{hp}) are produced (Johnson, 1975). By transfer of zygote pronuclei between heterozygous T^{hp} and wild-type embryos, it was shown that the lethal effect is transmitted via the maternal pronucleus and not by the maternal ooplasm (McGrath and Solter, 1984b). Apparently the deleted portion of chromosome 17 contains genes necessary for development when maternally derived, but the same alleles are inactive when paternally derived. These results confirm the previous observation that paternal duplication–maternal deficiency for the proximal part of chromosome 17 results in embryonic mortality, while maternal duplication–paternal deficiency for this part of chromosome 17 is without effect (Lyon and Glenister, 1977).

In the second example, embryos derived from DDK eggs fertilized with non-DDK sperm usually die, while the reciprocal cross or fertilization by DDK sperm gives normal development (Wakasugi, 1974). To investigate the incompatibility between DDK egg and non-DDK sperm, Mann (1986) transferred pronuclei of embryos derived by mating DDK females with non-DDK males into enucleated zygotes of non-DDK origin. These nuclear transfer embryos developed as well as control nuclear transfer embryos, suggesting that incompatibility between the female DDK and male non-DDK pronuclei is not the reason for developmental failure. In another series of nuclear transfers, Renard and Babinet (1986) showed that when enucleated zygotes, derived from mating DDK females with non-DDK males, are used as nuclear recipients, development is poor regardless of the genotype of the transferred nuclei. These two sets of experiments indicate that there is a specific detrimental interaction between DDK ooplasm and non-DDK sperm that is initiated immediately after fertilization and persists for some time. Conceivably "alien" paternally derived pronuclei, in contrast to DDK paternally derived pronuclei, actively express alleles in DDK ooplasm which have a lethal effect on subsequent development. Nuclear transfer experiments also established that these same alleles are not expressed by "alien" maternal pronuclei in DDK ooplasm (Renard and Babinet, 1986). Note that the differentially inactive allele appears to be derived through the female germ cell lineage for DDK and through the male lineage for T^{hp}.

The combined results from nuclear transfer and genetic experiments clearly indicate that at the moment of fertilization, the male and female genomes are functionally different. This unexpected finding suggests a series of developmentally relevant questions such as these: What are the molecular mechanisms that lead to the generation, maintenance, and expression of functional differences between gametes? How long do these differences persist? What proportion of the genome is involved? Do the differences affect all cells in the embryo or are these effects restricted to specific tissues? Although complete answers to these questions are not available, some recent experiments attempt to address these problems.

The complex series of events which occur during gametogenesis lead to end products, the sperm and the egg, with very different structural and functional chromatin characteristics (Wassarman, 1983; Bellve and O'Brien, 1983). Sperm have highly modified chromatin in which much of the histone has been replaced with protamine, the nucleosome structure has been lost, and the DNA is extensively methylated. In contrast, the chromatin of the ovum has an essentially conventional structure. Upon resumption of transcriptional activity after fertilization (Wolgemuth, 1983), one might expect structure and function of the two parental genomes to remain somewhat different, perhaps a reflection of their past history (Groudine and Conkin, 1985). The effect of the extensive changes in the sperm chromatin on its function in the fertilized egg is not clear. Rapid general remodeling occurs prior to DNA synthesis, a process which involves rehydration, loss of DNA-associated protamines, and the development of chromatin with a normal histone composition. The methylation pattern of all genes examined, with the possibly irrelevant exception of satellite DNA, differs between oocyte and sperm. These differences in methylation are seemingly maintained after fertilization (Sanford, 1986) and may affect the activity of some genes. Since the observed differences are so extensive, it seems unlikely that they all relate to differential gene regulation. In addition, whenever a specific paternal gene was examined, it was found to be active very soon after fertilization (Sawicki *et al.*, 1981; Szollosi and Yotsuyanagi, 1985; Renard and Babinet, 1986). Similarly, in the few instances where activation of both paternal and maternal genes was examined, they appeared to be activated at the same time (Table III) (Gilbert and Solter, 1985; Chapman *et al.*, 1977). Two-dimensional gel analysis of embryo protein synthesis patterns at day 2 and day 3 in culture shows that they are nearly identical for androgenetic, gynogenetic, and normal embryos when the most actively synthesized polypeptides are compared (Petzoldt *et al.*, 1981; Solter *et al.*, 1985). The inability to detect significant differences in expression between maternally and paternally derived genes during early development is not unexpected if one considers the genetic data which show that about half the chromosomes studied do not have developmental effects when present as a parental disomy/nullisomy (Cattanach and Kirk, 1985). Assuming that the genes which differ are not clustered, the data support an estimate of perhaps 10 genes which should show large differential effects, depending on their parental origin.

The stability of differences between the paternal and maternal genome during early development was examined experimentally by testing the ability of haploid nuclei from androgenetic and gynogenetic embryos to substitute for a male or female pronucleus in a partially enucleated zygote (Surani *et al.*, 1986a). Zygotes in which the female pronuclei were replaced by a haploid nucleus from a gynogenetic 4-, 8-, or 16-cell stage embryo developed to birth. Similar results were obtained in zygotes in which the male pronucleus was replaced by a haploid androgenetic nucleus from the 2- or 4-cell stage embryo. The simplest explanation of these results, assuming near-normal development of haploid embryos, is that the male and female character of the genome persists to at least the 4-cell and 16-cell stage, respectively.

TABLE III

EARLY EXPRESSION OF SOME MATERNALLY AND PATERNALLY DERIVED GENES

| "Gene" | Developmental stage | | References |
	Paternal	Maternal	
Non-DDK sperm	1 Cell	Inactive	Renard and Babinet (1986)
β_2-Microglobulin variant	2 Cells	NI[a]	Sawicki *et al.* (1981)
IAP[b] expression level	2 Cells	NI[a]	Szollosi and Yotsuyanagi (1985)
t^{12}/t^{12}	2 Cells	NI[a]	Sherman and Wudl (1977)
t^{w32}/t^{w32}	2 Cells	NI[a]	Sherman and Wudl (1977)
c^{25h}/c^{25h}	4 Cells	NI[a]	Lewis (1978)
A^Y/A^Y (agouti, yellow)	4 Cells	4 Cells	Pedersen (1974)
Protein synthesis patterns	2 Cells	2 Cells	Petzoldt *et al.* (1981)
β-Galactosidase variant	4 Cells	NI[a]	Chapman *et al.* (1977)
β-Glucuronidase level	8 Cells	NI[a]	Esworthy and Chapman (1981)
HPRT[c] activity	8 Cells	8 Cells	Kratzer and Gartler (1978)
GPI[d] isozyme	16 Cells	16 Cells	Gilbert and Solter (1985)

[a] NI, No information.
[b] IAP, Intracisternal A particle.
[c] GPI, Glucose-phosphate isomerase.
[d] HPRT, Hypoxanthine phosphoribosyl transferase.

The functional difference between the paternal and maternal X chromosome persists even longer, so that the paternally derived X chromosome is preferentially inactivated in the extraembryonic membranes of postimplantation embryos (Takagi and Sasaki, 1975).

Although it is known that ICM size, development of extraembryonic membranes, growth, and body shape are affected, the actual genes that are differentially expressed according to the parental origin of gametes have not been identified (Surani, 1985; Cattanach and Kirk, 1985). These genes appear to belong to a common category, as first pointed out by Searle and Beechey (1978), who discussed "the possibility that haploid expression of particular maternal or paternal genes is important for normal mouse development," and subsequently by Cattanach and Kirk (1985). If the difference between the paternal and maternal allele is the presence or absence of a gene product(s), then differential activity of the maternally or the paternally derived genome may be thought of as a specialized case of dosage compensation. Specific gene products might be detrimental if expressed at either too high or too low a level (i.e., those encoded by chromosomes 6 and 17), and in some instances, both extremes might be detrimental (chromosomes 2 and 11). Regardless of the exact mechanism, the functional differences between male and female genomes which are mutually compensatory provide an immediate, near-absolute, short-term advantage to sexual reproduction. Once this mechanism is established and fixed at multiple loci, it can explain the absence of asexual reproduction (Williams and Mitton, 1973).

III. Stability or Reprogramming of the Embryonic Genome

"Nuclear reprogramming" is a loosely defined term used by Gurdon (1974) "to denote fundamental changes in gene activity." Changes in genomic activity following fertilization might be considered reprogramming, but the term is usually reserved for phenomena associated with changes in gene activity following specific experimental manipulation. In this section we consider the ability of the mammalian embryonic genome to support normal development in the fertilized egg cytoplasm, questioning whether the egg cytoplasm can reverse the genomic changes that occur during early embryogenesis. The intuitive expectation—that is, that nuclei derived from totipotent embryonic cells will be totipotent in the egg cytoplasm and that the nuclei from highly differentiated cells will be resistant to reprogramming—might prove incorrect if the nuclear and cytoplasmic balance is important.

Nuclear transfer studies using amphibian embryos suggest at least a degree of reprogramming and totipotency of embryonic nuclei; that is, nuclei from the blastula stage support complete development of the embryos in a large proportion of cases (Briggs and King, 1952; Gurdon, 1974). This capability is progressively reduced as nuclei from later stages are tested, but even adult keratinocyte-derived (Gurdon, 1974) and erythrocyte-derived (Di Berardino and Hoffner, 1983) nuclei can support complete early development. The frequency of successful early development is low, and development does not progress to the adult form. Comparable studies in mammals have produced conflicting results. Illmensee and Hoppe (1981) reported that mouse ICM nuclei, when injected into enucleated zygotes, could support complete development with reasonable frequency, and the birth of appropriate genetically marked individuals derived from those transfers was described. Attempts to repeat these results in mice using a slightly different technique have repeatedly failed (Table IV), even when nuclei from as early as the 4-cell stage were transplanted (McGrath and Solter, 1984c; Surani et al., 1986a; Robl et al., 1986). However, when blastomeres from 8- to 16-cell sheep embryos were fused with enucleated eggs with a reduced cytoplasmic volume, complete development ensued (Willadsen, 1986).

At the present time, we probably do not have all the necessary experimental data to explain these apparent discrepancies; however, careful analysis of the available data provides some clues as to the problem of nuclear reprogramming in mammals. First, we will examine the possible influence of the various techniques used in these experiments. Illmensee and Hoppe (1981) introduced the donor nucleus directly into the cytoplasm using a small-bore needle, and the same needle was subsequently used to remove the host pronucleus. The pronuclei invariably burst, since they were larger than the lumen of the needle. Thus the pronuclear contents may have been released into the cytoplasm. In contrast, the technique used by us and others involves removal of pronuclei intact within a karyoplast. If some factor(s) closely associated with the pronuclei are indispensable for normal development, karyoplast removal would eliminate them from the egg; however, if the pronuclei rupture during removal, some pronuclear-associated factor or structure(s) might be left behind. For example, the cytoplasmic asters, necessary for microtubule organization and for pronuclear movement (Schatten et al., 1986), are associated with the pronuclei and would be removed in the karyoplast. However, it is unlikely that these or other major parts of the mitotic apparatus are responsible for developmental failure of nuclear transfer embryos, since these embryos usually divide several times before undergoing developmental arrest.

An alternative explanation for failure of the zygote to develop following transfer of nuclei from blastomeres is that insufficient time is

TABLE IV
DEVELOPMENT OF NUCLEAR TRANSFER EMBRYOS CONTAINING POSTZYGOTIC NUCLEI

Species	Enucleated host[a]	Nuclear donor	N[b]	Developmental Stage			References
				Submorula	Blastocyst	Progeny	
Mouse	Z	ICM[c]	66	34	7	4	Hoppe and Illmensee (1982)
	Z	ICM[d]	142	48	48	3	Illmensee and Hoppe (1981)
Mouse	Z	2 Cell	151	123	19	—	McGrath and Solter (1984c)
	Z	4 Cell	81	77	0	—	McGrath and Solter (1984c)
	Z	8 Cell	111	111	0	—	McGrath and Solter (1984c)
	Z	ICM	84	84	0	—	McGrath and Solter (1984c)
Mouse	Z	8 Cell	32		0	—	Robl et al. (1986)
	2B	2 Cell	43		40	—	Robl et al. (1986)
	2B	8 Cell	89		45	—	Robl et al. (1986)
Sheep	O[e]	8 Cell	100	25	40	—	Willadsen (1986)
	O[e]	8 Cell	—		4	3	Willadsen (1986)
	O[e]	16 Cell	29	6	14	—	Willadsen (1986)
	O[e]	16 Cell	—		6	3	Willadsen (1986)

[a] Z, Zygote; 2B, two-cell stage blastomere; O, oocyte.
[b] N, Number of embryos surviving surgery and either cultured or reimplanted.
[c] Parthenogenetic.
[d] Normal.
[e] Cytoplasmic mass was reduced by ~50%.

available for donor nuclei to adapt to the cytoplasm of the zygote. In our initial experiments, nuclear transfer was performed during the latter half of the first cell cycle. It has been shown that remodeling of adult nuclei introduced into the egg cytoplasm diminishes with increased time between egg activation and the introduction of the nucleus (Czolowska *et al.*, 1984). For this reason we introduced, by either Sendai-mediated fusion or electrofusion, karyoplasts derived from 8-cell embryos into oocytes 3 hours after activation (McGrath and Solter, 1986b). Several hours later, the newly formed female pronucleus was removed and development of these embryos monitored *in vitro*. Over 70% of the control oocytes that received zygote pronuclei developed to blastocysts, while 3% of the experimental embryos reached the morula–blastocyst stage. This is a very small yet definite improvement in development compared with our previous results with midcleavage nuclei transferred to the zygote, which never supported development to the blastocyst (McGrath and Solter, 1984c). Normal development to birth of sheep nuclear transfer embryos was observed when the part of the oocyte containing the second meiotic spindle was removed and the remaining part fused with an 8- or 16-cell stage blastomere (Willadsen, 1986). Mouse embryos produced by this type of manipulation develop poorly, and only a few reached blastocyst stage (J. Aronson and D. Solter, unpublished results). Further extending the time of donor nucleus transit in the egg cytoplasm by serial transfer through several enucleated eggs may improve the development of these reconstituted embryos, but the results suggest that an additional mechanism is required to account for the developmental arrest of these embryos.

Mouse preimplantation development is crucially dependent on the early and normal expression of the embryonic genome (Johnson, 1981; Magnuson and Epstein, 1981). We therefore speculated that reprogramming of donor nuclei is not complete, resulting in failure of synthesis of some crucial stage-specific gene products. Since major changes in gene expression (as determined by monitoring the changes in the polypeptides synthesized during preimplantation development) occur between the zygote and two-cell stage (Levinson *et al.*, 1978; Howe and Solter, 1979; Flach *et al.*, 1982), one could hypothesize that the cytoplasm of late two-cell embryos might be better suited to support development of transferred cleavage stage nuclei. Such a possibility is supported by the recent experiment in which enucleated two-cell blastomeres served as recipients for nuclei from eight-cell embryos (Robl *et al.*, 1986). These reconstituted embryos implanted and developed *in vivo* to midgestation. Although development was not observed beyond day 10 of gestation, it is very likely that, with technical improvement, transfer of eight-cell stage nuclei into two-cell stage cytoplasm could result in live births. These results strongly indicate that the activity of the embryonic genome in the zygote and possibly in the early two-cell embryo is essential to normal development (Solter, 1986). Thus the midcleavage donor nucleus either cannot be sufficiently reprogrammed in the zygote or the conditions and/or length of time allowed for reprogramming is not adequate.

As previously mentioned, nuclei from cleavage stage embryos transferred to activated oocytes can support the complete development of sheep embryos, a result which suggests a significant difference between embryos from different mammalian species. However, successful development of sheep nuclear transfer embryos may not be dependent on substantial reprogramming of the genome of the donor nucleus, since single 8-cell stage sheep blastomeres are capable of developing to term albeit at reduced frequency (Willadsen, 1981), while single 8-cell stage mouse blastomeres are not. Moreover, ultrastructural changes of the nucleoli, consistent with active rRNA synthesis, is observed in mouse embryos at the 2-cell stage (Hillman and Tasca, 1969) but not until the 16-cell stage in sheep embryos (Calarco and McLaren, 1976). Activation of the embryonic genome might occur at a later stage in the sheep than in the mouse; transfer of cleavage stage sheep nuclei would then require little or no reprogramming.

A survey of the presently available evidence suggests that cloning by nuclear transfer is not feasible in mice, a failure attributed to incomplete reprogramming of the donor nucleus in the zygote cytoplasm. This failure might be related to the inability of the egg cytoplasm under any condition to reverse activation–deactivation of certain genes (e.g., methylation differences initiated before fertilization), or it might reflect the inability fully to reprogram the genome in the fertilized egg cytoplasm in the short time available.

IV. Conclusions and Perspectives

Reproducible and easily performed nuclear transfer techniques have allowed us to explore the role of the major components of the fertilized egg in mouse embryonic development. Paternal and maternal genomes are functionally different and complementary; thus the presence of both is required for complete development. It is likely that functional differences exist for only small numbers of specific genes, while most of the male and female genome is comparable. These somewhat unexpected results further emphasize the need for identification and characterization of genes which regulate early mammalian development. The existence and the extent of reprogramming of the mammalian genome exemplified by the ability of embryonic nuclei to support development of enucleated eggs remains an open question. Transfer of early embryonic nuclei into enucleated zygotes is unlikely to result in complete development, at least in the mouse. Limited reprogramming might occur in other mammalian species, although it is not proven. Regardless of the reasons for the developmental failure of nuclear transfer embryos, they will continue to be an excellent model for analyzing mechanisms which control early mammalian development. Numerous factors including the role of the cell cycle, nuclear–cytoplasmic ratio, and the need for specific gene products remain to be explored. It will be also crucial to demonstrate, using two-dimensional gel analysis, that the ongoing program of gene expression is reversed following nuclear transfer and that a new and appropriate program is initiated.

ACKNOWLEDGMENTS

This work was supported in part by grants HD-12487 and HD-17720 from the National Institute of Child Health and Human Development, CA-10815 and CA-25875 from the National Cancer Institute, and 8502155 from the U.S. Department of Agriculture. Critical comments by Drs. Barbara B. Knowles and James McGrath are gratefully acknowledged.

REFERENCES

Altman, P. L., and Dittmer, D. S. (1972). "Biology Data Book," 2nd Ed., Vol. 1, p. 529. Fed. Am. Soc. Exp. Biol., Bethesda, Maryland.

Anderegg, C., and Markert, C. L. (1986). *Proc. Natl. Acad. Sci. U.S.A.* **83**, 6509–6513.

Barton, S. C., Surani, M. A. H., and Norris, M. L. (1984). *Nature (London)* **311**, 374–376.

Barton, S. C., Adams, C. A., Norris, M. L., and Surani, M. A. H. (1985). *J. Embryol. Exp. Morphol.* **90**, 267–285.

Beatty, R. A. (1957). "Parthenogenesis and Polyploidy in Mammalian Development." Cambridge Univ. Press, Cambridge and New York.

Bell, G. (1982). "The Masterpiece of Nature," pp. 342–347. Univ. of California Press, Berkeley.

Bellvé, A. R., and O'Brien, D. A. (1983). *In* "Mechanism and Control of Animal Fertilization" (J. F. Hartmann, ed.), pp. 55–137. Academic Press, New York.

Briggs, R., and King, T. J. (1952). *Proc. Natl. Acad. Sci. U.S.A.* **38**, 455–463.

Calarco, P. G., and McLaren, A. (1976). *J. Embryol. Exp. Morphol.* **36**, 609–622.

Cattanach, B. M. (1986). *J. Embryol. Exp. Morphol.* **97** (Suppl.), 137–150.

Cattanach, B. M., and Kirk, M. (1985). *Nature (London)* **315**, 496–498.

Chapman, V. M., West, J. D., and Adler, D. A. (1977). *In* "Concepts in Mammalian Development" (M. I. Sherman, ed.), pp. 95–135. MIT Press, Cambridge, Massachusetts.

Cuellar, O. (1977). *Science* **197**, 837–843.

Czolowska, R., Modlinski, J. A., and Tarkowski, A. K. (1984). *J. Cell Sci.* **69**, 19–34.

Di Berardino, M. A., and Hoffner, N. J. (1983). *Science* **219**, 862–864.

Esworthy, S., and Chapman, V. M. (1981). *Dev. Genet.* **2**, 1–12.

Evans, M. J., Bradley, A., Kuehn, M. R., and Robertson, E. J. (1985). *Cold Spring Harbor Symp. Quant. Biol.* **50**, 685–689.

Flach, G., Johnson, M. H., Braude, P. R., Taylor, R. A. S., and Bolton, V. N. (1982). *EMBO J.* **1**, 681–686.

Gilbert, S. F., and Solter, D. (1985). *Dev. Biol.* **109**, 515–517.

Graham, C. F. (1974). *Biol. Rev.* **49**, 399–422.

Groudine, M., and Conkin, K. F. (1985). *Science* **228**, 1061–1068.

Gurdon, J. B. (1974). "The Control of Gene Expression in Animal Development." Clarendon, Oxford.

Hillman, N., and Tasca, R. J. (1969). *Am. J. Anat.* **126**, 151–174.

Hoppe, P. C., and Illmensee, K. (1977). *Proc. Natl. Acad. Sci. U.S.A.* **74**, 5657–5661.

Hoppe, P. C., and Illmensee, K. (1982). *Proc. Natl. Acad. Sci. U.S.A.* **79**, 1912–1916.

Howe, C. C., and Solter, D. (1979). *J. Embryol. Exp. Morphol.* **52**, 209–225.

Illmensee, K., and Hoppe, P. C. (1981). *Cell* **23**, 9–18.

Johnson, D. R. (1975). *Genet. Res.* **24**, 207–213.

Johnson, M. H. (1981). *Biol. Rev.* **56**, 463–498.

Kaufman, M. H. (1983). "Early Mammalian Development: Parthenogenetic Studies." Cambridge Univ. Press, Cambridge and New York.

Kaufman, M. H., Barton, S. C., and Surani, M. A. H. (1977). *Nature (London)* **265**, 53–55.

Kaufman, M. H., Robertson, E. J., Handyside, A. H., and Evans, M. J. (1983). *J. Embryol. Exp. Morphol.* **73**, 249–261.

Kratzer, P. G., and Gartler, S. M. (1978). *Nature (London)* **274**, 503–504.

Levinson, J., Goodfellow, P., Vadeboncoeur, M., and Devitt, H. M. (1978). *Proc. Natl. Acad. Sci. U.S.A.* **75**, 3332–3336.

Lewis, S. E. (1978). *Dev. Biol.* **65**, 553–557.

Lyon, M. F., and Glenister, P. H. (1977). *Genet. Res.* **29**, 83–92.

McGrath, J., and Solter, D. (1983). *Science* **220**, 1300–1302.

McGrath, J., and Solter, D. (1984a). *Cell* **37**, 179–183.

McGrath, J., and Solter, D. (1984b). *Nature (London)* **308**, 550–551.

McGrath, J., and Solter, D. (1984c). *Science* **226**, 1317–1319.

McGrath, J., and Solter, D. (1985). *In* "Genetic Manipulation of the Early Mammalian Embryo" (F. Costantini and R. Jaenisch, eds.), pp. 31–42. Banbury Report, Cold Spring Harbor Laboratory, Cold Spring Harbor, New York.

McGrath, J., and Solter, D. (1986a). *In* "Manipulation of Mammalian Development" (R. B. L. Gwatkin, ed.), pp. 37–55. Plenum, New York.

McGrath, J., and Solter, D. (1986b). *J. Embryol. Exp. Morphol.* **97** (Suppl.), 277–289.

Magnuson, T., and Epstein, C. J. (1981). *Biol. Rev.* **56**, 369–408.

Mann, J. R. (1986). *J. Reprod. Fertil.* **76**, 779–781.

Mann, J. R., and Lovell-Badge, R. H. (1984). *Nature (London)* **310**, 66–67.

Markert, C. L. (1982). *J. Hered.* **73**, 390–397.

Modlinski, J. A. (1980). *J. Embryol. Exp. Morphol.* **60**, 153–161.

Pedersen, R. A. (1974). *Exp. Zool.* **188**, 307–320.

Petzoldt, U., Illmensee, G. R., Burki, K., Hoppe, P. C., and Illmensee, K. (1981). *Mol. Gen. Genet.* **184**, 11–16.

Pincus, G. (1939a). *J. Exp. Zool.* **82**, 85–114.

Pincus, G. (1939b). *Proc. Natl. Acad. Sci. U.S.A.* **25**, 557–559.

Renard, J. P., and Babinet, C. (1986). *Proc. Natl. Acad. Sci. U.S.A.* **83**, 6883–6886.

Robertson, E. J., Evans, M. J., and Kaufman, M. H. (1983). *J. Embryol. Exp. Morphol.* **74**, 297–309.

Robl, J. M., Gilligan, B., Critser, E. S., and First, N. L. (1986). *Biol. Reprod.* **34**, 733–739.

Sanford, J. P. (1986). DNA methylation in early mouse development: Possible means for gametic imprinting. Ph.D. thesis, State University of New York, Buffalo, New York, unpublished.

Sawicki, J. A., Magnuson, T., and Epstein, C. J. (1981). *Nature (London)* **294**, 450–451.

Schatten, H., Schatten, G., Mazia, D., Balczon, R., and Simerly, C. (1986). *Proc. Natl. Acad. Sci. U.S.A.* **83**, 105–109.

Searle, A. G., and Beechey, C. V. (1978). *Cytogenet. Cell Genet.* **20**, 282–303.

Searle, A. G., and Beechey, C. V. (1985). *In* "Aneuploidy: Etiology and Mechanisms" (V. L. Dellarco, P. E. Voytek, and A. Hollaender, eds.), pp. 363–376. Plenum, New York.

Sherman, M. I., and Wudl, L. R. (1977). *In* "Concepts in Mammalian Embryogenesis" (M. I. Sherman, ed.). MIT Press, Cambridge, Massachusetts.

Solter, D. (1986). *In* "Molecular Genetics in Developmental Neurobiology" (Y. Tsukada, ed.), pp. 91–100. Japan Scientific Societies Press, Tokyo.

Solter, D., Aronson, J., Gilbert, S. F., and McGrath, J. (1985). *Cold Spring Harbor Symp. Quant. Biol.* **50**, 45–50.

Stevens, L. C. (1978). *Nature (London)* **276**, 266–267.

Stevens, L. C., Varnum, D. S., and Eicher, E. M. (1977). *Nature (London)* **269**, 515–517.

Surani, A. (1985). *In* "Genetic Manipulation of the Early Mammalian Embryo" (F. Costantini and R. Jaenisch, eds.), pp. 43–55. Banbury Report, Cold Spring Harbor Laboratory, Cold Spring Harbor, New York.

Surani, M. A. H., and Barton, S. C. (1983). *Science* **222**, 1034–1036.

Surani, M. A. H., Barton, S. C., and Norris, M. L. (1984). *Nature (London)* **308**, 548–550.

Surani, M. A. H., Barton, S. C., and Norris, M. L. (1986a). *Cell* **45**, 127–136.

Surani, M. A. H., Reik, W., Norris, M. L., and Barton, S. C. (1986b). *J. Embryol. Exp. Morphol.* **97** (Suppl.), 123–136.

Szollosi, D., and Yotsuyanagi, Y. (1985). *Dev. Biol.* **111**, 256–259.

Takagi, N., and Sasaki, M. (1975). *Nature (London)* **256**, 640–641.

Wakasugi, N. (1974). *J. Reprod. Fertil.* **41**, 85–96.

Wassarman, P. M. (1983). *In* "Mechanism and Control of Animal Fertilization" (J. F. Hartmann, ed.), pp. 1–54. Academic Press, New York.

Willadsen, S. M. (1981). *J. Embryol. Exp. Morphol.* **65**, 165–172.

Willadsen, S. M. (1986). *Nature (London)* **320**, 63–65.

Williams, G. C., and Mitton, J. B. (1973). *J. Theor. Biol.* **39**, 545–554.

Wolgemuth, D. J. (1983). *In* "Mechanism and Control of Animal Fertilization" (J. F. Hartmann, ed.), pp. 415–452. Academic Press, New York.

CHAPTER 4

OVUM FACTOR AND EARLY PREGNANCY FACTOR

Halle Morton, Barbara E. Rolfe, and Alice C. Cavanagh

DEPARTMENT OF SURGERY
UNIVERSITY OF QUEENSLAND
ROYAL BRISBANE HOSPITAL
HERSTON QUEENSLAND 4029
AUSTRALIA

I. Introduction

The conceptus from very early in its development produces or stimulates the production of substances that will create the most advantageous environment for its survival. During the pre- and peri-implantation periods, conceptus secretory proteins provide a signal for the continuing production of progesterone in order to maintain the uterine environment. These proteins may act directly on the corpus luteum as antiluteolysins, or indirectly by inducing antiluteolysins from the endometrium (Godkin *et al.*, 1984). The maintenance of the uterine environment is essential for the production of uterine secretory proteins, thought to provide nutrition for the various stages of embryonic development (Beier, 1974). With successful implantation and the development of the placenta, placental proteins are produced, almost always by trophoblast cells. Many placental proteins have been described; their occurrence and possible biological function has been reviewed by Bohn (1985). The properties of early pregnancy factor (EPF) do not suggest that it can be grouped with any of the previously described pregnancy-dependent proteins; it differs in its time course, source of production, and activity both *in vivo* and *in vitro*.

EPF is produced from maternal tissue (ovary) as the result of stimulation by a signal (ovum factor) released from the ovum on fertilization (Cavanagh *et al.*, 1982). EPF can be detected in serum of all species yet tested within 24 hours of a fertile mating, and thus provides the first means of determining *in vitro* that pregnancy has commenced (Morton *et al.*, 1976; Rolfe, 1982). Ovarian production continues from fertilization until shortly after implantation, by which time the placenta has commenced development and becomes the second source of

73

EPF (Morton *et al.*, 1982a; Morton, 1984). EPF has been purified from sheep serum (Wilson *et al.*, 1983, 1984), and from medium conditioned either by mouse ovaries and oviducts (Cavanagh, 1984) or by a choriocarcinoma cell line (Cavanagh, 1985). A partial amino acid sequence of EPF purified from the two latter sources has shown that it is a novel protein (Cavanagh *et al.*, unpublished data).

EPF is detected by its ability to bind lymphocytes, both *in vivo* and *in vitro,* and in so doing to release suppressor substances (Rolfe, 1985). It is these suppressor substances that are active in the bioassay for EPF, the rosette inhibition test (Morton *et al.*, 1976; Rolfe *et al.*, 1984). The stimulation of suppressor release by EPF has led to the proposal that EPF is involved in modulating the mother's immune system during pregnancy to prevent rejection of the embryo (Noonan *et al.*, 1979; Rolfe *et al.*, 1987).

In this chapter evidence will be presented to show that EPF in serum is an indication of the presence of a viable conceptus. The tissues involved in the production of EPF will be discussed, and finally the role of EPF in the maintenance of the embryo will be considered.

II. Assay for EPF: The Rosette Inhibition Test

EPF was originally detected by Morton *et al.* (1974, 1976) using a modification of the rosette inhibition test (Bach *et al.*, 1968, 1969). Bach and his colleagues defined the rosette inhibition titer (RIT) of an antilymphocyte serum (ALS) as the titer to which an ALS can inhibit rosette formation between lymphocytes and heterologous red blood cells to less than 75% of the number formed in the absence of ALS. This titer did not vary more than two doubling dilutions when tested with lymphocytes from different normal donors. Morton *et al.* (1974, 1976) showed that if either lymphocytes from pregnant mice or lymphocytes from nonpregnant mice, preincubated in pregnancy serum, were used to estimate the RIT of an ALS, the RIT was significantly increased above that obtained with untreated nonpregnancy lymphocytes. As a result of these findings, EPF was defined as a soluble factor capable of eliciting an increase in RIT of an ALS in this assay; all subsequent studies on EPF have relied on detection of this increase.

Various groups have used this method for the detection of EPF in serum as a means of diagnosing pregnancy in humans (Morton *et al.*, 1977; Smart *et al.*, 1982a–c; Tinneberg *et al.*, 1984; Chen *et al.*, 1985), sheep (Morton *et al.*, 1979; Nancarrow *et al.*, 1979), and pigs (Morton *et al.*, 1983). In these studies, sera were tested with lymphocytes from the same species and ALS prepared from these lymphocytes. The details of the methods used are fully discussed in these publications. Several groups (Cooper and Aitken, 1981; Thompson *et al.*, 1980) have been critical of the method as they have failed to repeat published results. However, neither group had carried out the assay as recommended but had introduced inappropriate modifications, which led to a failure to detect EPF. Some causes of apparent false-negative results are discussed by Morton and colleagues (1982b).

The assay for EPF in human serum, using human lymphocytes and anti-human ALS, consistently detects the presence of EPF but its sensitivity is restricted by a difference of only one to three doubling dilutions of ALS between pregnancy and nonpregnancy samples (Morton *et al.*, 1977; Smart *et al.*, 1982c; Rolfe *et al.*, 1984). Rolfe and co-workers (1984) modified the assay so that EPF in human pregnancy serum can be detected with mouse lymphocytes. Interference resulting from incubation of lymphocytes with heterologous serum proteins is prevented by the introduction of an ion-exchange chromatography step. This is a simple and rapid method for separating EPF from interfering serum proteins which can also be applied to serum from other species. The rosette inhibition test using mouse lymphocytes and anti-mouse ALS has the advantage of showing a greater difference in RIT values (more than three alternate doubling dilutions of ALS) between pregnancy and nonpregnancy serum samples (see Fig. 1). Furthermore, the ready availability of a defined population of spleen cells from control-bred mice suggests that the mouse assay system could provide a universally applicable method capable of a considerable degree of standardization.

The reliability of the mouse assay system has been investigated by Rolfe *et al.* (1987). They reported results obtained with the rosette inhibition test on serum from a group of 19 nonpregnant mice. In each test lymphocytes from a male donor mouse were preincubated in test serum before a further incubation in each of eight ALS dilutions (alternate doubling dilutions from 12 to 26; see Fig. 1). The results have been analyzed using a random-effect, one-way classification (by mice) statistical model (see, for example, Miller, 1986). The analysis of results based on the logarithm of percentage change within each test led to a lower 5% point of 76.03%. Using a binomial distribution with index 8 (corresponding to eight ALS dilutions per test), the probability of rosette counts being less than 76.03% in two ALS dilutions was estimated to be 0.057, and in three ALS dilutions reduced to the acceptable level of 0.006. A positive assay for EPF is defined therefore as an RIT of at least three alternate doubling dilutions of ALS above the RIT with the negative controls; in Fig. 1, the negative control RIT is 10, so an RIT of 16 or greater would be a positive assay for EPF.

In a recent study, Wong *et al.* (1987) tested for EPF in serum from

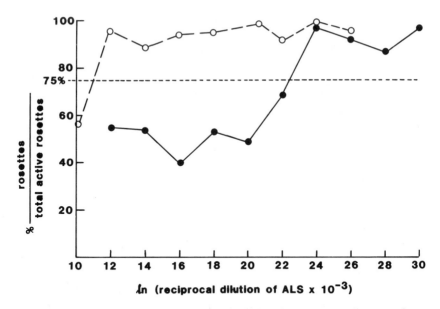

Fig. 1. Titration curves with lymphocytes incubated in mouse pregnancy and non-pregnancy serum. The number of rosettes formed at each dilution of ALS is expressed as a percentage of total active rosettes (i.e., those formed without ALS). The RIT of each serum sample is the highest dilution of ALS [expressed as ln (reciprocal dilution of ALS × 10^{-3})] in which the number of rosettes is <75%. ●——●, Pregnancy serum, RIT 22; ○- - - - -○, nonpregnancy serum, RIT 10.

16 nonmated female mice and 30 mated female mice, 32 hours after mating. The mated mice were autopsied 10 days later and examined for the presence of viable embryos. The RIT with lymphocytes incubated in serum from nonmated mice gave a mean of 9.6 (SE 0.2; $n = 16$). Four of the mated mice gave an RIT of 10 and were not pregnant on examination at 10 days. Of the 26 mice with RIT ranging from 22 to 28, mean RIT 25.1 (SE 0.45), 25 were pregnant when examined. One mouse gave a positive EPF assay (RIT 22) at 32 hours but was not pregnant 10 days later; this may have been due to error in the assay or to spontaneous abortion after 32 hours gestation. The correlation between the presence of EPF (RIT of ≥16) and pregnancy was highly significant ($p < 0.001$, χ^2 test).

III. EPF in Preimplantation Pregnancy Serum

EPF in serum has been investigated as a marker for fertilization and implantation. In animals, EPF has been detected in the serum 6–24 hours after a fertile mating (Morton *et al.*, 1976, 1979, 1983), and in women, several workers have reported the appearance of EPF within 2 days following estimated ovulation and fertilization (Rolfe, 1982; Smart *et al.*, 1982a–c; Tinneberg *et al.*, 1984; Mesrogli and Maas, 1985). EPF is not produced as the result of ovulation alone nor after infertile intercourse (Morton *et al.*, 1977). The appearance of EPF in serum thus provides the earliest indication of fertilization.

The incidence of fertilization and the progress of the early embryo has been monitored by assay of serum EPF. In a study of 13 nulliparous women, Rolfe (1982) detected EPF after ovulation and intercourse in 18 of the 28 cycles investigated, giving a fertilization rate of 67%. However she also found a high incidence of embryonic loss (78%), with EPF disappearing from the circulation before the onset of menstruation in 14 cases. In the remaining 4 cases EPF production continued beyond 14 days and the presence of a viable embryo was confirmed by β-human chorionic gonadotrophin (β-hCG) assay. Smart and co-workers (1982c) in a similar study also found a fertilization rate of 67% but only 38% fetal loss. This latter group contained multiparous as well as nulliparous women, which could account for the higher rate of implantation. Mesrogli and Maas (1985) looked for EPF in serum in 66 cycles of a group of 38 women undergoing artificial insemination because of abnormalities in the husband's sperm or pathological cervical factors. They showed that in 1 of 3 cycles, EPF was detectable in serum, tested 2 days before the due date of menstruation, signifying fertilization of the ovum. Of these 22 EPF-positive cycles, 7 (31%) resulted in a confirmed pregnancy. These authors concluded that EPF is a valuable means of diagnosis of conception.

A positive assay for EPF in serum is the only means of demonstrating the existence of a viable embryo *in vivo* during the preimplantation period other than by surgery. Therefore, it is not possible at this stage to confirm by other means that serum EPF monitors the viability of the early conceptus. However, two approaches that have provided convincing evidence have been the appearance of EPF in serum after embryo transfer and its disappearance after induced abortion.

IV. Serum EPF after Embryo Transfer

The appearance of EPF in serum after embryo transfer has been reported in sheep (Nancarrow *et al.*, 1981) and women (Chen, 1985; Chen *et al.*, 1985; Mesrogli and Maas, 1985). A study has also been carried out (Gidley-Baird, Cavanagh, Rolfe, Morton, and Quinn, unpublished results) in which serum EPF, tested at various times after transfer, was related to the presence of fertilized ova.

In this study, injection of pregnant mares' serum gonadotropin and hCG was used to synchronize the estrous cycle of a group of mice (Edwards and Gates, 1959); these were then stimulated into pseudo-pregnancy by mating with vasectomized males and animals on day 3 of pseudopregnancy were used as recipients of transferred fertilized ova. The fertilized ova were obtained from other mice on day 1 (one-cell), day 3 (eight-cell), or day 4 (blastocyst) of pregnancy, or unfertilized ova were obtained within 24 hours of ovulation; ova were washed twice in Whitten's medium (Whitten, 1956) prior to transfer. Groups of nine pseudopregnant mice received five ova per uterine horn from one of the above categories. Three mice within each group were then killed at 12, 24, and 48 hours after transfer. Ova were recovered from the reproductive tract and examined. Serum samples were obtained from each mouse, coded, and sent to another group for EPF assay. After all tests were completed, results were correlated.

Table I shows serum EPF and the state of recovered ova in mice at various times after transfer. In some cases, unfertilized, degenerating ova of the recipient mouse were recovered with the transferred ova. EPF was detected in serum only in animals in which healthy cleaving ova or blastocysts were recovered at the time of autopsy. It was not detected in animals which received healthy eggs but from which only degenerating ova were recovered (e.g., in animals 24 and 48 hours after asynchronous transfer) nor in animals receiving unfertilized ova or sham operations. EPF was not detected in the serum of four animals from which apparently healthy preimplantation ova were recovered; the reason for this is unclear. Nevertheless, the results show that the appearance of EPF in the serum is directly related to the presence of a viable conceptus.

Nancarrow and his group (1981) found EPF in serum of synchronized ewes, 24 hours and 12 days after embryo transfer. The ewes were examined after slaughter at 9 weeks; two of the four had maintained their pregnancies.

Serum EPF after embryo transfer in women has been investigated by Chen and his group (Chen, 1985; Chen et al., 1985). In this study 3 patients had transfers that presented technical difficulties and the success of the procedure was uncertain. No EPF was found in the serum of these patients when tested at various times after transfer. Of 22 patients in whom the embryo was definitely placed within the uterus, elevated levels of EPF activity were observed in all patients up to day 7. In 14 of these cases EPF was not detectable beyond this time and all failed to become pregnant. In the remaining 8 cases activity was present on the third and subsequent days of transfer up to day 15, at which time pregnancy was confirmed by β-hCG assay. All 25 cases were negative for EPF before transfer.

In a similar study, Mesrogli and Maas (1985) also found that by monitoring serum EPF, *in vitro* fertilization patients could be classified into three groups: (1) no successful transfer, (2) successful transfer but failure to implant, and (3) confirmed pregnancy.

V. Serum EPF after Induced Abortion

Although the disappearance of EPF has been noted after spontaneous abortion (Rolfe, 1982; Smart *et al.*, 1982c), more decisive results have been obtained by determining the time course of EPF in serum after surgical removal of the embryo. A study was done in pigs in which the occurrence of serum EPF before and after surgical removal of the ova was related to the development of these ova in culture (Koch *et al.*, 1982). The results indicated that (1) EPF disappears from the serum within 24 hours of removal of fertilized eggs; (2) in the presence of unfertilized eggs, EPF is absent from the serum; and (3) for the polytocous pig, more than one fertilized and viable egg seems to be necessary to signal the production of EPF. In sheep, Nancarrow and coworkers (1979) showed that levels of serum EPF rapidly declined following the removal of the conceptus from the oviducts and uteri, with no EPF detectable 24 hours later.

The decline of EPF activity in serum after therapeutic abortion has also been evaluated in a group of women 6–8 weeks pregnant (Mettler *et al.*, 1985). EPF values and concentration of luteinizing hormone (LH), β-hCG, estradiol, progesterone, and prolactin were compared on the basis of the relative decrease from levels found immediately prior to abortion. The results obtained are reproduced in Fig. 2 (from Mettler *et al.*, 1985). From their experiments, the authors concluded that EPF can be regarded as a sensitive parameter for the surveillance of early pregnancy, as embryonic mortality is detected earlier than with the commonly used hormone determinations.

VI. EPF Production: Tissues of Source

In the preimplantation stage the fertilized egg does not itself liberate EPF; it does not have this capacity until it reaches the blastocyst stage (Morton *et al.*, 1982a). Prior to development of trophoblast, the fertilized egg liberates an EPF-releasing factor (ovum factor; see Section VII) rather than EPF. Morton *et al.* (1980) and Cavanagh *et al.* (1982) have shown that medium from fertilized mouse ova, cultured *in vitro,* does not have any detectable EPF at least until ova develop to

TABLE I

SERUM EPF AND OVA RECOVERED AT VARIOUS TIMES AFTER EMBRYO TRANSFER[a]

Treatment[b]	12 hours		24 hours		48 hours	
	EPF (RIT)[c]	Ova recovered[c]	EPF (RIT)[c]	Ova recovered[c]	EPF (RIT)[c]	Ova recovered[c]
One-cell fertilized ova	28	3 × 2-cell; 4 × 1-cell; 8 degenerated	12	7 × 2-cell; 1 × 1-cell	10	1 compacted 4-cell
	30	3 × 2-cell; 6 × 1-cell	12	—	10	8 × 2-cell compact; 1 abnormal 4-cell
	12	9 × 1-cell; 10 degenerated	12	10 × 2-cell	10	1 degenerated
Eight-cell fertilized ova	22	8 × 8-cell	10	—	10	—
	20	3 × 8-cell; 5 degenerated	—	5 × 16-cell; 1 morula; 1 blastocyst	22	3 small implantation sites; 2 compact
	10	5 × 8- to 16-cell; 3 × 8-cell	18	5 morulae; 5 blastocysts	12	6 blastocysts without zona
Blastocysts	20	2 blastocysts; 5 degenerated	10	7 blastocysts; 5 degenerated	—	—

	20	5 blastocysts; 3 degenerated	16	4 blastocysts	—	—
	24	7 blastocysts; 4 degenerated	10	4 blastocysts	—	—
Unfertilized ova	10	4 unfertilized	10	5 unfertilized	10	—
	12	21 unfertilized; 3 degenerated; 8 abnormal	10	12 unfertilized; 6 abnormal	10	—
	10	19 unfertilized; 6 degenerated; 10 abnormal	10	—	10	—
Sham operation	10	6 unfertilized; 5 degenerated	10	—	—	—
	10	4 unfertilized, degenerated	10	3 unfertilized, degenerated	—	—
	10	3 unfertilized; 1 degenerated	12	2 unfertilized	—	—

[a] These results are from a collaborative study of the authors with Dr. A. A. Gidley-Baird, Department of Veterinary Physiology, University of Sydney, and Dr. P. Quinn, Department of Biological Sciences, University of Newcastle, New South Wales, Australia.

[b] Five ova were transferred to each uterine horn of each mouse on day 3 of pseudopregnancy. At autopsy at the times indicated, ova were flushed from the uterus and serum was obtained.

[c] Each group of results (i.e., serum EPF + ova recovered) shows values from an individual mouse. RIT >14 indicates the presence of EPF.

81

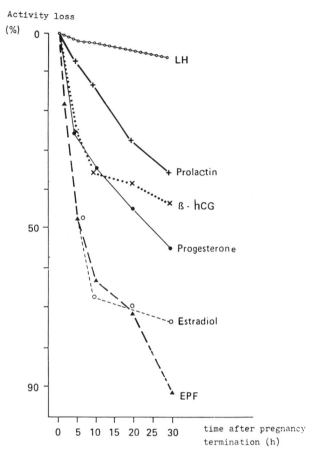

F𝐼𝐺. 2. Activity loss of six pregnancy-associated substances in serum following therapeutic abortion. (From Mettler *et al.*, 1985, with permission.)

the blastocyst stage; at this stage the production of embryonic EPF
commences (Morton *et al.*, 1982a). Nancarrow *et al.* (1981) similarly
showed that infusates prepared from fertilized mouse ova did not contain EPF activity. A. C. Cavanagh (unpublished data) tested human
embryo culture medium (supplied by Dr. Alan Trounson, Melbourne,
Australia) and once again found no EPF. This work has been confirmed
recently by Chen and co-workers (1985), who were unable to find any
EPF-like activity in their human embryo cultures; in their experiments, the test only became positive when exogenous EPF was added
to the culture medium.

To determine the early source of EPF, various tissues from 24-hour pregnant, estrous, and diestrous mice were cultured *in vitro* for 24 hours, after which the culture medium was tested for EPF (Morton *et al.*, 1980). Ova (fertilized and unfertilized) were flushed from the oviducts before incubation; then ovaries, oviducts, and ova were incubated separately and together. EPF activity was found in the medium from the culture of ovaries plus oviducts from 24-hour pregnant mice. The cultures with estrous or diestrous ovaries plus estrous oviducts could be stimulated to produce EPF if both fertilized ova and pituitaries were added to the culture system (Morton *et al.*, 1980).

These studies in mice seemed to indicate that EPF consisted of two components, both of which were required for activity in the rosette inhibition test. These were termed EPF-A from the oviduct and EPF-B from the ovary. The components appeared to have *in vitro* counterparts, as demonstrated by Clarke *et al.* (1980) in their studies on ammonium sulfate fractions of 24-hour pregnant ewes' serum. EPF-A was shown to have an inhibitory effect on EPF activity (Morton *et al.*, 1980); this was further demonstrated in pigs in which excess EPF-A was found in serum of some pigs during the first 3 weeks of pregnancy, resulting in a negative assay for EPF (Morton *et al.*, 1983).

More recent studies which are still in progress have further clarified the nature of these two components. EPF activity has been shown to reside entirely in the ovarian component, EPF-B, while EPF-A appears to play a regulatory role. The latter has an inhibitory effect on EPF-induced suppressor release, i.e., in the presence of EPF-A, higher concentrations of EPF (EPF-B) are required for suppressor induction. The range of concentrations over which EPF is able to affect lymphocytes is thereby extended, raising the possibility that as an inhibitory binding protein, EPF-A may be an important biological regulator of EPF (A. C. Cavanagh, unpublished data).

A need for the ovaries in EPF production has been confirmed *in vivo* in a group of ovariectomized mice (Gidley-Baird *et al.*, unpublished data). The ovaries were removed at various times after mating, and the mice maintained on progesterone (1 mg in sesame oil daily; McLaren, 1971) until autopsy 3 days later. Serum collected at autopsy was tested for EPF and the reproductive tract examined for embryos and implantation sites. All four mice ovariectomized on day 4 of pregnancy had normal implants at the time of autopsy, while the four mice ovariectomized on day 3 had normal blastocysts in the uterus at autopsy; both groups had EPF in their serum (RIT >16; negative control group, RIT 10). In contrast, normal blastocysts were recovered from only one of the four mice ovariectomized on day 2 of pregnancy; EPF was present in the serum of this animal (RIT 22). The other three animals in the group had poorly developed or degenerating eggs and no EPF was detectable in serum (RIT 8–10). Thus if the maternal source of EPF is removed, EPF can be produced only from the time embryos have reached the blastocyst stage.

VII. Ovum Factor: Embryonic Signal for EPF Production

The existence of an EPF-releasing factor of embryonic origin was first recognized by Morton et al. (1980) in the mouse; it has been termed ovum factor (Cavanagh et al., 1982). Ovum factor was shown to cooperate with the pituitary in stimulating ovarian production of EPF. Release of ovum factor is initiated at virtually the time of penetration of the ova by spermatozoa (Cavanagh et al., 1982), suggesting that it is already in the ovum and that fertilization acts as a trigger for its release. The alternative proposition that ovum factor is a sperm product, released upon interaction with the ovum, seems unlikely as processes which parthenogenetically activate the ovum are capable also of liberating ovum factor from the unfertilized egg. However, a specific stimulus is needed, e.g., spermatozoa, hyaluronoglucuronidase, or Ca^{2+}- and Mg^{2+}-free medium; ovum factor is not released either by diffusion or by sonication (Cavanagh et al., 1982). On stimulation, human ova (A. C. Cavanagh, unpublished data), pig and sheep ova (H. Morton, unpublished data), as well as mouse ova (Cavanagh et al., 1982) have all been found to produce ovum factor. Moreover, the ability of this substance to stimulate the production of EPF from the ovary is not species specific; ovum factor produced from cultured human and pig embryos stimulates EPF production from mouse ovaries in vitro similarly to mouse ovum factor (H. Morton and A. C. Cavanagh, unpublished data). In vivo, Nancarrow and his group (1981) have shown that after an infusion of culture medium from fertilized mouse ova, EPF can be detected in serum of estrous sheep.

An initial characterization of ovum factor (Cavanagh et al., 1982) showed that it is produced by the conceptus from fertilization at least until blastulation. Ovum factor appears to exist in forms of relative molecular mass (M_r) approximately 160,000, 2,800, and 1,500. The large and a combination of the two smaller forms will stimulate the production of EPF when injected intraperitoneally into estrous mice (Fig. 3; see Cavanagh et al., 1982).

Orozco and co-workers (1986) found that synthetic platelet-activating factor (PAF) acts similarly to ovum factor in stimulating EPF production from the ovaries of mature female mice. Embryo-derived PAF was first described by O'Neill (1985a–c) as a product of the zygote

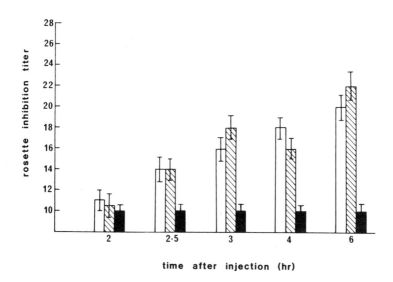

time after injection (hr)

Fig. 3. EPF production was stimulated in estrous mice by injection of low- and high-M_r preparations of ovum factor. Results are expressed as the RIT; values >14 indicate the presence of EPF in the serum. Each bar represents the mean of three animals; standard errors of the mean are shown. Open bars, EPF after low-M_r ovum factor injection; crosshatched bars, EPF after high-M_r ovum factor injection; closed bars, EPF after injection of buffer. (From Cavanagh et al., 1982, with permission.)

which causes a reduction in peripheral blood platelet count; its biochemical and physiological properties were shown to be similar to the well-characterized PAF (Snyder, 1985). The conclusion drawn by Orozco and his group, as a result of their *in vivo* studies, was that ovum factor, produced by the ovum at fertilization, is the same as embryo-derived PAF. These two substances have similar M_r, and both appear to bind to carrier molecules in the circulation. Induction of EPF activity and altered maternal platelet physiology may be two of the roles of this very early embryonic signal.

VIII. Cooperation of Prolactin with Ovum Factor in EPF Release from the Ovary

Experiments in mice have shown that ovum factor requires the cooperative action of a soluble factor from the pituitary in order to stimulate EPF production. Initially an *in vitro* system, described by Cavanagh et al. (1982), was used to investigate the identity of the pituitary factor. Ovaries from nonpregnant mice were incubated with medium conditioned by fertilized ova (a source of ovum factor) and with various pituitary hormones. EPF could be detected in supernatant 24 hours later only if both ovum factor and prolactin were present. Prolactin could not be replaced by follicle-stimulating hormone, luteinizing hormone, a combination of these two, or by ovine growth hormone; nor was it successful when used alone. If prolactin was omitted, ovum factor alone was unable to stimulate EPF production.

Confirmation of the essential role played by prolactin was provided by a series of *in vivo* experiments (Gidley-Baird *et al.*, unpublished data). Hypophysectomy of mice 6 hours after confirmed mating resulted in the disappearance of EPF from serum within 48 hours. However, EPF production could be maintained by injections of 10 μg prolactin, twice daily (see Morton *et al.*, 1982a). Within 48 hours of subsequent withdrawal of prolactin, EPF was no longer detectable in serum. Injections of growth hormone were unable to produ   similar effects.

In all of these studies, both *in vivo* and *in vitro,* the simultaneous presence of both prolactin and ovum factor is required for EPF production. Their action on the ovary appears to be cooperative but the mechanism of the action remains to be elucidated.

IX. Passive Immunization of Pregnant Mice with Monoclonal Antibodies to EPF

Having established that EPF is present during preimplantation pregnancy, the question arises whether or not it is necessary for the survival, and later the development, of the embryo. To investigate the need for EPF in the maintenance of fetal viability, Wong and co-workers (1987) have prepared monoclonal antibodies against EPF for use as specific agents to neutralize EPF *in vivo*. EPF used as the immunogen in the preparation of the antibodies was purified from medium conditioned by the choriocarcinoma cell line BeWo (ATCC CCL 98). Isolation procedures have been fully described by Cavanagh (1985), and a partial amino acid sequence of the purified protein has shown it to be unique (Cavanagh *et al.*, unpublished data). Monoclonal antibodies isolated from ascitic fluid, when tested against EPF in the rosette inhibition test (Rolfe *et al.*, 1984), neutralized the suppressor-releasing activity of EPF derived from either mouse pregnancy tissue or human choriocarcinoma cells; the activity of 500 pg EPF was neutralized by 40 ng anti-EPF monoclonal antibody but not by 4 ng. The control monoclonal antibody not of anti-EPF specificity, used in the experiments described below, did not neutralize EPF activity at any concentration. Anti-EPF monoclonal antibodies identified from the early fusions were all of class IgM, probably due to mice receiving small doses of immunogen (10–50 ng per injection); this was all that was available at that time.

Wong and co-workers (1987) described the results of administering varying doses of specific anti-EPF IgM monoclonal antibodies to female mated mice. The mice received two injections of antibody, one 32 hours after mating and a second 24 hours later; only 7 of the 21 mice were still pregnant at 10 days of gestation. These results were significantly different from those of the two control groups, tested in parallel ($p < 0.001$; χ^2 test). The first control group received injections of an IgM monoclonal antibody not of anti-EPF specificity. All of 14 mice in this group were still pregnant at day 10. The second control group received injections of 0.9% NaCl; 17 of the 18 mice maintained their pregnancies. These results indicate that EPF is necessary to maintain embryonic viability since neutralization of EPF *in vivo* during the preimplantation period terminated pregnancy in a significant number of cases.

Nevertheless, this particular monoclonal antibody did not terminate pregnancy in all mice. This may have been due to the antibody being of class IgM, which does not diffuse freely across membranes. With more purified EPF becoming available, mice have been immunized with greater amounts of EPF (1–20 μg per injection) and IgG monoclonal antibodies have been produced. It will now be possible to determine more precisely the dose of antibody needed to terminate pregnancy, and the effect of administering the antibody at different times during gestation.

X. Role of EPF in Pregnancy

One possible role for EPF in the maintenance of pregnancy is that of immunoregulation to prevent the rejection of an antigenically alien embryo (Noonan et al., 1979). An immunosuppressive role was first suggested for EPF as a result of its reaction with lymphocytes in the rosette inhibition test; in this assay EPF augments the suppressive effect of ALS (Morton et al., 1976; Morton, 1984; Rolfe et al., 1984). Further studies investigated the effect of EPF on the adoptive transfer of contact sensitivity to trinitrochlorobenzene (TNCB) by lymphocytes from sensitized mice to naive, syngeneic mice (Noonan et al., 1979; Rolfe, 1985; Rolfe et al., 1983, 1987). The adoptive transfer of contact sensitivity is an *in vivo* assay which measures the delayed-type hypersensitivity (DTH) reaction (Asherson and Zembala, 1973) and involves the same T-lymphocyte population that is active in skin graft rejection (Loveland and McKenzie, 1982). These experiments showed that preincubation of lymphocytes in EPF completely suppressed the transfer of sensitivity. Inhibitory activity of EPF in the assay was not species specific; partially purified sheep (Noonan *et al.*, 1979) and human (Rolfe *et al.*, 1983) EPF as well as highly purified mouse EPF (Rolfe *et al.*, 1987) were able to suppress the transfer of sensitivity by mouse lymphocytes.

Studies have shown that the activity of EPF in both the rosette inhibition test and the adoptive transfer assay is not due to EPF as such but is mediated by the induction of suppressor cells (Rolfe, 1985; Rolfe *et al.*, 1987). EPF binds to a small population of lymphocytes, stimulating these cells to release suppressor factors. These substances in turn bind to a further population of lymphocytes, modifying their reactivity in the assays mentioned above. Unlike the reaction of EPF in stimulating the recruitment of suppressor cells, which is neither strain nor species restricted, the reaction of the suppressor factors is genetically restricted (Rolfe, 1985; Rolfe *et al.*, 1987). EPF will bind to lymphocytes from C57BL/6, C3H, and BALB/c mice, stimulating suppressor factor release. After separation from the inducing EPF, these substances will modify the reaction of syngeneic but not allogeneic lymphocytes in both the rosette inhibition test and the adoptive transfer assay.

Analysis by gel filtration chromatography indicated that EPF stimulates the release of two factors detectable in the rosette inhibition test: EPF-S$_1$ (M_r 14,000) and EPF-S$_2$ (M_r 55,000). The experiments mentioned above showed that EPF-induced suppressor factors were strain restricted in their activity. Since the interaction between suppressor factors and lymphocytes is frequently restricted by genes mapping to the major histocompatibility complex (MHC) (Green *et al.*, 1983), experiments were designed to investigate whether the EPF-induced suppressor factors were restricted in this way. Suppressor factors were prepared from the spleen cells of BALB/c (H-2^d) mice and separated by gel filtration. The two fractions (EPF-S$_1$ and EPF-S$_2$) were then tested in the rosette inhibition test with cells from the congenic strains BALB.b (H-2^b) and BALB.k (H-2^k), and with cells from DBA/2 mice (H-2^d; H-2 compatible but with a different genetic background). The results showed that the activity of EPF-S$_1$ is H-2 restricted, since it suppressed H-2-compatible DBA/2 cells but had no effect on cells from either of the congenic BALB/c strains. In contrast, EPF-S$_2$ appeared to be restricted to a locus outside the H-2 region, since it suppressed cells of the BALB/c congenic strains but not those of DBA/2 mice. Rolfe *et al.* (1987) went on to show by further experiments with H-2 recombinant mouse strains that the genetic restriction of EPF-S$_1$ mapped to the I region of the H-2 complex.

The existence of pregnancy-associated suppressor systems has been reported previously (Clark and McDermott, 1981; Chaouat and Voisin, 1979, 1981; Smith and Powell, 1977), although their relationship to the EPF-induced suppressor system is unclear. Chaouat and Voisin (1979, 1981) have described a suppressor T cell which acts in the mixed lymphocyte reaction via soluble products and is I-region restricted. However, this system has been found to be active only in multiparous mice. The suppressor system described by Clark and McDermott (1981) nonspecifically impairs the generation of cytotoxic T lymphocytes against paternal H-2 antigens; the kinetics of suppression during pregnancy are similar to that of EPF, but, unlike EPF, suppression can be detected also in pseudopregnant mice.

A number of model suppressor systems have complex pathways involving induction of suppressor cells and their factors (Germain and Benacerraf, 1981). The suppressor system described for EPF may form such a pathway, initiated in this case by fertilization and the release of ovum factor. EPF liberated from the ovary in response to stimulation by ovum factor is present in the circulation at very low concentrations and binds to a small population of lymphocytes. The proposed system by which EPF initiates the sequential induction of suppressor cells and subsequent release of soluble suppressor factors would provide a means of amplification and prolongation of the effect of EPF in maintaining the viability of the embryo.

XI. Conclusions

The experimental evidence described in this chapter shows that production of EPF is initiated by fertilization and that its presence in serum monitors the viability of the conceptus for at least the first half of gestation. Furthermore, EPF is necessary for the continued survival of the conceptus; neutralization by monoclonal antibodies will interrupt pregnancy.

The role of EPF in maintaining embryonic viability is not yet fully understood but may involve immunological protection. The characteristics of EPF meet the criteria needed for an effective immunosuppressant capable of inhibiting maternal rejection of the embryo. Immunomodulation begins within hours of fertilization and is reversible within 24 hours of loss of the embryo. The effect of EPF is selective; it binds to a specific lymphocyte population, recruiting suppressor cells which in turn release soluble suppressor factors, genetically restricted in their behavior. The target cells affected by these suppressor factors are of the same T-lymphocyte population as those involved in graft rejection.

The discovery of EPF and the ensuing research has depended on the activity of EPF in the rosette inhibition test. This test is extremely sensitive and reproducible but very time-consuming, so that only a few samples can be tested in 1 day. Furthermore, it is an assay that needs considerable immunological expertise to carry out successfully. Research has been directed toward finding the most productive source of EPF for purification, in order to characterize EPF and to develop polyclonal and monoclonal antibodies of high affinity. EPF has now been shown by a partial amino acid sequence to be a novel protein, while anti-EPF IgG monoclonal antibodies have been prepared and are being incorporated into an immunoassay for EPF in serum. The availability of such an assay would facilitate more extensive studies of the diagnostic value of EPF in pregnancy as well as furthering our understanding of the role of EPF in the maintenance of embryonic viability.

ACKNOWLEDGMENTS

Work from the authors' laboratories was supported by grants from the Lalor Foundation, Queensland Cancer Fund, and Mayne Bequest Fund, University of Queensland. We thank Dr. David Chant for statistical analysis of the data on the rosette inhibition test and Bernadette Brady for the excellent preparation of the manuscript.

REFERENCES

Asherson, G. L., and Zembala, M. (1973). *Nature (London) New Biol.* **244**, 176–177.

Bach, J. F., and Antoine, B. (1968). *Nature (London)* **217**, 658–659.

Bach, J. F., Dormont, J., Dardenne, M., and Balner, H. (1969). *Transplantation* **8**, 265–280.

Beier, H. M. (1974). *J. Reprod. Fertil.* **37**, 221–237.

Bohn, H. (1985). *In* "Early Pregnancy Factors" (F. Ellendorff and E. Koch, eds.), pp. 127–137. Perinatology Press, New York.

Cavanagh, A. C. (1984). *J. Reprod. Fertil.* **71**, 581–592.

Cavanagh, A. C. (1985). *In* "Early Pregnancy Factors" (F. Ellendorff and E. Koch, eds.), pp. 179–189. Perinatology Press, New York.

Cavanagh, A. C., Morton, H., Rolfe, B. E., and Gidley-Baird, A. A. (1982). *Am. J. Reprod. Immunol.* **2**, 97–101.

Chaouat, G., and Voisin, G. A. (1979). *J. Immunol.* **122**, 1383–1388.

Chaouat, G., and Voisin, G. A. (1981). *J. Immunol.* **127**, 1335–1339.

Chen, C. (1985). *In* "Early Pregnancy Factors" (F. Ellendorff and E. Koch, eds.), pp. 215–226. Perinatology Press, New York.

Chen, C., Jones, W. R., Bastin, F., and Ford, C. (1985). *Ann. N.Y. Acad. Sci.* **442**, 420–428.

Clark, D. A., and McDermott, M. R. (1981). *J. Immunol.* **127**, 1267–1273.

Clarke, F. M., Morton, H., Rolfe, B. E., and Clunie, G. J. A. (1980). *J. Reprod. Immunol.* **2**, 151–162.

Cooper, D. W., and Aitken, R. J. (1981). *J. Reprod. Fertil.* **61**, 241–245.

Edwards, R. G., and Gates, A. H. (1959). *J. Endocrinol.* **18**, 292–304.

Germain, R. N., and Benacerraf, B. (1981). *Scand. J. Immunol.* **13**, 1–10.

Godkin, J. D., Bazer, F. W., and Roberts, R. M. (1984). *Endocrinology* **114**, 120–130.

Green, D. R., Flood, P. M., and Gershon, R. K. (1983). *Annu. Rev. Immunol.* **1**, 439–463.

Koch, E., Morton, H., Niemann, H., and Ellendorff, F. (1982). *Acta Endocrinol.* **99** (Suppl. 246), 4.

Loveland, B. E., and McKenzie, I. F. C. (1982). *Transplantation* **33**, 217–220.

McLaren, A. (1971). *J. Endocrinol.* **50**, 515–526.

Mesrogli, M., and Maas, D. H. A. (1985). *In* "Early Pregnancy Factors" (F. Ellendorff and E. Koch, eds.), pp. 233–235. Perinatology Press, New York.

Mettler, L., Hanf, V., and Tinneberg, H.-R. (1985). *In* "Early Pregnancy Factors" (F. Ellendorff and E. Koch, eds.), pp. 227–231. Perinatology Press, New York.

Miller, R. G. (1986). "Beyond ANOVA: Basics of Applied Statistics," pp. 95–105. Wiley, New York.

Morton, H. (1984). *Aust. J. Biol. Sci.* **37**, 393–407.

Morton, H., Hegh, V., and Clunie, G. J. A. (1974). *Nature (London)* **249**, 459–460.

Morton, H., Hegh, V., and Clunie, G. J. A. (1976). *Proc. R. Soc. London Ser. B* **193**, 413–419.

Morton, H., Rolfe, B., Clunie, G. J. A., Anderson, M. J., and Morrison, J. (1977). *Lancet* **1**, 394–397.

Morton, H., Nancarrow, C. D., Scaramuzzi, R. J., Evison, B. M., and Clunie, G. J. A. (1979). *J. Reprod. Fertil.* **56**, 75–80.

Morton, H., Rolfe, B. E., McNeill, L., Clarke, P., Clarke, F. M., and Clunie, G. J. A. (1980). *J. Reprod. Immunol.* **2**, 73–82.

Morton, H., Rolfe, B., and Cavanagh, A. (1982a). *In* "Pregnancy Proteins" (J. G. Grudzinskas, B. Teisner, and M. Seppala, eds.), pp. 391–405. Academic Press, Sydney.

Morton, H., Morton, D. J., and Ellendorff, F. (1983). *J. Reprod. Fertil.* **68**, 437–446.

Morton, H., Tinneberg, H. R., Rolfe, B. E., Wolf, M., and Metter, L. (1982b). *J. Reprod. Immunol.* **4**, 251–261.

Nancarrow, C. D., Evison, B. M., Scaramuzzi, R. J., and Turnbull, K. E. (1979). *J. Reprod. Fertil.* **57**, 385–389.

Nancarrow, C. D., Wallace, A. L. C., and Grewal, A. S. (1981). *J. Reprod. Fertil. Suppl.* **30**, 191–199.

Noonan, F. P., Halliday, W. J., Morton, H., and Clunie, G. J. A. (1979). *Nature (London)* **278**, 649–651.

O'Neill, C. (1985a). *J. Reprod. Fertil.* **68**, 437–446.

O'Neill, C. (1985b). *J. Reprod. Fertil.* **73**, 567–577.

O'Neill, C. (1985c). *In* "Early Pregnancy Factors" (F. Ellendorff and E. Koch, eds.), pp. 261–266. Perinatology Press, New York.

Orozco, C., Perkins, T., and Clarke, F. M. (1986). *J. Reprod. Fertil.* **78**, 549–555.

Rolfe, B. E. (1982). *Fertil. Steril.* **37**, 655–660.

Rolfe, B. E. (1985). *In* "Early Pregnancy Factors" (F. Ellendorff and E. Koch, eds.), pp. 117–125. Perinatology Press, New York.

Rolfe, B. E., Morton, H., and Clarke, F. M. (1983). *Clin. Exp. Immunol.* **51**, 45–52.

Rolfe, B. E., Cavanagh, A. C., Forde, C., Bastin, F., Chen, C., and Morton, H. (1984). *J. Immunol. Methods* **70**, 1–11.

Rolfe, B. E., Cavanagh, A. C., Quinn, K. A., and Morton, H. (1987). Submitted.

Smart, Y. C., Fraser, I. S., Clancy, R. L., Roberts, T. K., and Cripps, A. W. (1982a). *Fertil. Steril.* **37**, 201–204.

Smart, Y. C., Fraser, I. S., Roberts, T. K., Clancy, R. L., and Cripps, A. W. (1982b). *Clin. Reprod. Fertil.* **1**, 177–184.

Smart, Y. C., Roberts, T. K., Fraser, I. S., Cripps, A. W., and Clancy, R. L. (1982c). *Fertil. Steril.* **37**, 779–785.

Smith, R. N., and Powell, A. E. (1977). *J. Exp. Med.* **146**, 899–904.

Snyder, F. (1985). *Med. Res. Rev.* **5,** 107–140.

Thompson, A. W., Milton, J. I., Campbell, D. M., and Horne, C. H. W. (1980). *J. Reprod. Immunol.* **2,** 263–268.

Tinneberg, H.-R., Staves, R. P., and Semm, K. (1984). *Am. J. Reprod. Immunol.* **5,** 151–156.

Whitten, W. K. (1956). *Nature (London)* **177,** 96–98.

Wilson, S., McCarthy, R., and Clarke, F. (1983). *J. Reprod. Immunol.* **5,** 275–286.

Wilson, S., McCarthy, R., and Clarke, F. (1984). *J. Reprod. Immunol.* **6,** 253–260.

Wong, T.-Y., Quinn, K. A., Athanasas, S., Rolfe, B. E., Cavanagh, A. C., and Morton, H. (1987). Submitted for publication.

CHAPTER 5

DEVELOPMENT OF THE HUMAN PREIMPLANTATION EMBRYO *IN VITRO*

Virginia N. Bolton* and Peter R. Braude

EMBRYO AND GAMETE RESEARCH GROUP
DEPARTMENT OF OBSTETRICS AND GYNAECOLOGY
UNIVERSITY OF CAMBRIDGE CLINICAL SCHOOL
THE ROSIE MATERNITY HOSPITAL
CAMBRIDGE CB2 2SW, ENGLAND

I. Introduction

The successful fertilization *in vitro* of human eggs and the *in vitro* culture of human preimplantation embryos, first achieved by Edwards *et al.* (1970, 1980), has become a daily challenge for hundreds of laboratories throughout the world. For notwithstanding the advent of human *in vitro* fertilization (IVF) and embryo replacement as an achievable and accepted form of therapy for infertility, in general the sad and frustrating reality that remains is the continuing inability, when confronted with any single individual or couple, to provide an accurate prognosis as to whether their eggs will fertilize, will cleave normally *in vitro,* will implant following replacement, or will lead to a full-term pregnancy following implantation. In fact, IVF represents a remarkably inefficient therapeutic procedure. Although fertilization can now be achieved with consistent success *in vitro,* the success rate of ongoing pregnancies is much lower (Osborn and Moor, 1985; Braude *et al.,* 1986). If an average is taken from the longest established IVF units, it can be seen that <15% of all embryos that are replaced will result in a clinical pregnancy (Table I). While it is not our intention to belittle this success, which has led to the birth of babies to hundreds of otherwise childless couples, it is essential that the reasons for this unacceptably high rate of embryonic loss following embryo replacement are investigated.

* Present address: Department of Obstetrics and Gynaecology, King's College Hospital, London SE5, England.

93

TABLE I

SUCCESS OF EMBRYO REPLACEMENT[a]

Number replaced	Replacements	Patients pregnant per replacement (%)	Patients pregnant per embryo replaced (%)
1	1003	12.7	12.7
2	826	24.2	12.1
3	502	28.9	9.6

[a] Pooled figures from seven units. From Osborn and Moor (1985) and Steptoe (1985).

The factors that might influence the success of IVF include (1) the uterine microenvironment, (2) embryo replacement technique, (3) culture conditions, and (4) egg or embryo quality.

Most therapeutic IVF units now use superovulatory regimes with clomiphene citrate (Lopata *et al.*, 1978; Quigley *et al.*, 1984), human menopausal gonadotrophin (hMG), pure follicle-stimulating hormone (FSH), or a combination of these hormones (Jones *et al.*, 1984), in order to achieve multiple folliculogenesis. This hyperstimulation of the ovary results in abnormally high levels of estrogens, which may render the endometrium less receptive to the implanting blastocyst. Attempts have been made to avoid the use of these regimes by performing egg aspiration during accurately timed natural cycles (Edwards *et al.*, 1980; I. Cooke and E. Lenton, personal communication). However, the practical problems that such procedures entail, including the provision of a 24-hour clinical service, and the lower pregnancy rate that is achieved with the replacement of single embryos, make this an unattractive proposition.

The procedure of embryo replacement is essentially "blind"; the clinician knows that the embryos have been introduced into the uterus, but their precise position remains unclear. Furthermore, it appears that there are certain "indefinable" factors that result in successful replacement; it is well recognized from embryo transfer in cattle that one clinician may achieve a higher pregnancy rate than another, although there may be no obvious differences in replacement technique (Newcomb, 1983).

Optimal culture conditions for human embryos have yet to be defined. The media used for culture of human eggs and embryos *in vitro* have been adapted from those derived originally for culture of animal embryos, primarily the mouse preimplantation embryo (Whittingham,

1971). Thus, although these media can clearly support human preimplantation embryonic development *in vitro*, as demonstrated by the successful outgrowth of blastocysts in culture (Edwards, 1980; Mohr and Trounson, 1982; Lopata *et al.*, 1982) as well as the live birth of healthy children, it is possible that they provide embryos with a suboptimal growth environment.

Although attempts are made to assess the quality of eggs and embryos obtained in IVF programs, the morphological criteria that are used have been shown to be unreliable (Bomsel-Helmreich, 1985). It has become clear that assessment of the "ripeness" of an egg, as judged by the expansion of the cumulus, and of the "viability" of an embryo, as judged by cleavage rate and the shape of blastomeres, will give no certain indication of whether or not a pregnancy will follow embryo replacement (Mohr, 1984).

For the developmental biologist, it is these latter two factors that are of the greatest concern in the identification of reasons for the high rate of failure of human IVF. In the past, animal embryos have been used in an attempt to approximate to events in early human embryogenesis, with most work being carried out on mouse (Johnson, 1981; Magnuson and Epstein, 1981), sheep (Moor and Crosby, 1985), and rabbit embryos (Brackett *et al.*, 1972; Van Blerkom, 1977). Indeed, many IVF units use mouse embryos routinely in order to perform "quality control" evaluations of culture media for human embryo growth (Hillier *et al.*, 1985). However, embryos of different animal species differ from each other, both in developmental rates and morphology and in key biochemical events (Van Blerkom, 1981). This throws into question the validity of the use of animal models and the extrapolation of information that they provide to investigations of human *in vitro* embryogenesis and culture conditions. While animal models are undoubtedly important in pinpointing possible critical stages in human embryogenesis that might yield important information (Bolton *et al.*, 1986), it has now become crucial that human preimplantation embryos are examined, in order to identify the normal parameters of development for these embryos, and to elucidate the factors that might be responsible for the high rate of embryo failure following IVF (Braude *et al.*, 1986).

II. The Source of Human Embryos for Research

In any therapeutic IVF program, it is difficult to perform experiments to test optimal *in vitro* culture conditions for human embryogenesis, since any maneuver that might endanger the already precarious outcome of embryo replacement could not be justified on ethical grounds. Similarly, any investigations into egg or embryo viability, other than the simple observation of morphology and cleavage rates, cannot be undertaken in the context of therapeutic IVF programs. Therefore, an alternative source of human eggs and embryos must provide the materials for such research. There are three potential sources of such human material.

A. "SPARE" EMBRYOS

As a consequence of therapeutic regimes that induce the formation of multiple follicles, many patients will yield more embryos than are required for replacement. Despite the fact that the chances of achieving a pregnancy following IVF increase significantly if more than one embryo is replaced (Table I), the increased risk of spontaneous abortion and the hazards to both mother and fetuses of multiple pregnancy (Kerin *et al.*, 1983; Lancaster, 1985) suggest that it is clinically irresponsible to replace more than four embryos. This means that a number of "spare" embryos will be generated. Such embryos have been used in the development of cryopreservation techniques for embryo storage (Fehilly *et al.*, 1985; Mohr *et al.*, 1985), and the increasing success of such procedures means that fewer spare embryos will be produced by therapeutic IVF.

B. EMBRYOS GENERATED FOR RESEARCH PURPOSES

Embryos may be derived from surplus eggs donated by patients undergoing IVF therapy (Wood *et al.*, 1984), although as with "spare" embryos, these are becoming fewer as egg donation programs become more accepted (Lutjen *et al.*, 1984) and as cryopreservation techniques improve. Alternatively, eggs may be donated to research programs by patients who have completed their families and are undergoing sterilization (Messinis *et al.*, 1986; Templeton *et al.*, 1984).

C. EMBRYOS ARISING AS BY-PRODUCTS OF THERAPEUTIC RESEARCH

Such embryos may be derived from eggs provided by patients undergoing sterilization who are willing to donate their eggs for research into the fertilizing capacity of spermatozoa from oligozoospermic men. It is from just such a research project, designed to derive objective semen parameters that might define male fertility, that the human embryonic material used in our investigations is derived (Braude *et al.*, 1984).

III. Factors Influencing the Success of Human Embryogenesis *in Vitro*

In order to achieve fertilization of human preovulatory oocytes *in vitro*, they are inseminated with between 50,000 and 100,000 sperm ~5 hours after aspiration from the follicle. Successful fertilization is confirmed by the presence of two pronuclei between 14 and 27 hours after insemination. Cleavage to the two-cell stage usually occurs between 26 and 34 hours postinsemination, and cleavage to the four-cell stage can be expected 36–48 hours after insemination. Compaction is reported to occur between the eight-cell and the sixteen-cell stages, with fully expanded blastocysts being detected ~110 hours after the addition of the sperm. However, culture of human embryos *in vitro* to the blastocyst stage has been remarkably unsuccessful compared with other species. In the mouse, for example, 60–75% of one-cell embryos fertilized *in vitro* will reach the fully expanded blastocyst stage in culture (Edgar *et al.*, 1987), whereas only 25–35% of human embryos derived from IVF will undergo development to this stage *in vitro* (Fehilly *et al.*, 1985; Mohr *et al.*, 1985).

A. CULTURE CONDITIONS

The development of 203 pronucleate embryos fertilized and cultured *in vitro* is shown in Fig. 1. Of the embryos left in culture, 95% progressed to the two-cell stage, and of these, 87% cleaved to the four-cell stage. However, after the four-cell stage there is a marked increase in the rate of embryonic failure, with only 58% of four-cell embryos undergoing cleavage to the eight-cell stage, and only 53% of these developing to the fully expanded blastocyst stage. Although the numbers are relatively small, they provide some indication of the stage of development at which human embryos are most susceptible to insult (e.g., by suboptimal culture conditions), or are most likely to manifest inherent inability to undergo further development. The adverse effects on preimplantation embryo development *in vitro* of nonphysiological pH (Chetowski *et al.*, 1985), temperature fluctuations (Moor and Crosby, 1985), and the presence of impurities in oil (Fleming *et al.*, 1987) and in water (Purdy, 1982) have been well described. Further undefined variables are introduced in culture systems used for human IVF by the routine use of serum supplements (bovine serum albumin, human serum albumin, human cord serum, patients' serum) in culture media.

One important observation to be drawn from these data is that, irrespective of the macromolecular supplement, the highest rate of

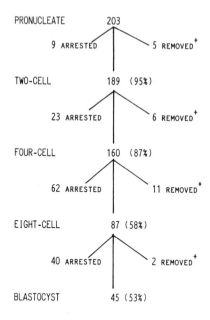

FIG. 1. Diagram illustrating the development of 203 human embryos cultured in Earle's balanced salt solution (EBS) after fertilization *in vitro*. Results pooled from King's College Hospital and The Rosie Maternity Hospital. Oocytes were inseminated either in EBS + 4 mg/ml Fraction V bovine serum (SIGMA) albumin or EBS + 10% heat-inactivated patient's serum. At 16–20 hours postinsemination, all pronucleate embryos were transferred to EBS containing 10% heat-inactivated patient's serum. Plus signs indicate embryos removed for biochemical analysis. Blastocyst formation rate from the 1-cell stage was 25%.

attrition to embryonic development occurs between the four- and eight-cell stages of human embryogenesis. This finding is confirmed by data from Fehilly *et al.* (1985), who attempted to culture human embryos surplus to those required for replacement during therapeutic IVF cycles to the blastocyst stage for cryopreservation. Of 784 pronucleate embryos, 75% (585) were able to develop to the five- to eight-cell stage *in vitro;* only 34% (197) of these progressed in culture to form expanded blastocysts.

Suboptimal culture conditions are undoubtedly responsible for a proportion of this embryonic failure. The relatively high pregnancy rate that is achieved with gamete intrafallopian transfer (GIFT; Asch *et al.,* 1985) indicates that the exposure of human embryos to a 1- to 2-

day period of culture *in vitro* is detrimental to subsequent rates of implantation.

B. EGG/EMBRYO FACTORS

Within a cohort of eggs obtained from the same individual, a proportion may not undergo fertilization after insemination, and of those eggs that are fertilized, a proportion will arrest in development before reaching the blastocyst stage *in vitro*. Furthermore, Buster *et al.* (1985) have shown that few oocytes derived by fertilization *in vivo* have the potential to form blastocysts. Of 25 embryos (aged between 93.5 and 130 hours postovulation) flushed from the uteri of women who had been inseminated for the purpose of embryo donation, only 5 had developed to the fully expanded blastocyst stage. These observations suggest that inadequate culture media cannot explain the full extent of early human embryonic failure, and that inherent and variable defects within individual eggs and/or embryos, which render normal development impossible, must be considered. Two possible factors that may contribute to embryonic attrition will be discussed. The first, that of chromosomal abnormalities, has been investigated in some detail by other laboratories (Angell *et al.*, 1983, 1986a,b), while the second, that of cytoplasmic incompetence and abnormal gene expression, has been the subject of our own research.

1. Chromosomal Abnormalities

With the ovarian hyperstimulation regimes used in IVF, embryos with multiple pronuclei arise with a frequency ranging from 2 to 28% (Wentz *et al.*, 1983; Rudak *et al.*, 1984; Mahadevan and Trounson, 1984), compared with an incidence of triploidy of only 1% in conceptions produced *in vivo* (Jacobs *et al.*, 1978). Although the incidence of chromosomal abnormalities is well documented both in live young born from pregnancies achieved *in vivo*, and in first and second trimester spontaneous abortus material (Evans, 1977; Boué and Boué, 1978), we do not know the contribution of chromosomal abnormalities to the high rate (52%; Edmonds *et al.*, 1982) of early pregnancy loss within 2 weeks of fertilization *in vivo* (Roberts and Lowe, 1975; Boué and Boué, 1978). Some of the embryonic failure following IVF may be a manifestation of this "natural wastage" that is seen *in vivo*. However, the failure of 85–90% of embryos derived from IVF to implant, together with the subsequent loss due to spontaneous abortion of 30% of those embryos that do implant (Seppala, 1985; Lancaster, 1985), indicates the need for a reevaluation of the frequency of chromosomal abnormalities in embryos fertilized *in vitro*.

Most of the chromosomal abnormalities that arise spontaneously are due to nondisjunction at the first meiotic division of oocyte maturation (Hassold et al., 1984), which takes place before egg aspiration for IVF. Animal studies have provided no evidence to suggest that superovulatory hormonal regimes increase the frequency of chromosomal nondisjunction (Hansmann and Probeck, 1979a,b), although the incidence of sister chromatid exchange may be elevated (Elbling and Colet, 1985; Sato and Marrs, 1984a,b). There is a need for data comparing the frequency and nature of chromosomal errors arising at the first and second meiotic divisions in both natural and superovulatory cycles in the human, with those of conceptuses produced in vivo and in vitro. These data could be provided by abortuses from conceptions achieved by in vivo and in vitro fertilization.

Data concerning the incidence of multipronucleate embryos in IVF are more easily obtained (Angell et al., 1986a). The occurrence of multiple pronuclei is thought to be due to the entry of more than one spermatozoon (Edwards et al., 1981; Jacobs et al., 1978), although failure of extrusion of the second polar body may also be a factor. The consequences of such abnormalities arising at fertilization are only now being elucidated (Angell et al., 1986a). Certainly, one-cell embryos with multiple pronuclei and other chromosomal abnormalities will undergo cleavage and appear morphologically indistinguishable from embryos with a normal diploid chromosome complement (Van Blerkom et al., 1984; Angell et al., 1986b). However, some multipronucleate embryos may have the capacity to "regulate" their chromosome complement, as evidenced by Rudak et al. (1984) who found that one of eight tripronucleate embryos had only two haploid chromosome sets after the first cleavage division. It is now widely advocated that in view of the potentially pathological consequences of aneuploidy (Edwards, 1984), clinics practicing IVF should ensure that one-cell embryos are examined for pronuclei so that multipronucleate embryos may be rejected (Wentz et al., 1983; Rudak et al., 1984; Van Blerkom et al., 1984).

An examination of the development of tripronucleate embryos in vitro can throw light on the origins of triploidy, restoration of diploidy, and gross aneuploidy (Angell et al., 1986a). One of three mechanisms appears to operate during the first mitotic division of the tripronucleate embryo. First, all three sets of chromosomes may gather on the metaphase plate, divide regularly, and produce two daughter cells, each with a triploid chromosome complement. Second, one set of chromosomes may be excluded from the metaphase plate, so that if the third chromosome set degenerates, a diploid embryo results. If this third excluded set represents the female chromosome complement, a hydatidiform mole may result (Bagshawe and Lawler, 1982; Kajii and Ohama, 1977; Edwards, 1984), whereas if it represents the male complement, a normal diploid embryo is produced. Finally, the three sets of chromosomes may gather on a tripolar spindle, which, although resulting in cleavage to three cells, would entail such disorganization of the spindle that gross aneuploidy might result (Angell *et al.*, 1986a).

The importance of the cytoskeleton, and in particular the spindle, requires considerable emphasis in any examination of factors influencing successful development of human embryos *in vitro*. Recent work using fluorescent antibodies to actin, tubulin, and microtubule-organizing center (MTOC)-associated material has enabled a detailed description of the changing localization and relationships of cytoskeletal structures and chromosomes in the unfertilized and fertilized mouse egg (Maro *et al.*, 1984, 1985, 1986; Longo and Chen, 1985; Howlett *et al.*, 1985; Webb *et al.*, 1986; Van Blerkom and Bell, 1986). Following ovulation and fertilization, microtubules function to maintain the integrity of the mitotic spindle and the metaphase chromosomes, to organize extrusion of the second polar body and migration of the male and female pronuclei. Microfilaments, which are concentrated in the newly ovulated egg in an actin-rich area immediately overlying the spindle, are required to effect spindle rotation and thereby polar body extrusion. Disruption of the correct spatial and temporal organization of these cytoskeletal components during oocyte maturation, fertilization, and mitosis is clearly of crucial importance in the establishment of a normal, euploid embryo. Cytoskeletal organization can be affected by temperature (Magistrini and Szollosi, 1980; Moor and Crosby, 1985), by drugs that disrupt cytoskeletal elements (Maro *et al.*, 1984, 1986; Schatten *et al.*, 1985), and by postovulatory age (Webb *et al.*, 1986). The progressive disorganization of the cytoskeleton that occurs with increased postovulatory age in the mouse egg is correlated with the developmental abnormality observed at activation (Webb *et al.*, 1986).

Thus, the earliest change in the cytoskeleton that occurs with age is the dispersal of the actin-rich area overlying the spindle, until actin becomes distributed uniformly around the cell cortex; at activation, this change is associated with a failure of polar body extrusion. Later, migration of the spindle from the periphery to the center of the cell occurs, and is associated at activation with the formation of a meiotic cleavage plane that divides the egg into two equal halves rather than a small discarded polar body and a large egg. Finally, progressive disintegration of the spindle microtubules occurs with further aging until the chromosomes are no longer organized on the metaphase plate, and cleavage fails altogether with both female pronuclei being retained.

Thus, fertilization of aging eggs may produce abnormalities including polyploidy and aneuploidy. Aging represents one source of such developmental anomalies, and it is clear that the complex intracellular reorganizations that take place during fertilization and the first mitotic division of embryogenesis make these stages of development particularly sensitive to insult, whether by exposure to inappropriate hormonal environment during superovulatory stimulation, temperature fluctuations during egg aspirations, or suboptimal culture conditions during the *in vitro* culture period. Further examination of the effects of each phase of IVF procedures is necessary in order to clarify their contribution to the high rate of early embryonic loss (Bolton *et al.*, 1987).

2. Cytoplasmic Incompetence and Abnormal Gene Expression

In the mammal, the contribution of a spermatozoon to the embryo is largely if not exclusively genetic, consisting of one set of chromosomes. In contrast, the egg carries in addition a considerable cytoplasmic inheritance, consisting of organelles and protein-synthetic apparatus, generated and stored during oocyte maturation. Deficiencies in this maternal, nongenetic, cytoplasmic inheritance might lead to deficiencies in the embryo. The high incidence of multiple pronuclei following IVF may be a manifestation of this, since Trounson *et al.* (1982) found a 30% rate of polyspermy in eggs inseminated immediately after aspiration, whereas this was reduced to negligible levels with a preincubation period of 4–6 hours before insemination. As the incidence of polyspermy is unrelated to the inseminated spermatozoal concentration (Mahadevan and Trounson, 1984), this result suggests that the preincubation period enabled the eggs to complete maturation in culture, thereby acquiring the capacity to express the normal block to polyspermy.

What other role might the maternal, cytoplasmic inheritance play in embryogenesis, and how might cytoplasmic incompetence be related to embryonic failure? Using the mouse embryo, certain facts have emerged concerning the importance of the "maternal program" in regulating development of the embryo until activation of the embryonic genome takes place, when the "embryo program" takes over (Pratt *et al.*, 1983). We have carried out detailed studies on patterns of protein synthesis and cleavage in the mouse embryo; and in light of the results obtained with this animal model, we have now begun to look at the protein synthetic and cleavage patterns of human embryos, as one approach to the examination of embryo viability.

The polypeptide-synthetic profiles of mouse one-cell embryos at varying times after insemination *in vitro* have been described (Pratt *et al.*, 1983; Howlett and Bolton, 1985; Howlett, 1986a). The first cell cycle of mouse embryogenesis is characterized by the synthesis of many polypeptides; most remain unchanged during the 20- to 24-hour period following ovulation, but some show temporal differences. Of those polypeptides whose pattern of synthesis changes in the one-cell mouse embryo, three complexes of polypeptides have been described in detail (Howlett and Bolton, 1985; Howlett, 1986a) and are summarized diagrammatically in Fig. 2. In the context of investigations of human embryogenesis, it is important to know the level at which the synthesis of these polypeptides and the changes in their patterns of synthesis are regulated. By incubating mouse one-cell embryos in the presence of the transcriptional inhibitor α-amanitin (11 μg/ml), and examining the patterns of polypeptide synthesis and embryo cleavage rates, it has been demonstrated that none of the polypeptides that are synthesized during the first cell cycle of mouse embryogenesis, nor the temporal changes that take place in their synthetic patterns, require new transcription (Fig. 3). Thus, following insemination *in vitro,* not only are identical proteins synthesized during the first cell cycle in the presence or absence of the transcriptional inhibitor, but the same changes take

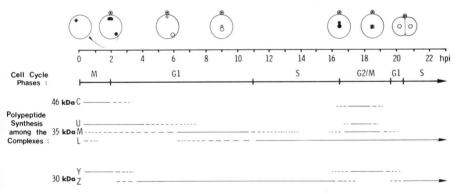

FIG. 2. Summary diagram to outline the changes in polypeptide synthesis of the 46-, 35-, and 30-kDa complexes during the 22 hours following fertilization (hpi) of the mouse egg. C, U, M, L, Y, Z refer to previous polypeptide complexes that can be identified on one-dimensional gel electrophoresis. Solid lines represent maximal synthesis, a dotted line represents lower levels of synthesis, and no line represents no detectable synthesis. The morphology of the fertilized eggs at various times after insemination are shown diagrammatically at the top of the figure. (See Howlett, 1986a, for details.)

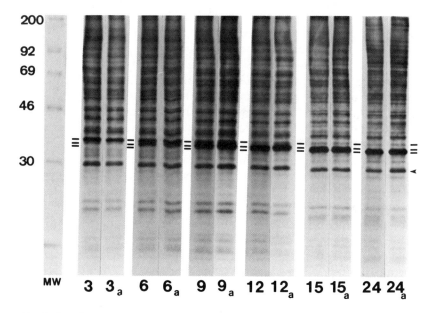

Fɪɢ. 3. One-dimensional sodium dodecyl sulfate–polyacrylamide gel electrophoretic (SDS–PAGE) separation of radiolabeled polypeptides synthesized by one- and two-cell mouse embryos. Embryos were labeled with [^{35}S]methionine for 3 hours beginning post-insemination *in vitro* at the times indicated (3–24 hours). Eggs were inseminated and cultured in control medium (tracks 3, 6, 9, 12, 15, 24) or in medium containing 11 μg/ml α-amanitin (tracks 3a, 6a, 9a, 12a, 15a, 24a). Bars indicate positions of bands U, M, and L of the 35-kDa complex of polypeptides, whose pattern of synthesis changes during this period of development (see Fig. 2). MW, Relative molecular weight radiolabeled markers.

place among these polypeptides in the absence of new mRNA synthesis (Fig. 3). Moreover, mouse embryos will undergo cleavage to the two-cell stage at precisely the same time whether or not they are cultured in the presence of α-amanitin (Fig. 4; Braude *et al.*, 1979; Flach *et al.*, 1982). Clearly then, the synthesis of these polypeptides, the changes in their patterns of synthesis, and the reorganization of the cytoskeleton and chromatin that is involved in the first cleavage division, all take place independently of any contribution from the embryonic genome, and therefore must be regulated by components already present in the egg before the transcriptional blockage is introduced, that is, by the maternal inheritance (Pratt *et al.*, 1983). It has indeed been demonstrated that the changes that occur in patterns of protein synthesis in the one-cell mouse embryo include cell cycle-related reversible post-translational modifications involving phosphorylation (Howlett,

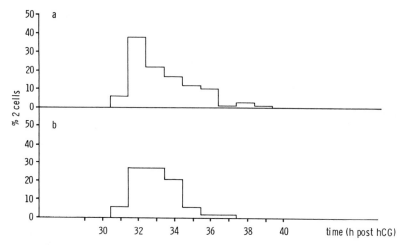

F<small>IG</small>. 4. Histograms showing the timing of the first cleavage division of mouse embryos after fertilization *in vitro*. (a) Embryos inseminated and cultured in control medium; (b) embryos inseminated and cultured in medium containing 11 μg/ml α-amanitin.

1986a). Complex levels of cytoplasmic regulation must operate in the one-cell mouse embryo in order to control the utilization of this maternal inheritance that programs the protein-synthetic apparatus and cytoplasmic organelles, resulting in the ordered temporal and spatial sequence of events that occurs during the 20- to 24-hour period following ovulation.

It is possible that an analogous situation occurs in the human embryo, whereby the human egg carries a maternal program for development that is, perhaps, responsible for maintaining the "housekeeping" functions of the newly fertilized egg, for initiating embryogenesis, and for laying down the basis for further development. If so, any defects in the cytoplasmic, maternal inheritance of the oocyte might be responsible for early embryonic failure. So far there has been little opportunity to examine this hypothesis. Preliminary data suggest that similar processes may operate in the human embryo, since on four occasions, pronucleate or early two-cell stage human embryos cultured in the presence of 100 μg/ml α-amanitin have undergone cleavage to four cells at the same time as control embryos, and fertilization can occur in the presence of the inhibitor (Bolton and Braude, unpublished observations). This result cannot be considered definitive evidence of the exclusively maternal regulation of human embryogenesis during the first two cell cycles until it has been established (1) that α-amanitin penetrates the human one-cell embryo and inhibits transcription at a concentration of 100 μg/ml and (2) that the polypeptide synthetic profiles of human embryos are not altered by culture in the presence of α-amanitin.

Nonetheless, this preliminary work does support the notion that the earliest stages of human preimplantation embryogenesis (at least until the four-cell stage) may be regulated at the posttranscriptional level, and that cytoplasmic incompetence produces eggs which are unable to carry out the maternal program for development. Such cytoplasmic incompetence could be due to egg immaturity at the time of follicular aspiration, and/or to suboptimal culture conditions during maturation *in vitro*, and/or to exposure to an inappropriate intrafollicular environment during hyperstimulatory hormonal therapy.

One possible way that cytoplasmic incompetence may manifest is by a failure to activate the embryonic genome properly. In the mouse, embryonic gene activation occurs in two phases during the two-cell stage (reviewed by Johnson *et al.*, 1984). The first phase of transcriptional activity occurs within 1 hour of the first cleavage division and is followed immediately by the translation of new mRNAs into a complex of heat-shock-like proteins of MW 68,000–70,000 (Bensuade *et al.*, 1983; Bolton *et al.*, 1984). The second phase, believed to represent the major activation of the embryonic genome, occurs after completion of DNA replication in the second cell cycle and results in a major transformation in the polypeptide-synthetic profile of two-cell embryos, with a cessation of synthesis of polypeptides characteristic of the one-cell stage, and commencement of synthesis of a new set of proteins (Van Blerkhom and Brockway, 1975; Flach *et al.*, 1982; Bolton *et al.*, 1984; Giebelhaus *et al.*, 1983). This major transition in the pattern of polypeptides synthesized by two-cell mouse embryos is demonstrated in Fig. 5 (see tracks 0 and M16), which also illustrates the timing of the onset of sensitivity to α-amanitin (Bolton *et al.*, 1984). Thus, two-cell embryos that were placed in α-amanitin within 8 hours of the first cleavage division cease synthesis of polypeptides characteristic of one-cell embryos, but do not commence synthesis of characteristic late two-cell polypeptides (tracks 5–8, Fig. 5). The introduction of α-amanitin >8 hours following the first cleavage division has no effect on the pattern of polypeptide synthesis, which is identical in control and drug-treated embryos (track 9, Fig. 5). The second cleavage division shows the same sensitivity to α-amanitin: embryos placed in α-amanitin up to 8 hours after the first cleavage division do not divide to four cells, while embryos placed into α-amanitin after this time do divide (Bolton *et al.*, 1984).

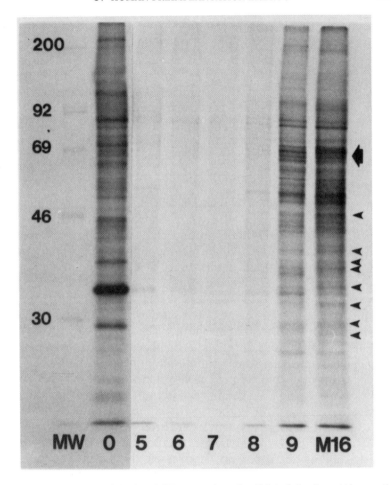

FIG. 5. One-dimensional SDS–PAGE separation of radiolabeled polypeptides synthesized by mouse embryos labeled with [^{35}S]methionine for 3 hours beginning at 0 hours
(track 0) or 24 hours (all other tracks) after the first cleavage division. Embryos were
cultured in control medium (tracks 0 and M16), or in medium to which 11 μg/ml α-
amanitin was added at 5, 6, 7, 8, or 9 hours after cleavage. MW, Relative molecular
weight markers as for Fig. 3. (From Bolton *et al.*, 1984.)

These results demonstrate that the maternal program for development becomes converted to the embryonic program during the two-cell
stage of mouse embryogenesis. But what is the developmental signal
that triggers activation of the embryonic genome? Attempts to identify
the component of maternal inheritance that is responsible have established that gene activation occurs in the absence of the preceding

rounds of cytokinesis or DNA replication (Petzoldt *et al.,* 1983; Bolton *et al.,* 1984). However, it appears that the first round of DNA replication must take place if the second, major phase of gene activation is to occur; the first phase, resulting in synthesis of heat-shock-like proteins, is independent of this round of DNA replication (Howlett, 1986b). The precise mechanism of the trigger remains unclear. What is clear is that the maternal cytoplasmic inheritance is responsible for the regulation of development up to this point of transition, and for the organization of the transition itself. Thus, it is possible to envisage that deficiencies in the cytoplasmic inheritance could prejudice this change.

In an attempt to identify whether or not the same principles apply in human embryogenesis, we have performed preliminary investigations of the protein-synthetic profiles of human embryos derived by fertilization *in vitro.* The [^{35}S]methionine-labeled polypeptides synthesized by individual human embryos at various stages of development are shown in Fig. 6. Unlike the situation in the mouse embryo, patterns of polypeptide synthesis appear remarkably similar throughout preimplantation development in the human, with no obvious stage of transition from synthesis of one characteristic set of proteins to that of another. However, unlike the experiments that have been described using mouse embryos, where the quantity of experimental material enabled the precise and detailed description of events by short (1-hour) labeling periods and the examination of multiple experimental groups (Howlett and Bolton, 1985), the paucity of human material means that long (3-hour) labeling periods were utilized, which may have masked brief but significant developmental changes in polypeptide-synthetic patterns. Moreover, it should be stressed that each track of Fig. 6 represents a single human embryo, and although the same results have been obtained in duplicate, the experimental embryos may not have been normal and, if left in culture, might not have developed. Indeed, from the data on developmental arrest presented in Fig. 1, it is likely that tracks 5 and 6 (Fig. 6), which show the protein-synthetic profiles of a four- and an eight-cell embryo, respectively, may represent developmentally incompetent embryos.

Though few, there are certain marked changes that take place in the pattern of proteins synthesized during human preimplantation embryogenesis, as illustrated in Fig. 6. For example, the synthesis of a polypeptide band in the MW 36,000 region of the gel increases up to the two-cell stage, but decreases dramatically thereafter; this is similar to the pattern shown by the MW 35,000-complex polypeptides in the mouse. In the MW 50,000 region of the gels, there is a band whose

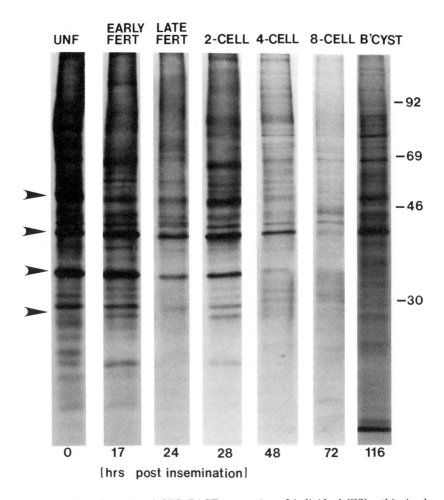

Fɪɢ. 6. One-dimensional SDS–PAGE separation of individual [35S]methionine-la-beled (0) unfertilized human egg, labeled 36–39 hours after hCG; human embryos la-beled for 3 hours at 17, 24, 28, 48, 72, and 116 hours postinsemination. Approximate molecular sizes (kDa, kilodaltons) are indicated on the right of the figure. Arrowheads indicate positions of polypeptides whose pattern of synthesis changes during the culture period.

synthesis decreases markedly during the four- to eight-cell stages, but increases again in the blastocyst. A band in the MW 40,000 region of the gels is synthesized by all but eight-cell embryos, and bands in the MW 25,000 and 30,000 regions show changes in synthesis that may be fertilization dependent.

The most noticeable stage-specific differences in protein patterns are between the patterns of four- and eight-cell embryos and those of embryos at earlier and later stages of development, which are remarkably similar. These differences, together with the evidence of a marked increase in the rates of embryonic loss at the four- to eight-cell stages, lead to the tempting speculation that these observations are manifestations of similar processes to those described in the mouse embryo. Thus, just as the maternal cytoplasmic inheritance in the mouse embryo regulates protein synthesis and cleavage to the two-cell stage in the absence of any contribution from the embryonic genome, the same form of maternal program may operate in the human embryo to regulate protein synthesis and cleavage to the four-cell stage. Preliminary data with α-amanitin would support this hypothesis. Similarly, just as gene activation in the mouse embryo is required for subsequent cleavage beyond the two-cell stage and for the synthesis of new, characteristic late two-cell polypeptides, the same process of gene activation in the human embryo may be necessary for cleavage and protein synthesis beyond the four-cell stage. Inherent deficiencies in the human embryo, resulting either in arrested development beyond the four-cell stage *in vitro* or in failure to implant following replacement, may be a consequence of inherent cytoplasmic deficiencies (deficiencies of the maternal program) and/or of a failure to switch on the embryonic genome (failure of the embryonic program). Since mouse embryos show acute sensitivity to insult around this period of transition (the late one-cell/early two-cell stages), e.g., by temperature fluctuations, resulting in developmental arrest at the two-cell stage, it seems likely that the same sensitivity may exist in human embryos during their transition period at the four- to eight-cell stage, resulting in a failure to undergo further development.

IV. Conclusions

The hypotheses we have drawn about the development of human embryos are based on few data from work which is still in progress and must therefore be regarded as highly speculative. Nevertheless, if these preliminary findings are confirmed, they have important implications for our understanding of early human development and for the clinical practice of IVF.

In most therapeutic IVF units, embryos are replaced into the recipient's uterus between 40 and 48 hours after insemination (the four- to eight-cell stage). Since this may coincide with the time at which the human embryo is most likely to undergo cleavage arrest *in vitro,* it may well be that many of the embryos that are replaced have no capacity for further development despite showing no overt morphological abnormalities. Indeed the manipulation of the embryos for transfer at this sensitive stage might increase the likelihood of cleavage arrest. Such considerations could explain (1) the low success rate of IVF and (2) why the chances of conceiving increase with an increase in the number of embryos that are replaced. Moreover, it could explain the disproportionately high rate of pregnancy that is achieved with those that are cultured *in vitro* to the blastocyst stage before cryopreservation and subsequent transfer. Finally, it highlights the dilemma facing clinicians and embryologists in selecting which embryos are to be replaced in a treatment cycle, when there are no reliable criteria by which to judge egg or embryo quality or viability. The dependence of the early embryo on extrachromosomal information inherited from the oocyte would suggest that further study of the human oocyte and its follicular environment might yield important information. Above all, our speculations emphasize the need for further research on the development of the preimplantation human embryo *in vitro*. Although animal models may serve to direct our attention toward important events in mammalian embryogenesis, it is only from a direct study of the human embryo that its unique developmental requirements will be revealed and its normal developmental mechanisms will be understood.

ACKNOWLEDGMENTS

We wish to thank Martin Johnson for his helpful criticism of the manuscript and Sheena Glenister for typing it. We are grateful to Ros Angell for allowing us to use unpublished material. This work is supported by an MRC program grant to P.R.B. and Martin Johnson.

REFERENCES

Angell, R. R., Aitken, R. J., Van Look, P. F. A., Lumsden, M. A., and Templeton, A. A. (1983). *Nature (London)* 303, 336–338.

Angell, R. R., Templeton, A. A., and Messinis, I. E. (1986a). *Cytogenet. Cell Genet.* 42, 1–7.

Angell, R. R., Templeton, A. A., and Aitken, R. J. (1986b). *Hum. Genet.* 72, 333–339.

Asch, R. H., Ellsworth, L. R., Balmaceda, J. P., and Wong, P. C. (1985). *Lancet* 2, 163.

Bagshawe, K. D., and Lawler, S. D. (1982) *Br. J. Obstet. Gynaecol.* 89, 255–257.

Bensuade, O., Babinet, C., Morange, M., and Jacob, F. (1983). *Nature (London)* 305, 331–333.

Bolton, V. N., Oades, P. J., and Johnson, M. H. (1984). *J. Embryol. Exp. Morphol.* 79, 139–163.

Bolton, V. N., Johnson, M. H., Maro, B., Howlett, S. K., Pickering, S., and Webb, M. (1987). *Proc. World Conf. In Vitro Fertil., 4th,* in press.

Bomsel-Helmreich, O. (1985). *Oxford Rev. Reprod. Biol.* 7, 1–72.

Boué, A., and Boué, J. (1978). In "Towards the Prevention of Fetal Malformation" (J. B. Scrimgeour, ed.), pp. 49–65. Edinburgh Univ. Press, Edinburgh.

Brackett, B. G., Mills, J. A., and Jeitles, G. G. (1972). Fertil. Steril. 23, 898–909.

Braude, P. R., Pelham, H. R. B., Flach, G., and Lobatto, R. (1979). Nature (London) 282, 102–105.

Braude, P. R., Bright, M. V., Douglas, C. P., Milton, P. J., Robinson, R. E., Williamson, J. G., and Hutchinson, J. (1984). Fertil. Steril. 42, 34–38.

Braude, P. R., Bolton, V. N., and Johnson, M. H. (1986). In "Embryo Research: Yes or No" (G. Bock and M. O'Connor, eds.), pp. 63–82. Ciba Foundation Symposium, Tavistock, London.

Buster, J. E., Bustillo, M., Rodi, I. A., et al. (1985). Am. J. Obstet. Gynecol. 153, 211–217.

Chetowski, R. J., Nass, T. E., Matt, D. W., Hamilton, F., Steingold, K. A., Randle, D., and Meldrum, D. R. (1985). J. IVF Embryol. Transf. 2, 207–212.

Cohen, J., Simons, R. F., Edwards, R. G., Fehilly, C. B., and Fishel, S. B. (1985). J. IVF Embryol. Transf. 2, 59–64.

Edgar, D. H., Whalley, K. M., and Mills, J. A. (1987). J. IVF Embryol. Transf. 4, 111–115.

Edmonds, P. K., Lindsay, K. S., Miller, J. F., Williamson, E., and Wood, P. J. (1982). Fertil. Steril. 38, 447–453.

Edwards, R. G. (1980). "Conception in the Human Female." Academic Press, London.

Edwards, R. G. (1984). In "In Vitro Fertilization and Embryo Transfer" (A. O. Trounson and C. Wood, eds.), pp. 217–250. Churchill Livingstone, Edinburgh.

Edwards, R. G., Steptoe, P. C., and Purdy, J. M. (1970). Nature (London) 227, 1307–1309.

Edwards, R. G., Steptoe, P. C., and Purdy, J. M. (1980). Br. J. Obstet. Gynaecol. 87, 737–756.

Edwards, R. G., Purdy, J. M., Steptoe, P. C., and Walters, D. E. (1981). Am. J. Obstet. Gynecol. 141, 408–416.

Elbling, L., and Colet, M. (1985). Mutat. Res. 147, 189–195.

Evans, H. J. (1977). J. Med. Genet. 14, 309–312.

Fehilly, C. B., Cohen, J., Simons, R. F., Fishel, S. B., and Edwards, R. G. (1985). Fertil. Steril. 44, 638–644.

Flach, G., Johnson, M. H., Braude, P. R., Taylor, R. A. S., and Bolton, V. N. (1982). EMBO J. 1, 681–686.

Fleming, T., Pratt, H. P. M., and Braude, P. R. (1987). Fertil. Steril. 47, 858–860.

Giebelhaus, D. H., Heikkila, J. J., and Schultz, G. A. (1983). Dev. Biol. 98, 148–154.

Hansmann, I., and Probeck, H. D. (1979a). Cytogenet. Cell Genet. 24, 115–125.

Hansmann, I., and Probeck, H. D. (1979b). Cytogenet. Cell Genet. 23, 70–77.

Hassold, T., Chin, D., and Yamane, J. A. (1984). Ann. Hum. Genet. 48, 129–144.

Hillier, S. G., Dawson, K. J., Afnan, M., Margara, R. A., Ryder, T. A., Wickings, E. J., and Winston, R. M. L. (1985). In "In Vitro Fertilization and Donor Insemination" (W. Thompson et al., eds.), pp. 125–137. Royal College of Obstetrics and Gynaecology, London.

Howlett, S. K. (1986a). Cell 45, 387–396.

Howlett, S. K. (1986b). Wilhelm Roux's Arch. Dev. Biol. 195, 499–505.

Howlett, S. K., and Bolton, V. N. (1985). J. Embryol. Exp. Morphol. 87, 175–206.

Howlett, S. K., Webb, M., Maro, B., and Johnson, M. H. (1985). Cytobios 43, 295–305.

Jacobs, P. A., Angell, R. R., Buchanan, J. M., Hassold, J. J., Matsuyama, A. M., and Manuel, B. (1978). Ann. Hum. Genet. 42, 49–57.

Jacobs, P. A., Szulman, A. E., Funkhauser, J., Matsura, J. S., and Wilson, C. C. (1982). Ann. Hum. Genet. 46, 223–231.

Johnson, M. H. (1981). *Biol. Rev.* **56**, 463–498.

Johnson, M. H., McConnell, J., and Van Blerkom, J. (1984). *J. Embryol. Exp. Morphol.* **83** (Suppl. 2), 197–231.

Jones, H. W., Acosta, A. A., Andrews, M. C., Garcia, J. E., Jones, G. S., Mayer, J., McDowell, J. S., Rosenwaks, Z., Sandow, B. A., Veeck, L. L., and Wilkes, C. A. (1984). *Fertil. Steril.* **42**, 826–834.

Kajii, T., and Ohama, K. (1977). *Nature (London)* **268**, 633–634.

Kerin, J. F., Quinn, P. J., Kirby, C., Seamark, R. F., Warnes, G. M., Jeffrey, R., Matthews, C. D., and Cox, L. W. (1983). *Lancet* **2**, 537–540.

Lancaster, P. A. L. (1985). *Br. Med. J.* **291**, 1160–1163.

Longo, F. J., and Chen, D. Y. (1985). *Dev. Biol.* **107**, 382–394.

Lopata, A., Brown, J. M., Leeton, J. F., Talbot, J. Mc., and Wood, C. (1978). *Fertil. Steril.* **30**, 27.

Lopata, A., Kohlman, D. J., and Kellow, G. N. (1982). *In* "Embryonic Development (Part B): Cellular Aspects," pp. 69–85. Liss, New York.

Lutjen, P., Trounson, A., Leeton, J., Findlay, J., Wood, C., and Renou, P. (1984). *Nature (London)* **307**, 174–175.

Magistrini, M., and Szollosi, D. (1980). *Eur. J. Cell Biol.* **22**, 699–707.

Magnuson, T., and Epstein, C. J. (1981). *Biol. Rev.* **56**, 369–408.

Mahadevan, M. M., and Trounson, A. O. (1984). *Fertil. Steril.* **42**, 400–405.

Maro, B., Johnson, M. H., Pickering, S. J., and Flach, G. (1984). *J. Embryol. Exp. Morphol.* **81**, 211–237.

Maro, B., Howlett, S. K., and Webb, M. (1985). *J. Cell Biol.* **101**, 1665–1672.

Maro, B., Johnson, M. H., Webb, M., and Flach, G. (1986). *J. Embryol. Exp. Morphol.* **92**, 11–32.

Messinis, I., Templeton, A., Angell, R., and Aitken, J. (1986). *Br. J. Obstet. Gynaecol.* **93**, 39–42.

Mohr, L. R. (1984). *In* "In Vitro Fertilization and Embryo Transfer" (A. O. Trounson and C. Wood, eds.), pp. 159–171. Churchill Livingstone, Edinburgh.

Mohr, L. R., and Trounson, A. O. (1982). *J. Reprod. Fertil.* **66**, 499–504.

Mohr, L. R., Trounson, A., and Freemann, L. (1985). *J. IVF Embryol. Transf.* **2**, 1–10.

Moor, R. M., and Crosby, I. M. (1985). *J. Reprod. Fertil.* **75**, 467–473.

Mortimer, D. (1985). *Curr. Problems Obstet. Gynecol.* **7**, 1–87.

Newcomb, R. (1983). *In* "In Vitro Fertilization and Embryo Transfer" (P. G. Crosignani and B. L. Rubin, eds.), pp. 261–270. Academic Press, London.

Osborn, J. C., and Moor, R. M. (1985). *In* "In Vitro Fertilization and Donor Insemination" (W. Thompson, D. N. Joyce, and J. Newton, eds.), pp. 101–114. Royal Coll. Obstet. Gynaecol., London.

Petzoldt, U., Burki, K., Illmensee, G. R., and Illmensee, K. (1983). *Wilhelm Roux's Arch. Dev. Biol.* **192**, 138–144.

Pratt, H. P. M., Bolton, V. N., and Gudgeon, K. A. (1983). "Molecular Biology of Egg Maturation," pp. 197–217. *Ciba Symp* **98**. Pitman, London.

Purdy, J. M. (1982). *In* "Human Conception *in Vitro*" (R. G. Edwards and J. M. Purdy, eds.), pp. 135–136. Academic Press, London.

Quigley, M. M., Schmidt, C. L., Beauchamp, P. J., Pace-Owens, S., Berkowitz, A. S., and Wolf, D. P. (1984). *Fertil. Steril.* **42**, 25–33.

Roberts, C. J., and Lowe, C. R. (1975). *Lancet* **1**, 498–499.

Rudak, E., Dor, J., Mashiach, S., Nebel, L., and Goldman, B. (1984). *Fertil. Steril.* **41**, 538–545.

Sato, F., and Marrs, R. P. (1984a). *Fertil. Steril.* **41** (Abstr. 56).

Sato, F., and Marrs, R. P. (1984b). *Fertil. Steril.* **41** (Abstr. 140).

Schatten, G., Simerly, C., and Schatten, H. (1985). *Proc. Natl. Acad. Sci. U.S.A.* **82**, 4152–4156.

Seppala, M. (1985). *Ann. N.Y. Acad. Sci.* **442**, 558–563.

Sher, G., Knutzen, V., Scratton, C., Chotiner, H., and Mayville, J. (1986). *Obstet. Gynaecol.* **67**, 309–315.

Steptoe, P. C. (1985). *In* "In Vitro Fertilization and Donor Insemination" (W. Thompson, D. N. Joyce, and J. Newton, eds.), pp. 241–251. Royal Coll. Obstet. Gynaecol., London.

Templeton, A., Van Look, P., Lumsden, M. A., Angell, R., Aitken, J., Duncan, A. W., and Baird, D. T. (1984). *Br. J. Obstet. Gynaecol.* **91**, 148–154.

Trounson, A., and Mohr, L. (1983). *Nature (London)* **305**, 707–709.

Trounson, A. O., Mohr, L. R., Wood, C., and Leeton, J. F. (1982). *J. Reprod. Fertil.* **64**, 285–294.

Van Blerkom, J. (1977). *In* "Immunobiology of Gametes" (M. Edidin and M. H. Johnson, eds.), pp. 187–206. Cambridge Univ. Press, London and New York.

Van Blerkom, J. (1981). *In* "Cellular and Molecular Aspects of Implantation" (S. R. Glasser and D. W. Bullock, eds.), pp. 155–176. Plenum, New York.

Van Blerkom, J., and Bell, H. (1986). *J. Embryol. Exp. Morphol.* **93**, 213.

Van Blerkom, J., and Brockway, G. O. (1975). *Dev. Biol.* **44**, 148–157.

Van Blerkom, J., Henry, G., and Porrecco, R. (1984). *Fertil. Steril.* **41**, 686–696.

Wassarman, P. M., and Fujurara, K. (1978). *J. Cell Sci.* **29**, 171–188.

Webb, M., Howlett, S. K., and Maro, B. (1986). *J. Embryol. Exp. Morphol.* **95**, 131–145.

Wentz, C. A., Repp, J. E., Maxson, W. S., Pittaway, D. E., and Torbitt, C. A. (1983). *Fertil. Steril.* **40**, 748–754.

Whittingham, D. G. (1971). *J. Reprod. Fertil. Suppl.* **14**, 7–21.

Whittingham, D. G. (1985). *In* "In Vitro Fertilization and Donor Insemination" (W. Thompson, D. N. Joyce, and J. Newton, eds.), pp. 269–274. Royal Coll. Obstet. Gynaecol., London.

Wood, C., Downing, B., Trounson, A. O., and Rogers, P. (1984). *Br. Med. J.* **289**, 978–980.

Zeilmaker, G. H., Alberda, A. T., Van Gent, I., Rijkmans, C. M. P. M., and Drogendijk, A. C. (1984). *Fertil. Steril.* **42**, 293–296.

CHAPTER 6

CELL LINEAGE ANALYSIS IN MAMMALIAN EMBRYOGENESIS

J. Rossant

DIVISION OF MOLECULAR AND DEVELOPMENTAL BIOLOGY
MOUNT SINAI HOSPITAL RESEARCH INSTITUTE
TORONTO, ONTARIO, CANADA M5G 1X5

I. Introduction

Cell lineage studies are a fundamental component of the comprehensive analysis of any developmental system (Stent, 1985). The aims of such studies are to define the fate of cells in the living embryo from egg until birth, to identify when and where cells are set aside or allocated to different cell lineages, and to determine the progenitor cell number as cells become allocated. To obtain all this information ideally requires a means of marking single defined cells in the intact embryo at any stage of development. The fate of all progeny of the marked cell should then be followed *in situ* in a quantitative and qualitative fashion throughout succeeding development, preferably in the living embryo. Detailed analysis of this sort in the intact embryo has been successfully undertaken in a variety of invertebrate and lower vertebrate species using either direct observation (Sulston *et al.,* 1983) or injection of lineage tracers (Weisblat *et al.,* 1978).

Lineage studies delineate the basic developmental decisions that occur during embryogenesis and provide the background for further investigation of mechanisms underlying these decisions. Knowledge of the normal fate of cells in the intact embryo allows one to assess their potency outside of their normal environment, thus ascertaining when cells are irreversibly committed to a given fate. Further, an understanding of when and where different cell lineages are established in the intact embryo provides a spatial and temporal map on which to search for expression of genes that may be involved in lineage differentiation. The complementary relationship between cell lineage analysis and the molecular genetics of development has been best illustrated by recent research in *Caenorhabditis elegans* and *Drosophila,* where mu-

115

tations in genes controlling lineage development have been characterized and the wild-type genes cloned (Gehring, 1985; Greenwald, 1985). The possibility that similar genes may exist in mammals, perhaps identified by "homeobox" sequences (Gehring, 1985), makes the quest for a fuller understanding of cell lineage development all the more important. Without a lineage map of the embryo, it will be very difficult to interpret the functional significance of patterns of expression of putative lineage controlling genes.

The fate of every individual cell in the intact mammalian embryo has not been followed directly from preimplantation stages to birth, but considerable lineage information has been obtained by less direct means. In this review I will describe different approaches to lineage analysis in the mouse embryo and discuss their limitations. I will emphasize newly developed techniques that provide new directions for lineage studies in mammalian embryogenesis. After consideration of methodology I will then discuss three examples of the questions that can be addressed using these techniques. These three questions represent areas of research in which new work has been undertaken since I last reviewed lineage in the mammalian embryo (Rossant, 1984). Finally, I will predict future directions for lineage analysis in mammals.

II. Techniques for Lineage Analysis in Mammalian Embryos

A. LINEAGE ANALYSIS IN CHIMERAS

1. Methods of Producing Chimeras

Until recently most information about cell lineage in the mammalian embryo has been obtained from addition of marked cells to embryos to produce chimeras. The original technique for making chimeras was developed in the 1960s by Tarkowski (1961) and Mintz (1962) and involves aggregation of entire embryos at the eight-cell stage to generate a mouse that is a mixture of the progeny of the two component embryos. This technique has limited direct application for studying cell lineage, since the fate of defined single cells cannot be assessed. Although single cells can be aggregated to cleavage-stage embryos, there have in fact been few attempts made to follow the fate of single cells by this technique. The technique of blastocyst injection developed by Richard Gardner (1968) has been used more extensively to study the fate of single defined cell types in later development. Single cells from the blastocyst stage (Gardner and Papaioannou, 1975) or even from certain tissues of the early postimplantation embryo (Moustafa and Brinster, 1972; Rossant et al., 1978) can incorporate into the blastocyst and contribute to later development. The power of the chimera approach is that, if suitable genetic markers are used, the fate of defined marked cells can be followed throughout subsequent development in the uterus (see Table I). Although, strictly speaking, chimera analysis cannot provide direct information on lineage in the intact embryo, this can be approached very closely by placing cells close to their normal position as, for example, in reconstituted blastocysts (Gardner *et al.*, 1973; Papaioannou, 1982). Further, the ability to follow cell fate after deliberately altering the cell's normal relationships in the embryo has proved extremely valuable for studying cell potency (reviewed Rossant, 1984; Pedersen, 1986).

Unfortunately, although chimeras can be made by rearrangement of cells at all preimplantation stages, production of chimeras after implantation is more difficult. Analysis of prospective fate of cells in postimplantation chimeras throughout development requires either the ability to return marked cells to their exact normal location in the embryo within the uterus or the capacity to reimplant postimplantation embryos after manipulation *in vitro*. The former is severely restricted by the inaccessibility of the embryo within the decidual mass at early postimplantation stages, and the latter has only proved successful in a very small number of cases (Beddington, 1985). There have been a few reports of successful establishment of postimplantation chimerism in certain tissue types by direct introduction of cells into the postimplantation embryo *in utero*. Hematopoietic chimerism has been established by introduction of fetal liver cells into the placental circulation at midgestation, although the injected cells seemed to require the selective advantage afforded by a genetically anemic host (Fleischman and Mintz, 1979). Postimplantation chimerism without use of a genetically deficient host has been achieved for the neural crest cell population. Neural crest cells isolated from cultured neural tubes can contribute to the melanocyte population in a reasonable proportion of cases after injection into the proamniotic cavity of early somite stage embryos (Jaenisch, 1985). Extension of this technique to a wide variety of cell types seems unlikely because of the imprecise manner in which cells are returned in the embryonic environment. Cells injected into the proamniotic cavity must by necessity relocate into their correct position in the interior of the embryo before they can contribute to later development; this property will probably be restricted to migratory cell types such as the neural crest and perhaps primordial germ cells.

Precise localization of marked cells can be achieved by establishing postimplantation chimerism *in vitro*. Cells can be grafted from one embryo to another at primitive-streak stages of development (Bed-

TABLE I

EXPERIMENTAL SYSTEMS FOR LINEAGE ANALYSIS

System	Characteristics				Information produced		
	Defined cell marking	Wide range of time of marking	Undisturbed development	Long-term analysis	Prospective fate	Progenitor cell number	Time of allocation
Chimeras							
Aggregation	−	−	−	+	±	?	−
Blastocyst injection	+	−	−	+	+	?	?
Postimplantation							
In vitro	+	−	−	−	+	−^a	−^a
In vivo	+	−	−	+	+	−	?
Tracer injections							
Preimplantation	+	−	+	−	+	−	±
Postimplantation	+	−	+	−	+	−	±
Genetic mosaics							
Spontaneous	−	+^b	+	+	−	±	−
X-Inactivation	−	−	+	+	−	±	−
DNA microinjection	−	−	+(?)	+	−	±	−
Retroviral infection							
Preimplantation	−	+	+	+	−^c	±^d	−
Postimplantation	−	+	+	+	+	+^d	+^d

^a Culture period too short.
^b But marking rare and uncontrolled.
^c No *in situ* marker for preimplantation infections yet.
^d But not performed yet.

dington, 1981, 1982; Copp *et al.*, 1986). This technique only allows short-term analysis of prospective cell fate, however, because complete postimplantation development cannot be achieved *in vitro* at present. If the embryos could be returned to the uterus after manipulation, this would dramatically increase the power of this technique. However, reimplantation of postimplantation embryos has proved to be extremely difficult (Beddington, 1985).

2. Marker Systems Used in Chimeras

The power of any technique of lineage analysis is determined by the kind of marker systems used. The properties of an ideal cell lineage marker have been described elsewhere (McLaren, 1976; West, 1984). The most important features are heritability, ubiquitous distribution, and *in situ* detection, since, in their absence, complete spatial and quantitative analysis of lineage cannot be achieved. A variety of different markers have been used to follow lineage in chimeras (West, 1984), few of which fulfill all the requirements of an ideal marker (see Table II for summary). Markers can be grouped into two main categories: short-term and genetic.

a. Short-Term Markers. Short-term markers have been used in both preimplantation and postimplantation chimeras. For example, preimplantation-stage embryos can be labeled with [^{3}H]thymidine and the labeled cells followed for two or three cell divisions after aggregation with unlabeled embryos (Hillman *et al.*, 1972; Garner and McLaren, 1974; Spindle, 1982). Additionally, tritiated thymidine has been applied to short-term analysis of postimplantation chimeras (Beddington, 1981, 1982). Other short-term markers such as fluorescein isothiocyanate (FITC) can also be used (Ziomek, 1982). Although these markers allow *in situ* detection of marked cells, they are limited in their usefulness by the fact that they are progressively diluted out as cell division proceeds. In particular, the rapid growth of the embryo that occurs shortly after implantation in the uterus (Snow, 1977) precludes their use for following lineage from preimplantation into postimplantation stages.

b. Genetic Markers. To follow the fate of cells throughout development in chimeras, some form of heritable marker must be used to circumvent dilution problems. Since chimeras can be made between many different mouse strains, there are numerous genetic differences that can be used to assess the contributions of the two components in later development (West, 1984). Most markers that have been used to date fail to fulfill one or other of the two vital criteria for an ideal cell marker; ubiquity and *in situ* detection. Markers such as isozymal vari-

TABLE II
Lineage Markers Used in Different Experimental Systems[a]

Marker	Heritability	In situ detection	Developmental neutrality	Ubiquitous detection	Used in	
					Chimeras	Intact embryo
Short term						
[3H]Thymidine	±	+	?	+	+	—
FITC	±	+	+	+	+	+
Oil droplets	—	+	+	±|	+	+
HRP	±	+	?	+	—	+
Rhodamine–dextran	±	+	?	+	—	+
Fluorescent latex beads	—	+	+	+	—	+
Conjugated lectins	—	+	?	—	—	+
Melanin granules	—	+	+	—	—	+
Genetic						
Pigmentation	+	+	+	—	+	+[b]
Chromosome	+	—	+	—	+	+[c]
Isozymes	+	—	+	+	+	+[c]
DNA polymorphisms	+	—	+	+	+	+[d]
Genetic: in situ						
Enzyme activity variants	+	+	+	—	+	+[e]
Interspecific satellite DNA	+	+	?	+	+	—
Exogenous DNA insertion	+	+	+(?)	+	+	—
Exogenous reporter gene insertion	+	+	?	?	?	+

[a] Only markers discussed in this review included. See West (1984) for review of additional markers.
[b] In spontaneous genetic mosaics.
[c] In X-inactivation mosaics.
[d] In DNA microinjection or retroviral mosaics.
[e] Ornithine carbamoyltransferase variants in X-inactivation mosaics only.

ants of glucose-phosphate isomerase (GPI) (Chapman *et al.*, 1971) and restriction-fragment length polymorphisms are ubiquitous but not detectable *in situ*, while markers such as activity variants of certain metabolic enzymes (Condamine *et al.*, 1971; Dewey *et al.*, 1976; West, 1976; Wareham *et al.*, 1983) are detectable *in situ* but only in certain tissues.

Considerable effort has been expended over the years to obtain a marker that would combine the ubiquity of GPI or DNA polymorphisms with ability to detect the gene marker *in situ*. Recent advances have been made in this area. Several markers are now available that can be readily detected *in situ* in many adult tissues and, importantly for the present discussion, during embryonic development. Gardner has shown that the null variant for cytoplasmic malic enzyme $Mod-1^n$ (Lee *et al.*, 1980), can be used as an *in situ* histological marker for chimera analysis at least in extraembryonic endoderm cells (Gardner, 1984) and may be applicable to other cell types as well. We have shown that a ubiquitous *in situ* marker can be developed using satellite DNA differences between two species of mice, *Mus musculus* and *Mus caroli* (Siracusa *et al.*, 1983). We originally used a radioactively labeled probe to *M. musculus* satellite DNA to show that we could distinguish labeled *M. musculus* cells from unlabeled *M. caroli* cells by *in situ* hybridization on sections of chimeras (Rossant and Chapman, 1983). Since then improvements in the methodology of *in situ* hybridization and our recent cloning of the major *M. caroli* satellite DNA sequence (J. Rossant and G. Fraser, unpublished) have combined to make this the most powerful reciprocal marker system known to date. When biotinylated probes are used and hybridization detected by streptavidin–horseradish peroxidase (HRP) binding (Rossant *et al.*, 1986), satellite probes from both species label practically every cell in sections of homologous tissue and fail to label any cells of the opposite species. This specificity and efficiency of labeling means that it is possible to identify single cells of the two genotypes in sections of chimeras at all stages of development. The only drawback of the system is the need to cross species boundaries in order to generate the marker. This leads to the possibility that cells may not behave in the same manner as in intraspecific chimeras, although we cannot detect any evidence for this at least within the lineages of the embryo itself (Rossant and Chapman, 1983).

It is now possible to utilize the *in situ* hybridization techniques developed for interspecific chimeras to detect DNA differences between animals of the same species. Transgenic mice that contain high copy numbers of inserted gene sequences have been produced by microinjection of DNA into the zygote stage of development (Brinster *et al.*, 1985). These new mouse strains can be used as chimera partners and the genotypic composition of the resulting chimeras can be detected *in situ* later in development. For example, using a mouse line generated by Cecilia Lo, which contains 1000 copies of a mouse β-globin gene plasmid inserted into its genome (Lo, 1986), one can distinguish cells of the transgenic strain from normal cells in chimeras by *in situ* hybridization. The advantage of this approach is not just that the marker is generated within one species, but that it can be obtained congenic to an established mouse strain. This will have considerable advantages for lineage studies that depend on quantitative analysis of chimera composition, since any strain-specific selection effects should be eliminated.

B. LINEAGE ANALYSIS BY EXOGENOUS TRACERS

The most direct approach to lineage analysis in the embryo is to investigate the fate of cells in the intact embryo itself. In some systems, most notably *C. elegans,* it is possible to follow cell fate in the intact embryo by simple visual observation using Nomarski optics (Sulston *et al.*, 1983). In the mouse embryo, although visual observation of early cleavage is feasible, there is no obvious polarity to the preimplantation embryo, which means that no blastomere possesses a unique identity that would allow its lineage to be defined. Thus, simple visual observation is of limited value. Recently it has been shown that morphogenetic movements of individual mesoderm cells can be studied by Nomarski optics during gastrulation in the living postimplantation mouse embryo in culture (Nakatsuji *et al.*, 1986). However, detailed lineage information requires introduction of exogenous markers.

During preimplantation development a variety of exogenous markers can be applied to study cell lineage and allocation. Microinjected oil droplets were the first exogenous markers used. When injected into single cells at early cleavage stages, the oil droplets can be used to follow cytoplasmic regionalization during succeeding divisions (Wilson *et al.*, 1972). However, the marker is not divided equally among progeny after cell division and so is very limited in its use. Workers have subsequently made use of two lineage tracers developed in other systems, namely, HRP (Weisblat *et al.*, 1978) and rhodamine-conjugated dextran (Gimlich and Braun, 1985). When microinjected into individual blastomeres, these tracer molecules disperse throughout the cytoplasm and thus are much more readily discernible than oil droplets. The fluorescent marker can be distinguished in the intact unsectioned embryo; HRP can also be visualized in the intact embryo or in more detail after histological sectioning (Pedersen *et al.*, 1986). These markers do not appear to be deleterious to the injected cells, since cell division occurs after injection and the marker is divided equally among the progeny of the injected cell (Balakier and Pedersen, 1986). This approach has allowed detailed *in situ* analysis of the lineage of individual marked cells during preimplantation development (Pedersen, 1986). It has not proved possible to use this method to follow the fate of cleavage-stage cells into postimplantation development because of dilution of the marker. HRP can, however, be used to study short-term fate in postimplantation embryos held in culture for 1–2 days (Lawson *et al.*, 1986).

There are several other exogenous markers that have been used to address specific questions of cell lineage development in the mouse embryo (Table II). These include melanin granules, which can be taken up by trophectoderm cells at the blastocyst stage and serve as a marker for these cells during later developmental stages (Gardner, 1975; Copp, 1979). Uptake of fluorescent latex beads by preimplantation blastomeres has also proved a useful lineage marker, this time not for individual cells but as a marker of all external cells in the embryo (Fleming, 1987). Conjugated lectins have been used to label cells facing the proamniotic cavity of the postimplantation embryo (Smits-Van Prooije *et al.*, 1986). In these last two experiments, information was obtained on the movements and allocations of entire cell populations rather than individual cells.

The chief advantage of all exogenous tracer experiments is that, unlike chimeras, there is no interference with the normal relationships of cells in the embryo. Further, marking the intact embryo eliminates any possible selection effects due to genetic differences between strains used to make chimeras, although proof that exogenous markers themselves do not affect cell viability is hard to find. The limitation of the technique is the short-term nature of the exogenous marker systems used to date, which means that complete lineage analysis of the intact embryo has not been achieved.

C. Lineage Analysis in Genetic Mosaics

Genetic mosaicism generated by introduction of a genetic marker into cells of the intact embryo has the potential to be a very powerful tool for lineage analysis. Such an approach would combine the advantages of having a long-term heritable marker, as available in chimeras, with the ability to mark cells in undisturbed development. For such an approach to be successful, it should be possible to control the time and position of cell marking (see Table I), and the marker generated should ideally be detectable *in situ*. Several forms of genetic mosaicism can be generated in mammalian embryos but none fulfills both of these criteria.

1. Spontaneous Genetic Mosaicism

A careful survey by Russell (1964) of the results of radiation experiments using the specific-locus method has revealed that genetic mosaicism can arise at various stages of embryogenesis, presumably by somatic mutation. Spontaneous reversion at two pigment loci, *pearl* (*pe*) and *pink-eye unstable* (p^{un}) has also been reported to generate mosaicism, the extent of which will depend on the stage of embryogenesis at which the reversion occurred (Russell, 1964; Melvold, 1971; Searle, 1978). Pigment mosaicism is normally the phenotype assayed in this approach; this provides an *in situ* marker of mosaicism but it is very limited in its tissue applicability. Somatic mutations in histochemically detectable enzyme loci could be sought to broaden the tissue range of scorable mosaicism, and increased rate of somatic mutation and control over time of onset of mosaicism might be produced by treatment with mutagens such as X rays at different times in development (Russell and Major, 1957). However, the full potential of this approach has not been realized in the mammalian embryo, chiefly because of the rare nature of spontaneous mutation and the extreme sensitivity of the early embryo to mutagens such as X rays (Pedersen *et al.*, 1978). The use of X rays to generate clones of cells marked by somatic mutation or recombination has been successfully used for lineage analysis in *Drosophila* (Garcia-Bellido and Ripoll, 1978) and in a limited manner in the zebra fish (Streisinger *et al.*, 1986).

2. X-Inactivation Mosaicism

Functional genetic mosaicism generated by random X-chromosome inactivation in female mammalian embryos can also provide some data on lineage relationships during development. In the cells of the primitive ectoderm which gives rise to the fetus itself (Gardner and Rossant, 1979), X inactivation is now known to occur randomly at some stage between 4.5 and 6.5 days of development (Monk and Harper, 1979; Rastan, 1982; Gardner *et al.*, 1985). Once the inactivation event is established, it is heritable (Lyon, 1961), so that the resulting mice contain approximately a 50:50 mixture of cells expressing genes from one or other of the X chromosomes. The resulting mosaicism can be detected using chromosomal (Cattanach, 1961) or isozymal markers (McMahon *et al.*, 1983) in a wide variety of tissues. Unfortunately, there are no X-linked polymorphisms that allow *in situ* detection of differential X-chromosomal activity in all tissues. A low-activity variant of the X-linked enzyme ornithine carbamoyltransferase (Wareham *et al.*, 1983) allows *in situ* analysis of mosaicism in the liver where the gene is expressed at high levels (Wareham and Williams, 1986); mosaicism at this gene locus cannot be detected in other tissues. X-inactivation mosaicism is also of limited use for lineage analysis because mosaicism is established at one time in development only.

3. Induced Genetic Mosaicism

Clearly, a means of generating genetic mosaicism at will at different stages of development and preferably in single defined cells would be extremely valuable. Techniques for manipulating the genome of the mouse embryo by introduction of exogenous DNA sequences offer such possibilities.

a. DNA Microinjection. Introduction of DNA into the zygote by microinjection (Gordon and Ruddle, 1981) or iontophoresis (Lo, 1983) has allowed the production of transgenic mice carrying foreign gene sequences in somatic tissues and the germ line. In most of these mice the added gene sequence is contained in all somatic cells, indicating that integration occurred at the one-cell stage. However in a certain number (probably between 10 and 30%; Wilkie *et al.*, 1986), the DNA appears to integrate at a later stage of development and the resulting mice are mosaic for the gene of interest. Quantitation of mosaicism can be achieved by Southern blot analysis of DNA in different tissues, but the sensitivity and accuracy of such quantitation has not been carefully determined. Again, the most powerful means of analyzing mosaicism in transgenic mice would be an *in situ* method. Wilkie and co-workers have shown that mosaicism can be detected *in situ* in the pancreas of transgenic mice containing an elastase–human growth hormone construct, using antibodies to growth hormone (Wilkie *et al.*, 1986). A more generally applicable method of studying mosaicism in transgenic mice has been developed by Cecilia Lo, who has shown that *in situ* hybridization to the inserted DNA itself can identify those cells within the mosaic animal that contain the injected gene (Lo, 1986). It is not yet clear whether this technique will be sensitive enough to detect accurately cells that contain low copy numbers of the injected sequence, although Lo claims that single-copy inserts can be detected (Lo, 1986).

Mosaic mice generated by DNA injection are unlikely to be widely used for elucidating lineage relationships in the embryo, even with *in situ* hybridization techniques that allow detection of mosaicism in a wide range of tissue types. There are several reasons for this. First it is not clear when mosaicism is established. Short-term studies, in which the expression of various promoter–*Escherichia coli lacZ* constructs has been followed *in situ* after DNA microinjection, have indicated that the most likely cause of mosaicism is integration after DNA synthesis at the zygote stage. Around 20 to 40% of embryos that express the injected constructs, as detected by *in situ* staining with the substrate X-gal, show expression restricted to some blastomeres, most frequently half the embryo (R. A. Pedersen, personal communication; Rossant and Clapoff, unpublished results). DNA iontophoresis has been reported to produce a higher proportion of mosaic animals, and it is possible that integration is delayed further in these embryos. However, it seems unlikely that it will be possible to control the time at which DNA integration occurs, a prerequisite for a truly powerful system of lineage tracing. Direct injection of exogenous DNA sequences into defined cells at different stages of embryogenesis would, of course, overcome some of these problems, provided that integration took place during the cell cycle directly following injection. Transgenic mice have been generated after injection into nuclei of two-cell stage embryos but the success rate was low (Brinster *et al.*, 1985). There are no reported cases of successful introduction of DNA into the embryo beyond the two-cell stage by direct nuclear injection, although Jaenisch and Mintz (1974) obtained a low frequency of transgenic mice following injection of SV40 DNA into the blastocoelic cavity. The technical difficulty of injecting nuclei at later stages of development would presumably lead to an unworkably low rate of integration of the injected sequences, making this approach to lineage analysis unfeasible.

b. *Retroviral Infection*. Generation of genetic mosaicism in the intact embryo during both preimplantation and postimplantation development can be achieved efficiently by retroviral infection. This approach has considerable potential for lineage analysis in mammalian development and has already been used to address questions of hematopoietic lineage in the adult mouse (Dick *et al.*, 1985). Preimplantation embryos can be infected with retroviruses at the four- to eight-cell stage *in vitro* (Jaenisch, 1976; Jahner and Jaenisch, 1980); integration of individual retroviral sequences into single blastomeres takes place at some unknown time after infection, probably not more than one or two cell cycles later (Stewart *et al.*, 1982). Mosaic mice are generated in which a varying proportion of the cells contain one or more retroviral inserts (Soriano and Jaenisch, 1986). Postimplantation embryos can be infected by injection of virus suspension (Jaenisch, 1980) or virus-producing cells (Stuhlmann *et al.*, 1984) directly into the embryo within the uterus. The exact stages of embryogenesis at which the zygote can be effectively infected have not been well defined, but presumably very early postimplantation-stage embryos will not be readily accessible to infection *in utero*. With this possible limitation, retroviral infection provides a means of genetically marking cells at many different stages of development.

Southern blot analysis can be used to provide a crude quantitative estimate of retroviral mosaicism in different tissues at later stages of development (Soriano and Jaenisch, 1986), but detailed lineage analysis requires *in situ* detection of retrovirally marked cells. Unlike DNA injection, in which multicopy concatamers are often inserted, retroviral infection only generates a single copy insertion which is not likely to be readily detectable by *in situ* hybridization. *In situ* analysis of mosaicism after retroviral infection would therefore seem to require insertion into the retrovirus of a gene whose product can be histologically detectable in the resulting mosaic embryos. The *E. coli lacZ* gene provides such a reporter or indicator gene: Nicolas and co-workers have recently shown that a retrovirus in which the *lacZ* gene is placed under the transcriptional control of the viral long terminal repeat (LTR) can be used to infect postimplantation embryos *in utero* and that the progeny of the infected cells can be detected *in situ* with X-gal (Sanes *et al.*, 1986). Provided that expression of the bacterial gene is not restricted to certain cell types in the embryo and provided that the multiplicity of infection can be controlled so that marked cells are clearly the clonal progeny of single cells, this method should allow clear delineation of both the time of lineage separation in the intact postimplantation embryo and the progenitor cell number of different lineages. The main problem with this approach is the imprecise site of infection; cells will be randomly marked and many mosaics will have to be analyzed if the fate of specific regions or cells is sought.

Before this approach can be used to trace lineage from preimplantation stages as well, the apparent inactivation of retroviral expression in preimplantation embryos will have to be addressed. In contrast to infection of postimplantation embryos, integration into the preimplantation embryo is accompanied by transcriptional inactivation which persists throughout the life-span of the animal with only rare episodes of activation (Stuhlmann *et al.*, 1981). The mechanism of this restriction is not altogether clear, although it has been correlated with inactivity of the viral enhancers (Linney *et al.*, 1984; Gorman *et al.*, 1985) and *de novo* methylation of viral sequences (Jahner *et al.*, 1982). These observations indicate that genes placed under the control of the retroviral LTR are not likely to be expressed following infection of preimplantation embryos. Accordingly, retrovirus vectors have been constructed in which exogenous genes are driven by internal nonretroviral promoters. These vectors have been shown capable of infecting preimplantation embryos and integrating into the germ line; however, expression of the foreign genes has been low or nonexistent (Van der Putten et al., 1985; Jahner et al., 1985; Huszar et al., 1985; Bernstein et al., 1986). Currently, vectors are being constructed carrying marker genes such as E. coli lacZ under the control of strong constitutive cellular promoters to determine whether retroviral inactivation in preimplantation embryos necessarily extends to independent transcriptional units carried within the virus.

III. Lineage Analysis: Experimental Results

A. Cell Allocation in the Preimplantation Embryo

Much attention has been given to studying the allocation of cells to the first two cell lineages to develop in the mammalian embryo, namely, inner cell mass (ICM) and trophectoderm. There are two main reasons for this focus of interest. First, the formation of these two cell types represents a simple model system for understanding general processes of development. Second, it is possible to manipulate the embryo extensively during preimplantation development so that the relationship between cell lineage and cell commitment can be examined in detail.

As cleavage proceeds, cells become smaller and more numerous so that inner and outer cell compartments are generated (Barlow et al., 1972). Pedersen and colleagues have used HRP injection to follow the fate of the progeny of outside cells at various stages during preimplantation development (Balakier and Pedersen, 1982; Pedersen et al., 1986). They have shown that at the 16-cell stage, 3–4 cells are internalized and that a further 2–4 inner cells are added at the next division. After this stage outer cells generate only outer descendants (Cruz and Pedersen, 1985; Pedersen et al., 1986). The numbers of inner and outer cells generated by this mechanism are completely consistent with the assumption that at the 32-cell stage inner cells go on to form ICM and outer cells generate trophectoderm. There are two important points to note about this analysis of ICM and trophectoderm lineage. First, generation of inner cells does not occur at one specific cell division; rather, cells are added to the inner pool over at least two cell cycles. Second, there is no fixed lineage from one embryo to the next. The exact number of inner cells at each division varies considerably. If few cells enter the inner compartment at the first cell division, then more will be added at the next cell division, and vice versa (Surani and Barton, 1984) (Fig. 1).

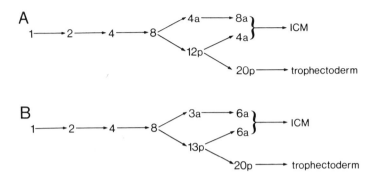

FIG. 1. Two possible cell lineage diagrams for the preimplantation mouse embryo. a, Apolar cells; p, polar cells.

The numerology of development provided by this analysis is very close to that predicted on simple geometrical grounds (Gardner and Rossant, 1976) and does not require any special preprogramming of cells to generate trophectoderm and ICM. However, other manipulative studies have shown that there is some predisposition of cells within the morula to contribute to ICM or trophectoderm. Division at the 8- to 16-cell stage generates two kinds of blastomeres, those in which certain membrane, cytocortical, and cytoplasmic components are polarized (polar cells), and apolar cells in which no such polarization is found (Johnson and Ziomek, 1981; Johnson and Maro, 1986). Polar cells are on the outside of the embryo and apolar cells take up an inside position during cleavage. When single polar or apolar cells were labeled with FITC and aggregated in various conformations with unlabeled blastomeres, polar cells were shown always to contribute at least one progeny cell to the trophectoderm of the blastocyst, whatever their original position in the aggregate (Ziomek and Johnson, 1982). Apolar cells seemed to differentiate much more according to their position. These experiments provide strong evidence that polarized cell division actually influences cell fate and indicate that lineage is not entirely constrained by simple positional effects in the preimplantation embryo. It appears as though each cell at the 8- to 16-cell stage has the underlying potential to generate an inner and an outer cell by polarized cell division, but the realization of this potential can be affected by various factors, including plane of cell division (Johnson and Ziomek, 1981), interactions with neighboring cells (Ziomek and Johnson, 1980), differential cell adhesiveness (Kimber et al., 1982), and cell number (Rand, 1985).

Although numerology and short-term lineage experiments indicate that the inner and outer compartments may be closed lineages by the 32-cell stage, this remains somewhat unclear. Cell potency experiments have indicated that ICM cells retain the potential to generate trophectoderm cells for some time after the beginning of blastocyst formation (Handyside, 1978; Spindle, 1978; Rossant and Lis, 1979b). Pedersen and colleagues have suggested that inner cells in the intact early blastocyst may in fact generate trophectoderm descendants in some instances. When ICM cells of early blastocysts were marked through the mural trophectoderm wall with HRP, some of the progeny of these cells appeared to contribute to the trophectoderm layer (G. A. Winkel and R. A. Pedersen, unpublished). Injection of HRP into single polar trophectoderm cells also suggested that polar trophectoderm cells might be displaced by cells derived from the ICM (Cruz and Pedersen, 1985). Thus in the intact embryo the outer trophectoderm compartment appears to be closed by the 32-cell stage, but the inside compartment may still contribute to the outer layer for some time beyond this stage. This area is still somewhat uncertain. Chimera experiments in which ICMs are placed inside other intact blastocysts have not revealed any ICM contributions to trophectoderm (Rossant and Lis, 1979a). A full understanding of mechanisms underlying ICM and trophectoderm development will have to take into account all this information on cell lineage and allocation during early preimplantation development.

B. Prospective Cell Fate in the Postimplantation Embryo

Recent advances in developing markers for *in situ* analysis of the later development of preimplantation chimeras, combined with new approaches to direct lineage analysis in the postimplantation embryo itself, have begun to provide information on the way in which cells are allocated to the later lineages that develop into the fetus.

The first kind of information that can be obtained relates to the mixing and movements of cells during development. Short-term analysis of aggregation chimeras made between [3H]thymidine-labeled and unlabeled embryos has shown that growth is essentially coherent during preimplantation development (Garner and McLaren, 1974; Kelly, 1979). Very little mixing was observed between the two component embryos up to the blastocyst stage. However, *in situ* analysis of early postimplantation embryos derived from aggregation of eight-cell embryos of *M. musculus* and *M. caroli* or from injection of *M. caroli* ICM into *M. musculus* blastocysts has shown that there is extensive cell mixing soon after implantation within the primitive ectoderm (Rossant, 1986, and unpublished). Cell mixing continues within the ectoderm layer of the egg cylinder up to primitive-streak formation. This mixing within what is apparently a columnar epithelium is somewhat surprising; however, a recent paper has suggested a "cortical tractor" mechanism whereby cells within intact epithelia may move relative to each other (Jacobson et al., 1986). Cell mixing appeared to be much less extensive within the visceral endoderm layer at the same stages of development (Rossant, 1986). Coherence of growth within this layer has been confirmed in later visceral yolk sac by application of the Mod-1^n enzyme marker (Gardner, 1984). Parietal endoderm, on the other hand, shows extensive intermingling of cells (Gardner, 1984). Thus, already at the early egg cylinder stage, different tissue lineages show different amounts of cell mixing. The extensive mixing that occurs within the primitive ectoderm suggests but does not prove that there is no rigidity of cell lineage at this stage of development. *In situ* analysis has not yet been undertaken to determine the exact extent of clonal mixing following single-cell marking in the preimplantation embryo.

Direct application of lineage tracers to single cells of the primitive ectoderm of the pre- or early primitive-streak stage embryo has also revealed that there is extensive cell movement and cell mixing (K. Lawson, personal communication). There is considerable net relocation of cells during primitive-streak formation. For example, cells marked at the early primitive-streak stage in the anterior ectoderm may produce progeny that have migrated posteriorly through the primitive streak into the mesoderm layer. Movement of cells through the primitive streak is perhaps not surprising, since there must be net migration of cells in order to generate a new layer of cells between the ectoderm and endoderm, and also to generate the definitive endoderm (Lawson et al., 1986). Similar movements and migrations have been observed in other vertebrate embryos (Vakaet, 1984; Kimmel and Warga, 1986). Unfortunately, one cannot yet follow HRP-marked cells *in vitro* from the pre-primitive-streak stage through to the time of organogenesis and beyond in order to determine whether there is any clonal restriction of cell lineage during this early stage. However, the extensive cell movements and intermingling suggest that this is unlikely. Certainly, single marked primitive ectoderm cells can give rise to both ectoderm and mesoderm derivatives (K. A. Lawson, personal communication).

Once the extensive cell movements of primitive-streak formation have occurred, it appears that different regions of the embryo may now be restricted to separate fates, at least in the intact embryo. Beddington (1982) has grafted [³H]thymidine-labeled fragments of different regions of late primitive-streak stage embryonic ectoderm to the

same regions in unlabeled embryos and shown that there is some regionalization of cell fate at this stage; anterior embryonic ectoderm
gives rise to head ectoderm and neuroectoderm, distal ectoderm produces gut endoderm and mesodermal tissues, and posterior ectoderm
gives rise to mesodermal tissues exclusively. Although the fate of ectoderm cells appears to be somewhat restricted by this stage in the intact
embryo, transplantation of the same fragments away from their original position has shown that they retain potential to form a much wider
spectrum of tissues (Beddington, 1982). The primitive streak region
itself retains the ability to generate endoderm, notochord, and mesoderm structures, though not extraembryonic mesoderm, until the
somite stage of development (Tam and Beddington, 1987).

There is some evidence for regional segregation of at least one
lineage by the primitive-streak stage, namely, the primordial germ
cell (PGC) lineage (Snow, 1981). Recent experiments suggest that the
cells that give rise to the PGC are restricted to the posterior end of the
primitive streak. Labeled grafts of this region but not of anterior lateral ectoderm and mesoderm produced PGC when transplanted to the
allantoic bud of an unlabeled embryo *in vitro* (Copp *et al.*, 1986). These
experiments do not address the question of whether individual cells
within the posterior primitive streak are committed to PGC formation
or whether single cells can still contribute to both somatic or germ cell
lineages, since the fate of single cells cannot be addressed by tissue
grafting experiments. Direct cell marking by HRP or retroviruses will
be required to address the time of complete separation of the germ cell
lineage.

In summary, the limited information available to date on lineage
analysis in the postimplantation embryo indicates that there is extensive cell intermingling during early postimplantation development
prior to and including primitive-streak formation itself. Allocation of
cells to specific somatic lineages has still not been conclusively demonstrated in the intact embryo. There is indication from grafting experiments of allocation of cells to anterior structures by the late primitive-
streak stage and there is evidence that PGC may be set aside during
primitive-streak formation. However, it seems likely that the major
allocation to different organ rudiments occurs at a slightly later stage
in development that cannot be addressed with current experimental
techniques, which are limited by the short-term nature of embryo culture and lineage markers used to date. The application of retroviral
infection, particularly of embryos *in vivo*, at different stages of development should provide important new information on allocation to somatic cell lineages later in development.

C. RETROSPECTIVE ANALYSIS OF PROGENITOR CELL NUMBER AND THE TIME OF ALLOCATION OF POSTIMPLANTATION LINEAGES

Various attempts have been made over the years to use retrospective analysis of the patterns of genetic mosaicism in adult animals to derive information on progenitor cell number of different tissues and thus make some inferences about time of allocation to different lineages. The use of retrospective analysis of genetic mosaicism to assess progenitor cell number of early cell lineages is fraught with difficulties, as has been reviewed many times elsewhere (McLaren, 1976; West, 1978; Rossant, 1984). Here I will outline general observations that have been made from retrospective analysis and describe some of the attempts to assess progenitor cell number of specific lineages by this method. The first general observation is that mosaicism is very similar between different tissues of one individual. This is true whether the mosaicism is induced by production of chimeras (Ford *et al.*, 1975; Rossant and Chapman, 1983) or within the intact embryo by X-inactivation mosaicism (Nesbitt, 1971), retroviral infection (Soriano and Jaenisch, 1986), or gene injection (Wilkie *et al.*, 1986). Although detailed analysis is hard to come by, it seems that there is more variation between different tissues in individual adult chimeras than between tissues in adult genetic mosaics. This is perhaps not surprising, since most chimeras have been made between different strains of mice and may be subject to strain-specific, tissue-specific selection effects (e.g., blood cells: Stephens and Warner, 1980; pigment cells: Gearhart and Oster-Granite, 1981; muscle: Peterson *et al.*, 1979). However, much of this variation can be avoided either by analysis of neonatal chimeras where cell selection effects seem more limited (Rossant and Chapman, 1983) or by production of chimeras between congenic strains of mice (Behringer *et al.*, 1984).

The general similarity of mosaic composition observed in adult somatic tissues indicates that there must be considerable cell mixing after initiation of genetic labeling but prior to allocation to specific tissues. Further, when allocation does occur, precursor cell numbers for each tissue must be fairly large. Since the same similarity in mosaic composition is observed whether genetic marking occurs during preimplantation development or in the early postimplantation embryo by X inactivation, allocation to specific adult tissues presumably occurs after X inactivation, that is, >6.5 days *post coitum*. This is consistent with what is now known about cell behavior and cell fate in the early-postimplantation embryo from direct prospective analysis (see Section III,B).

A further observation which can now be explained by direct knowledge of the behavior of cells in the early embryo is that there is little variation in the mean level of mosaicism between different X-inactivation mosaics (Nesbitt, 1971; McMahon et al., 1983), but a considerable range of mosaic composition is seen in chimeras (Falconer and Avery, 1978; West et al., 1984) or mosaics generated by gene introduction during preimplantation development (Soriano and Jaenisch, 1986; Wilkie et al., 1986). The main factor influencing this difference is the time of cell marking (West et al., 1984). X-inactivation mosaicism marks cells at random in the primitive ectoderm when this cell population is already quite large. We should expect, therefore, little variation from the initial ratio of marked cells (i.e., 50:50) in different adult X-inactivation mosaics. However, if cells are genetically marked during preimplantation development, be it by production of aggregation chimeras or by gene introduction, cells are marked in a small cell population before the primitive ectoderm lineage is allocated. Since cell lineage studies have shown that little cell mixing occurs during the preimplantation stages of development (Garner and McLaren, 1974; Kelly, 1979), a widely varying proportion of cells of one particular genotype may end up in the primitive ectoderm which gives rise to the fetus itself, even if the original ratio of component genotypes were 50:50. This proportion should depend on the relationship between the position of the ICM in the blastocyst and the borderline between the cells of the two genotypes (Falconer and Avery, 1978).

As well as explaining the wider variation in mosaics generated preimplantation to those generated postimplantation, this hypothesis also predicts that the mosaic composition of the other two cell lineages generated during preimplantation development should not be the same as that of the primitive ectoderm in any one conceptus (Falconer and Avery, 1978). This hypothesis has been tested for derivatives of the primitive ectoderm and primitive endoderm using chimeras carrying isozymal variants (West et al., 1984). There was no correlation between the mosaic composition of the two lineages in a series of chimeras, but they were not exactly inversely correlated, as might be expected if this were the only allocation event involved in generating the variation. Clearly there is a previous allocation event not taken into account in this analysis, namely, allocation to trophectoderm. Variation in mosaic composition between fetus and placenta observed in DNA injection (Wilkie et al., 1986) and retroviral infection mosaics (Soriano and Jaenisch, 1986) suggests nonrandom allocation to ICM and trophectoderm. In situ analysis of a series of aggregation chimeras between M. musculus and M. caroli at 6.5 days of development has confirmed directly that allocation of the two genotypes to all three preimplantation lineages is nonrandom (unpublished observations).

The general observations derived from retrospective analysis of chimeric and mosaic mice are therefore consistent with what is now becoming known from direct lineage analysis in the embryo. It is important to try to determine whether new information can be obtained from retrospective analysis of mosaicism that has not been obtained to date from direct lineage analysis.

1. Progenitor Cell Number for the Embryo

Prospective analysis of cell fate has shown that the fetus is derived in its entirety from the primitive ectoderm cell lineage, which is first established in the 4.5-day embryo and contains ~20 cells at the time that it can first be identified (Gardner and Rossant, 1979). There have been various attempts to use retrospective analysis to determine whether all cells of the primitive ectoderm actually contribute progeny to the later fetus. An early claim of three cells alone giving rise to the embryo was based on the proportion of nonmosaics in a series of aggregation chimeras (Mintz, 1971). This estimate of progenitor cell number based on the binomial theorem is subject to many limitations, most notably in this instance the fact that the estimate is not valid if there is any coherence of growth before the time of allocation (McLaren, 1972; Lewis et al., 1972). Coherence of growth is known to occur during preimplantation development, as already discussed.

A more accurate means of determining progenitor cell number is to use what I have termed the minimum descendant clone size estimation method (Rossant, 1984). In this terminology a descendant clone represents all the progeny of a single early progenitor cell (West, 1978). In a series of chimeras it should be possible to detect some minimum contribution of one genotype to a lineage, be it primitive ectoderm or any later lineage. This minimum contribution should represent one descendant clone. If the minimum contribution ever observed is 1/n of the lineage, then n is the progenitor cell number of that lineage. Further, there should also be chimeras in which the proportions of the two genotypes are 2/n, 3/n, etc. Soriano and Jaenisch (1986) have used this approach to attempt to determine progenitor cell number for the entire embryo after retroviral infection at preimplantation stages. In a series of retroviral mosaics the smallest contribution ever observed from one retrovirus to the adult mouse by Southern blot analysis was 12%. This led to the conclusion that there could be up to eight progenitor cells (12% = 1/8) for the mouse. Leaving aside the question of the accuracy of quantitation of mosaicism, what remains uncertain about this estimate, as with many others using retrospective analysis, is the stage of development at which these eight cells are found. Does the number obtained reflect the number of cells at the time of marking that can contribute at least some of their progeny to the adult mouse, or are eight cells specifically selected to give rise to the fetus at some stage later in development from a larger pool of primitive ectoderm cells? Given that retroviral infection occurred during preimplantation development, the small progenitor cell number most likely reflects the maximum number of cells at the time of integration that can contribute progeny to the fetus. The second possibility is also consistent with the data.

If the time of marking is the factor that determines the apparent progenitor cell number for the fetus, then this number should vary when cells are marked at different stages of development. The progenitor cell number for the entire fetus is calculated as between 20 and 40 from the analysis of variation between different X-inactivation mosaics (Nesbitt, 1971; McMahon *et al.*, 1983), which is consistent with the prediction, since X inactivation occurs later in development than retroviral infection. More information on mosaics generated by specifically marking cells at defined times in development is required to elucidate the exact progenitor numbers for the fetus in the early embryo.

2. Progenitor Cell Numbers for Specific Cell Lineages

As noted previously, quantitation of mosaicism in different organs of adult mice indicates that progenitor cell numbers for nearly all these organs must be large. This observation derives from the similarity in mosaic composition between almost all tissues of such chimeras or mosaics. If progenitor cell number is large for any given organ or tissue, then the actual number becomes very difficult to determine. When genetic mosaics are generated by any method used to date, cells are labeled prior to allocation of different organ rudiments. If these cells continue to proliferate evenly and become randomly mixed prior to allocation of the later lineages, then the level of mosaicism in a given tissue may reflect the original genotype composition of the cells that give rise to the fetus itself and not the number of actual progenitor cells for that tissue. This is illustrated diagrammatically in Fig. 2. If one uses a marker that only distinguishes mosaicism in one particular tissue and calculates a small progenitor cell number, one cannot distinguish whether this represents the true progenitor cell number for the tissue, or reflects the embryo progenitor cell number at the time of marking. For example, a recent claim of 15 progenitor cells for the

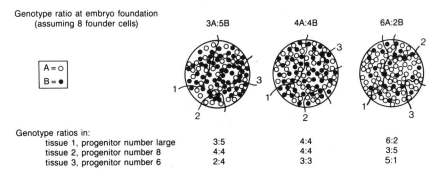

Genotype ratio at embryo foundation
(assuming 8 founder cells)   3A:5B   4A:4B   6A:2B

A = ○
B = ●

Genotype ratios in:

	3A:5B	4A:4B	6A:2B
tissue 1, progenitor number large	3:5	4:4	6:2
tissue 2, progenitor number 8	4:4	4:4	3:5
tissue 3, progenitor number 6	2:4	3:3	5:1

Fig. 2. The effect of initial genotype ratio in the primitive ectoderm and tissue progenitor cell numbers on final genotype ratios in different tissues of mosaics. Cells are assumed to be randomly mixed prior to tissue allocation. Mosaic composition in tissues whose progenitor cell number is large (tissue 1) will always reflect the initial genotype ratio, whereas tissues with small progenitor cell numbers (tissues 2 and 3) may show the same ratio as the initial ratio but may also deviate considerably from it. Use of the minimum descendant clone size estimation alone for tissues 1 and 2 would generate the same predicted progenitor cell number, namely, 8.

liver, based on quantitation of X-linked ornithine carbamoyltransferase activity *in situ* in liver sections (Wareham and Williams, 1986), is very similar to the progenitor cell number of the entire fetus calculated at the time of X inactivation (Nesbitt, 1971; McMahon *et al.*, 1983). In this instance mosaicism could not be analyzed in any other tissue by the marker used.

If there is indeed a small progenitor cell number for any specific tissue, then several other criteria should hold. The contributions of the two genotypes within the particular tissue analyzed should not always be identical to the mosaic composition of the animal as a whole. Further, the genotype ratios of the particular tissue should vary in a quantal manner between mice (Fig. 2). Tissues which have a large progenitor cell number may also show variation from the mean mosaic composition of the mouse but only within a normal distribution around the mean. Extreme differences from the mean imply small progenitor cell numbers.

Few attempts have been made to derive a truly quantitative estimate of mosaic composition in specific cell types in later development in order to estimate progenitor cell number. The reason for this lies chiefly in the absence of suitable *in situ* markers. However, Herrup and colleagues have used *in situ* analysis to determine progenitor cell number for specific neuron cell types. Quantitative *in situ* analysis of the development of Purkinje cells (Wetts and Herrup, 1982) and facial nerve nucleus (Herrup *et al.*, 1984) in chimeras revealed quantal contributions of the two genotypes, consistent with a limited progenitor cell number of 8–11 (depending on strain) for Purkinje cells in each side of the cerebellum, and 12 for the cells of the facial nerve nucleus. Although in this case no markers of chimerism in other tissues were included, the mosaic composition was different for the same cell group in left and right halves of the brain and for different cell groups within the brain of the same animal. This suggests that the calculated small progenitor numbers represent the actual progenitor cell numbers at the time of allocation of the specific cell types involved and are not simply a reflection of the small progenitor cell number for the embryo itself at the time of production of the chimeras. The time of allocation of these progenitor cells cannot be directly determined, but it is suggested that they arise at the neural-plate stage, based on various assumptions about cell division rates (Wetts and Herrup, 1982).

It seems clear that true progenitor cell number at the time of lineage allocation cannot be readily calculated by retrospective analysis based on establishment of mosaicism at one particular early stage of development. Further delineation of progenitor cell numbers and time of allocation must be derived from a marking procedure which is able to mark single cells at later stages of development. Retroviral infection combined with *in situ* detection of virally marked progeny seems to be the most promising approach.

3. Progenitor Cell Number and Time of Allocation of the Germ Line

The pattern of genetic mosaicism in the germ line has been used to assess the progenitor cell number of the germ line in a similar manner to the calculations described for progenitor cell number of somatic tissues. Breeding data have been collected from chimeras (McLaren, 1978), spontaneous genetic mosaics (Russell, 1964; Searle, 1978), DNA injection mosaics (Wilkie *et al.*, 1986), and retroviral infection mosaics (Soriano and Jaenisch, 1986), and in general there is a reasonable correlation between germ line mosaicism and somatic mosaicism. However, animals which show somatic mosaicism do not always show mosaicism in the germ line. The relatively high-frequency occurrence of single-genotype progeny in all these situations could be explained if the germ line arose from a very small number of cells, resulting in a high probability that one of the component genotypes of the mosaic embryo could be excluded from the PGC population. However, breeding data by necessity only sample a small proportion of the total germ cell population and thus might provide a biased representation of the genotype composition of the entire germ line.

There has been little direct analysis of the genotype composition of either germ cells or gametes in mosaics. McMahon and colleagues (1983) analyzed germ line mosaicism by isozymal analysis of PGK variants in germ cells extracted from fetal ovaries prior to the apparent time of X reactivation (Kratzer *et al.*, 1981). They could not detect any noticeable skewing of the genotype composition of the germ cells when compared with mosaicism in somatic tissues, leading them to propose that the germ line has a large progenitor cell number similar to that of the various somatic tissues analyzed. Wilkie and co-workers (1986) have undertaken a limited direct analysis of mosaicism in the sperm populations of mosaic mice generated by DNA injection and have shown that extreme mosaicism in transmission of the injected gene is reflected in skewed sperm DNA mosaicism in most cases. In one mouse that did not transmit the injected gene to its progeny there was evidence for the existence of sperm carrying the gene. However, it is possible that in this case the injected DNA had caused a dominant mutation affecting the viability of sperm carrying the injected sequence (Palmiter *et al.*, 1984). Clearly, more direct analysis of this sort in different kinds of mosaics would be informative.

If we accept at face value the small progenitor cell number for the germ line suggested from preimplantation mosaics and the larger number suggested from X-inactivation mosaics, then the only way these data can be reconciled is to suggest that a small number of germ line progenitors is set aside from the progenitors of the somatic tissues well before X inactivation. Proliferation of these progenitors would then have to be sufficient to generate essentially identical mosaicism in somatic and germ lineages when all cells are marked at X inactivation. McMahon and colleagues (1983) observed that the proportions of the two PGK isozymes in their mosaics often deviated from the expected 50:50 and always in the same direction in germ cell and somatic lineages. They interpret this to mean that lineages must be drawn from a common pool after X inactivation. However, as West *et al.* point out (1984), the mice they analyzed could well have been polymorphic for *Xce* alleles that affect the randomness of X inactivation, making interpretation of the deviations from 50:50 difficult.

The suggestion of a small germ line progenitor cell number based on the production of nonmosaic progeny from mosaic mice does not of itself prove an early allocation, although, of course, it is compatible with this possibility. If allocation did occur early, then it should also be possible to observe the opposite situation to that described above, namely, the production of mosaic progeny from nonmosaic mice. Searle (1978) has shown that, in a large series of mice in which spontaneous genetic mosaicism was fairly common, no large clusters of revertant genotype were observed in the offspring of apparent nonmosaic founders. This would suggest that an early separation of the germ line from the somatic tissues was unlikely. On the other hand, Soriano and Jaenisch (1986) have observed viral integration events in some of the progeny of their retroviral mosaics that were not observed in the somatic tissues of the founder mice. This can only be readily explained by assuming separate origin of the germ line very early in development. However, these experiments were carried out with replication-competent virus, and the possibility of cross-infection of germ cells cannot be excluded.

Thus, retrospective analysis of chimeras and mosaics has not yet clearly resolved the issue of the time of allocation of the germ line in mammalian embryos, which is still very controversial. In many other vertebrates and invertebrates, there is good evidence that the germ line is segregated from the somatic lineages very early in development (McLaren, 1984). However, in mammals, it is generally believed that germ cells differentiate from a common pool of progenitors with the somatic lineages around the time of primitive-streak formation (Falconer and Avery, 1978; Snow, 1981; Copp et al., 1986). This belief is based partly on the absence of any evidence for "germ plasm" in mammalian embryos. No marker has been found that can trace germ cell precursors prior to their first morphological appearance in the hindgut region of the 8.5-day embryo (Ozdzenski, 1967; Heath, 1978). The only direct evidence on time of germ line allocation comes from experiments of Gardner and colleagues (Gardner et al., 1985), which show that single primitive ectoderm cells from the 4.5-day mouse blastocyst can generate both somatic and germ line mosaicism after blastocyst injection, indicating no separation of somatic and germ line at this stage. The experiments that show that germ cell progenitors are restricted to the caudal region of the primitive streak later in development (Copp et al., 1986) cannot address the question of whether germ line and somatic tissues are separate lineages by this stage, since multicellular grafts were used to follow fate. Direct labeling of single cells at different later stages of development will be required to assess the precise progenitor cell number and time of origin of the germ line.

IV. Conclusions and Perspectives

There have been recent important advances in all three main techniques for lineage analysis in mammalian embryos (Table I and II). Development of ubiquitous in situ genetic markers has greatly enhanced the power of chimera analysis, such that this technique is currently by far the most powerful for later lineage analysis from cells marked in preimplantation stages. It is of limited use for marking cells in postimplantation development. Injection of exogenous tracers has elucidated lineage relationships in the intact preimplantation embryo and the precision of marking has also allowed generation of short-term fate maps of the postimplantation embryo. However, dilution effects severely limit this approach. Induced genetic mosaicism, especially using retroviruses expressing histologically detectable gene products, provides the most exciting new approach to lineage analysis, since cells can be marked at virtually all stages of development and followed throughout succeeding stages. If the problems of inactivation of the retrovirus by the preimplantation embryo can be overcome, this approach will only be limited by the spatial imprecision of marking.

Many of the unresolved questions of cell lineage allocation, particularly in the postimplantation embryo, can potentially be answered by this technique. Both time of lineage allocation and progenitor cell number can be addressed. If injection at one stage of development produces clones that cross a particular tissue boundary, then one can conclude that allocation to the two lineages concerned has not yet occurred. The stage at which infection generates clones that are restricted to one or other tissue represents the time of tissue allocation. The proportion of the resultant tissue that is derived from a single cell marked at the time of tissue allocation provides an estimate of progenitor cell number.

As with all experiments on cell lineage in the intact embryo, one must always bear in mind that restriction of cells to different lineages *in situ* does not necessarily imply that the cells are restricted in their potential at this stage. This can only be tested by taking the cells from their normal environment and testing their potency in other embryonic situations. Testing potency in later embryos is likely to be a difficult task. However, although information on potency and cell commitment is an important component in understanding postimplantation development, new approaches toward *in situ* analysis of gene expression in the postimplantation embryo rest more upon lineage analysis in the intact embryo than on potency studies. Identification of genes that may control lineage development will require the ability to trace the expression of these genes in the progenitors of that lineage during postimplantation development. For this reason, more detailed information on lineage in the intact embryo will be very important for understanding mechanisms of lineage restriction.

NOTE ADDED IN PROOF

There have been several new contributions to cell lineage analysis in the mammalian embryo since the literature review for this chapter was completed. On the technical side, somatic mosaicism in mice homozygous for the pink-eyed unstable mutation has been used to look at late-developing clones in the retinal pigment epithelium (Bodenstein and Sidman, 1987). The use of retroviral vectors carrying the *E. coli* β-galactosidase gene as lineage tracers has been shown to be applicable to the nervous system later in development (Price *et al.*, 1987). Two groups have shown that the apparent inactivation of retroviral expression in the early embryo need not extend to transcription units contained within the vector, provided that transcription is under the control of an internal promoter (Soriano *et al.*, 1986; Stewart *et al.*, 1987). This opens the possibility of using vectors to follow lineage *in situ* from the earliest stages of development.

New experimental results pertinent to the areas of lineage analysis covered by this review are continuing to appear. Fleming (1987) has elegantly confirmed the model of allocation to ICM and trophectoderm described here by labeling all outside cells in the preimplantation embryo and following their contribution to inner and outer compartments. Tam and Beddington (1987) have used grafting techniques and *in situ* labeling with WGA-Au to delineate further the formation of mesodermal tissues in the postimplantation mouse embryo. Finally, the controversy surrounding the calculation of progenitor cell number from retrospective analysis of chimeras continues. Mead and co-workers (1987) criticize the "quantal" approach to calculating progenitor cell number (Herrup *et al.*, 1984; Soriano and Jaenisch, 1986), based partly on statistical arguments and partly on their own observations which indicate that the assumption of equal proliferation of progenitor cells throughout development is unlikely to occur. The question of whether tissues differ in their modes of proliferation remains unanswered. What is clear is that retrospective analysis of mosaicism in the mouse needs to be supplemented with prospective analysis of clonal expansion.

ACKNOWLEDGMENTS

I would like to thank Drs. V. Chapman, K. Herrup, D. Huszar, C. Kimmel, A. McLaren, R. Pedersen, and D. Solter for their comments and discussion on this manuscript in its various incarnations. Special thanks are due to Dr. Sue Varmuza for hours of discussion on the problems of cell lineage analysis in mammals. I would also like to thank Drs. K. Lawson and J.-F. Nicolas for permission to quote their work prior to publication. Patient and careful secretarial assistance was provided by Pauline Vine and Mary Postar. My own work is supported by grants from the National Cancer Institute of Canada, the Medical Research Council of Canada, and the Natural Sciences and Engineering Research Council of Canada, and a Research Associateship from the NCIC.

REFERENCES

Balakier, H., and Pedersen, R. A. (1982). *Dev. Biol.* **90**, 352–362.
Barlow, P., Owen, D. A. J., and Graham, C. F. (1972). *J. Embryol. Exp. Morphol.* **27**, 431–445.
Beddington, R. S. P. (1981). *J. Embryol. Exp. Morphol.* **64**, 87–104.
Beddington, R. S. P. (1982). *J. Embryol. Exp. Morphol.* **69**, 265–285.
Beddington, R. S. P. (1985). *J. Embryol. Exp. Morphol.* **88**, 281–291.
Behringer, R. R., Eldridge, P. W., and Dewey, M. J. (1984). *Dev. Biol.* **101**, 251–256.
Bernstein, A., Dick, J. E., Huszar, D., Robson, I., Rossant, J., Magli, C., Estrov, Z.,

Freedman, M., and Phillips, R. A. (1986). *Cold Spring Harbor Symp. Quant. Biol.* **51,** 1083–1091.

Bodenstein, L., and Sidman, R. L. (1987). *Dev. Biol.* **121,** 205–219.

Brinster, R. L., Chen, H. Y., Trumbauer, M. E., Yagle, M. K., and Palmiter, R. D. (1985). *Proc. Natl. Acad. Sci. U.S.A.* **82,** 4438–4442.

Cattanach, B. M. (1961). *Z. Vererbungsl.* **92,** 165–182.

Chapman, V. M., Whitten, W. K., and Ruddle, F. H. (1971). *Dev. Biol.* **26,** 153–158.

Condamine, H., Custer, R. P., and Mintz, B. (1971). *Proc. Natl. Acad. Sci. U.S.A.* **68,** 2032–2036.

Copp, A. J. (1979). *J. Embryol. Exp. Morphol.* **51,** 109–120.

Copp, A. J., Roberts, H. M., and Polani, P. E. (1986). *J. Embryol. Exp. Morphol.* **95,** 95–115.

Cruz, Y. P., and Pedersen, R. A. (1985). *Dev. Biol.* **112,** 73–83.

Dewey, M. J., Gervais, A. G., and Mintz, B. (1976). *Dev. Biol.* **50,** 68–81.

Dick, J. E., Magli, M.-C., Huszar, D., Phillips, R. A., and Bernstein, A. (1985). *Cell* **42,** 71–79.

Falconer, D. S., and Avery, P. J. (1978). *J. Embryol. Exp. Morphol.* **43,** 195–219.

Fleischman, R. A., and Mintz, B. (1979). *Proc. Natl. Acad. Sci. U.S.A.* **76,** 5736–5740.

Fleming, T. P. (1987). *Dev. Biol.* **119,** 520–531.

Ford, C. E., Evans, E. P., and Gardner, R. L. (1975). *J. Embryol. Exp. Morphol.* **33,** 447–457.

Garcia-Bellido, A., and Ripoll, P. (1978). *In* "Results and Problems in Cell Differentiation" (W. J. Gehring, ed.), Vol. 9, pp. 119–156. Springer-Verlag, Berlin and New York.

Gardner, R. L. (1968). *Nature (London)* **220,** 596–597.

Gardner, R. L. (1975). *Symp. Soc. Dev. Biol., 33rd,* pp. 207–238.

Gardner, R. L. (1984). *J. Embryol. Exp. Morphol.* **80,** 251–288.

Gardner, R. L., and Papaioannou, V. E. (1975). *Symp. Br. Soc. Dev. Biol., 2nd,* pp. 107–132.

Gardner, R. L., and Rossant, J. (1976). *Ciba Found. Symp.* pp. 5–25.

Gardner, R. L., and Rossant, J. (1979). *J. Embryol. Exp. Morphol.* **52,** 141–152.

Gardner, R. L., Papaioannou, V. E., and Barton, S. C. (1973). *J. Embryol. Exp. Morphol.* **30,** 561–572.

Gardner, R. L., Lyon, M. F., Evans, E. P., and Burtenshaw, M. D. (1985). *J. Embryol. Exp. Morphol.* **88,** 349–363.

Garner, W., and McLaren, A. (1974). *J. Embryol. Exp. Morphol.* **32,** 495–503.

Gearhart, J., and Oster-Granite, M. L. (1981). *J. Hered.* **72,** 3–5.

Gehring, W. J. (1985). *Cell* **40,** 3–5.

Gimlich, R., and Braun, J. (1985). *Dev. Biol.* **109,** 509–514.

Gordon, J. W., and Ruddle, F. H. (1981). *Science* **214,** 1244–1246.

Gorman, C. M., Rigby, P. W. J., and Lane, D. P. (1985). *Cell* **42,** 519–526.

Greenwald, I. (1985). *Cell* **43,** 583–590.

Handyside, A. H. (1978). *J. Embryol. Exp. Morphol.* **45,** 37–53.

Heath, J. K. (1978). *In* "Development in Mammals" (M. H. Johnson, ed.), pp. 267–298. North Holland Publ., Amsterdam.

Herrup, K., Diglio, T. J., and Letsou, A. (1984). *Dev. Biol.* **103,** 329–336.

Hillman, N., Sherman, M. I., and Graham, C. F. (1972). *J. Embryol. Exp. Morphol.* **28,** 263–278.

Huszar, D., Balling, R., Kothary, R., Magli, M.-C., Hozumi, N., Rossant, J., and Bernstein, A. (1985). *Proc. Natl. Acad. Sci. U.S.A.* **82,** 8587–8591.

Jacobson, A. G., Oster, G. F., Odell, G. M., and Cheng, L. Y. (1986). *J. Embryol. Exp. Morphol.* **96,** 19–49.

Jaenisch, R. (1976). *Proc. Natl. Acad. Sci. U.S.A.* **73,** 1260–1264.

Jaenisch, R. (1980). *Cell* **19,** 181–188.

Jaenisch, R. (1985). *Nature (London)* **318,** 181–183.

Jaenisch, R., and Mintz, B. (1974). *Proc. Natl. Acad. Sci. U.S.A.* **71,** 1250–1254.

Jahner, D., and Jaenisch, R. (1980). *Nature (London)* **287,** 456–458.

Jahner, D., Stuhlmann, H., Stewart, C. L., Harbers, K., Lohler, J., Simon, I., and Jaenisch, R. (1982). *Nature (London)* **298,** 623–628.

Jahner, D., Haase, K., Mulligan, R., and Jaenisch, R. (1985). *Proc. Natl. Acad. Sci. U.S.A.* **82,** 6927–6931.

Johnson, M. H., and Maro, B. (1986). *In* "Experimental Approaches to Mammalian Embryogenesis" (J. Rossant and R. A. Pedersen, eds.) pp. 35–65. Cambridge Univ. Press, London and New York.

Johnson, M. H., and Ziomek, C. A. (1981). *Cell* **24,** 71–80.

Kelly, S. J. (1979). *J. Exp. Zool.* **207,** 121–130.

Kimber, S. J., Surani, M. A. H., and Barton, S. C. (1982). *J. Embryol. Exp. Morphol.* **70,** 133–152.

Kimmel, C. B., and Warga, R. M. (1986). *Science* **231,** 365–368.

Kratzer, P. G., and Chapman, V. M. (1981). *Proc. Natl. Acad. Sci. U.S.A.* **78,** 3093–3097.

Lawson, K. A., Meneses, J. J., and Pedersen, R. A. (1986). *Dev. Biol.* **115,** 325–339.

Lee, C.-Y., Chasalow, F., Lee, S.-M., Lewis, S., and Johnson, F. M. (1980). *Mol. Cell. Biochem.* **30,** 143–149.

Lewis, J. H., Summerbell, D., and Wolpert, L. (1972). *Nature (London)* **239,** 276–278.

Linney, E., Davis, B., Overhauser, J., Chao, E., and Fan, H. (1984). *Nature (London)* **308,** 470–472.

Lo, C. (1983). *Mol. Cell. Biol.* **3,** 1803–1814.

Lo, C. (1986). *J. Cell Sci.* **81,** 143–162.

Lyon, M. F. (1961). *Nature (London)* **190,** 372–373.

McLaren, A. (1972). *Nature (London)* **239,** 274–276.

McLaren, A. (1976). "Mammalian Chimaeras." Cambridge Univ. Press, London and New York.

McLaren, A. (1978). *In* "Genetic Mosaics and Chimeras in Mammals" (L. B. Russell, ed.), pp. 125–134. Plenum, New York.

McLaren, A. (1984). *In* "Chimeras in Developmental Biology" (N. Le Douarin and A. McLaren, eds.), pp. 111–129. Academic Press, New York.

McMahon, A., Fosten, M., and Monk, M. (1983). *J. Embryol. Exp. Morphol.* **74,** 207–220.

Mead, R., Schmidt, G. H., and Ponder, B. A. J. (1987). *Dev. Biol.* **121,** 273–276.

Melvold, R. W. (1971). *Mutat. Res.* **12,** 171–174.

Mintz, B. (1962). *Am. Zool.* **2,** 432.

Mintz, B. (1971). *Symp. Soc. Exp. Biol., 25th,* pp. 345–370.

Monk, M., and Harper, M. I. (1979). *Nature (London)* **281,** 311–313.

Moustafa, L. A., and Brinster, R. L. (1972). *J. Exp. Zool.* **181,** 193–202.

Nakatsuji, N., Snow, M. H. L., and Wylie, C. C. (1986). *J. Embryol. Exp. Morphol.* **96,** 99–109.

Nesbitt, M. N. (1971). *Dev. Biol.* **26,** 252–263.

Ozdzenski, W. (1967). *Zool. Pol.* **17,** 367–379.

Palmiter, R. D., Wilkie, T. M., Chen, H. Y., and Brinster, R. L. (1984). *Cell* **36,** 869–877.

Papaioannou, V. E. (1982). *J. Embryol. Exp. Morphol.* **68,** 199–209.

Pedersen, R. A. (1986). *In* "Experimental Approaches to Mammalian Embryonic Development" (J. Rossant and R. A. Pedersen, eds.), pp. 3–33. Cambridge Univ. Press, London and New York.

Pedersen, R. A., Spindle, A. I., and Takehisa, S. (1978). *In* "Developmental Toxicology of Energy-Related Pollutants" (D. D. Mahlum, M. R. Sikov, P. L. Hackett, and F. D. Andrew, eds.), p. 152. U.S. Dept. of Energy, Washington, D.C.

Pedersen, R. A., Wu, K., and Balakier, H. (1986). *Dev. Biol.* **117**, 581–595.

Peterson, A. C., Frair, P. M., Rayburn, H. R., and Gross, D. R. (1979). *Symp. Soc. Neurosci.* **4**, 258–273.

Price, J., Turner, D., and Cepko, C. (1987). *Proc. Natl. Acad. Sci. U.S.A.* **84**, 156–160.

Rand, G. F. (1985). *J. Exp. Zool.* **236**, 67–70.

Rastan, S. (1982). *J. Embryol. Exp. Morphol.* **71**, 11–24.

Rastan, S., Kaufman, M. H., Handyside, A. H., and Lyon, M. F. (1980). *Nature (London)* **288**, 172–173.

Rossant, J. (1984). *In* "Chimeras in Developmental Biology" (N. Le Douarin and A. McLaren, eds.), pp. 89–109. Academic Press, New York.

Rossant, J. (1986). *Philos. Trans. R. Soc. London Ser. B* **312**, 91–100.

Rossant, J., and Chapman, V. M. (1983). *J. Embryol. Exp. Morphol.* **73**, 193–205.

Rossant, J., and Lis, W. T. (1979a). *Dev. Biol.* **70**, 249–254.

Rossant, J., and Lis, W. T. (1979b). *Dev. Biol.* **70**, 255–261.

Rossant, J., Gardner, R. L., and Alexandre, H. (1978). *J. Embryol. Exp. Morphol.* **48**, 239–247.

Rossant, J., Vijh, K. M., Grossi, C. E., and Cooper, M. D. (1986). *Nature (London)* **319**, 507–511.

Russell, L. B. (1964). *In* "Role of Chromosomes in Development" (M. Locke, ed.), pp. 153–181. Academic Press, New York.

Russell, L. B., and Major, M. H. (1957). *Genetics* **42**, 161–175.

Sanes, J. R., Rubenstein, J. L. R., and Nicolas, J.-F. (1986). *EMBO J.* **5**, 3133–3142.

Searle, A. G. (1978). *In* "Genetic Mosaics and Chimeras in Mammals" (L. B. Russell, ed.), pp. 209–224. Plenum, New York.

Siracusa, L. D., Chapman, V. M., Bennett, K. L., Hastie, N. D., Pietras, D. F., and Rossant, J. (1983). *J. Embryol. Exp. Morphol.* **73**, 163–178.

Smits-van Prooije, A. E., Poelmann, R. E., Dubbeldam, J. A., Mentink, M. M. T., and Vermeij-Keers, C. (1986). *Stain Technol.* **61**, 97–106.

Snow, M. H. L. (1977). *J. Embryol. Exp. Morphol.* **42**, 293–303.

Snow, M. H. L. (1981). *J. Embryol. Exp. Morphol.* **65** (Suppl.), 269–287.

Soriano, P., and Jaenisch, R. (1986). *Cell* **46**, 19–29.

Soriano, P., Cone, R. D., Mulligan, R. C., and Jaenisch, R. (1986). *Science* **234**, 1409–1413.

Spindle, A. I. (1978). *J. Exp. Zool.* **203**, 483–489.

Spindle, A. (1982). *J. Exp. Zool.* **219**, 361–367.

Stent, G. (1985). *Philos. Trans. R. Soc. Ser. B* **312**, 3–19.

Stephens, T. J., and Warner, C. M. (1980). *Cell. Immunol.* **56**, 132–141.

Stewart, C., Stuhlmann, H., Jahner, D., and Jaenisch, R. (1982). *Proc. Natl. Acad. Sci. U.S.A.* **79**, 4098–4102.

Stewart, C. L., Schuetze, S., Vanek, M., and Wagner, E. F. (1987). *EMBO J.* **6**, 383–388.

Streisinger, G., Coale, F., Taggart, C., Walker, C., and Grunwald, D. J. (1986). *Dev. Biol.* (submitted).

Stuhlmann, H., Jahner, D., and Jaenisch, R. (1981). *Cell* **26**, 221–232.

Stuhlmann, H., Cone, R., Mulligan, R. C., and Jaenisch, R. (1984). *Proc. Natl. Acad. Sci. U.S.A.* **81**, 7151–7155.

Sulston, J. E., Schierenberg, E., White, J. G., and Thomson, J. N. (1983). *Dev. Biol.* **100,** 64–119.

Surani, M. A. H., and Barton, S. C. (1984). *Dev. Biol.* **102,** 335–343.

Tam, P. P. L., and Beddington, R. S. P. (1987). *Development* **99,** 109–126.

Tarkowski, A. K. (1961). *Nature (London)* **190,** 857–860.

Vakaet, L. (1984). *In* "Chimeras in Developmental Biology" (N. Le Douarin and A. McLaren, eds.), pp. 71–88. Academic Press, New York.

Van der Putten, H., Botten, F. M., Miller, A. D., Rosenfeld, M. G., Fan, H., Evans, R. M., and Verma, I. M. (1985). *Proc. Natl. Acad. Sci. U.S.A.* **82,** 6148–6152.

Wareham, K. A., and Williams, E. D. (1986). *J. Embryol. Exp. Morphol.* **95,** 239–246.

Wareham, K. A., Howell, S., Williams, D., and Williams, E. D. (1983). *Histochem. J.* **15,** 363–371.

Weisblat, D. A., Sawyer, R. T., and Stent, G. S. (1978). *Science* **202,** 1295–1298.

West, J. D. (1976). *J. Embryol. Exp. Morphol.* **36,** 151–161.

West, J. D. (1978). *In* "Development in Mammals" (M. H. Johnson, ed.), Vol. 3, pp. 413–460. North Holland Publ., Amsterdam.

West, J. D. (1984). *In* "Chimeras in Developmental Biology" (N. Le Douarin and A. McLaren, eds.), pp. 39–67. Academic Press, New York.

West, J. D., Bucher, T., Linke, I. M., and Dunnwald, M. (1984). *J. Embryol. Exp. Morphol.* **84,** 309–329.

Wetts, R., and Herrup, K. (1982). *J. Neurosci.* **2,** 1494–1498.

Wilkie, T. M., Brinster, R. L., and Palmiter, R. D. (1986). *Dev. Biol.* **118,** 9–18.

Wilson, I. B., Bolton, E., and Cuttler, R. H. (1972). *J. Embryol. Exp. Morphol.* **27,** 467–479.

Ziomek, C. A. (1982). *Wilhelm Roux's Arch. Dev. Biol.* **191,** 37–41.

Ziomek, C. A., and Johnson, M. H. (1980). *Cell* **21,** 935–942.

Ziomek, C. A., and Johnson, M. H. (1982). *Dev. Biol.* **91,** 440–447.

CHAPTER 7

CELLULAR INTERACTIONS OF MOUSE FETAL GERM CELLS IN *IN VITRO* SYSTEMS

Massimo De Felici and Susanna Dolci

DEPARTMENT OF ANATOMY AND CELL BIOLOGY
II UNIVERSITY OF ROME,
00173 ROME, ITALY

I. Introduction

When one studies the historical development of knowledge about gonad differentiation in the mammalian embryo, one realizes that, despite numerous descriptive histological studies (for a review, see Gondos, 1978), very little is known about the role that cellular interactions play in germ cell differentiation. During the last few years much effort has been devoted to developing suitable systems for *in vitro* culture that could be utilized as experimental models to facilitate the study of such complex biological phenomena. In our laboratory, organ, tissue, and dissociated-cell culture of fetal gonads have been used to examine various aspects of the early gonadal differentiation in the mouse. The choice of which system was to be employed was usually dictated by the nature of the questions posed (De Felici and McLaren, 1983; De Felici *et al.*, 1985; De Felici and Siracusa, 1985). The data reported in this review are for the most part from the most recent of these studies.

II. Germ Cell Differentiation in the Mouse Embryo

The development of germ cells in the mouse embryo, as well in all other mammals, can be schematically divided into four main periods: migratory, proliferative, sex differentiation, and cell death (Fig. 1).

A. The Migratory Period

In the mouse embryo primordial germ cells (PGCs) can be first identified by their high alkaline phosphatase (APase) activity at the posterior end of the primitive streak about 8 days *post coitum* (dpc)

147

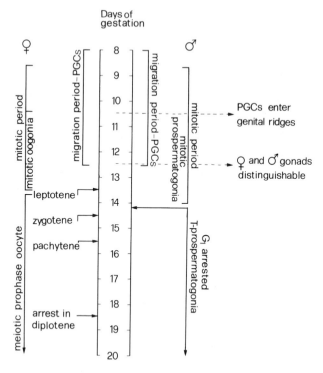

FIG. 1. The timing of female and male germ cell development in the mouse embryo.

(Tam and Snow, 1981). PGCs later become located at the base of the allantois and then in the hindgut epithelium, probably carried along passively by morphogenetic movements. After leaving the gut epithelium, they migrate actively up the dorsal mesentery, and at 10–11 dpc they enter the gonadal ridges. These are fully colonized by 13.5 dpc (Tam and Snow, 1981). Germ cells that have entered the gonadal ridges are now called gonia.

B. THE PROLIFERATIVE PERIOD

During the migratory period and for 2–3 days after their arrival in the gonadal ridges, germ cells proliferate actively. In about eight replicative cycles (population doubling time 14–15 hours), their number increases from ~50 at the beginning of migration to ~25,000 around 13.5 dpc (Mintz and Russell, 1957; Tam and Snow, 1981). Inside the gonadal ridges gonia lie closely together in groups connected by intercellular bridges (Ruby et al., 1969).

C. The Period of Sex Differentiation

Between 13 and 15 dpc, after a final round of DNA replication, oogonia enter meiotic prophase and are subsequently called oocytes. In ~2 days, oocytes pass through leptotene and zygotene into pachytene, until by the time of birth or soon afterward most are blocked in diplotene. At about the time oogonia are entering meiosis, prospermatogonia undergo mitotic arrest in the G_1 stage of the cell cycle. At 12.5 dpc, the testis is visibly distinguishable from the ovary (Fig. 2) by its larger size and larger blood supply, and by the presence of cords of somatic cells developing from the central region toward the periphery, enclosing strings of prospermatogonia. In the mouse ovary no cords are

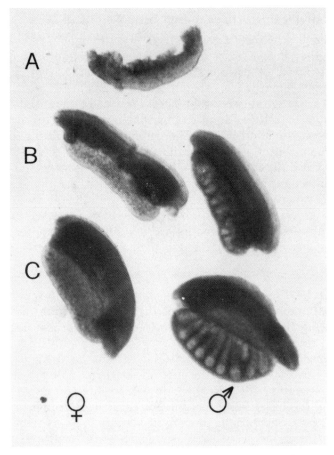

FIG. 2. (A) Urogenital ridge (mesonephros plus gonadal ridge) from 11.5-dpc mouse embryo. (B, C) Ovary and testis with attached mesonephros from 12.5- and 13.5-dpc embryos, respectively. ×20.

formed and groups of oocytes still linked by intercellular bridges are scattered in the stroma in contact with adjacent somatic cells.

D. THE PERIOD OF CELL DEATH

In all mammalian embryos, waves of degeneration drastically reduce the number of germ cells before birth. As far as we know, no detailed studies on germ cell degeneration in the fetal mouse ovary have been performed. One may assume that, by analogy with other related species (e.g., rat: Beaumont and Mandl, 1962), both oogonia and oocytes undergo extensive degeneration. Considerable degeneration of prospermatogonia is seen in the mouse testis 1–2 days before birth (A. McLaren, personal communication).

III. Cellular Interactions during Early Germ Cell Differentiation

A peculiar feature of germ cells is that throughout their entire life history they do not exist as an independent tissue, but are always associated with other cells from which they may derive nutrients as well as developmental signals. It is likely that the sequential expression of the different genes that direct germ cell differentiation may be modulated by cellular interactions that involve cell contact and cell position as a function of time. There is evidence suggesting that during the developmental periods mentioned above germ cells are involved in at least two different kinds of cellular interactions: germ cell–extracellular matrix and germ cell–somatic cell interactions. Homotypic interaction between germ cells is perhaps a third kind of interaction that plays a role in germ cell differentiation (Hilscher, 1981) (Fig. 3). The latter interaction, only hypothetical and difficult to approach experimentally, will not be examined in the present review.

A. PGC INTERACTIONS WITH EXTRACELLULAR MATRIX (ECM)

PGCs interact with ECM components both when they pass through the basal lamina of the hindgut epithelium to the outer mesenchyme, and during their active migration from the dorsal mesentery to the gonadal ridges.

In the early part of day 10, PGCs located in the hindgut epithelium start to move actively into the outer mesenchyme along the base of the dorsal mesentery. PGCs appear to escape into the mesenchyme by breaking the basal lamina of the gut epithelium (Zamboni and Merchant, 1973). Short-range proteolytic activity is likely to be involved: the neutral serine protease, plasminogen activator (PA), has properties which suggest that it might participate in such degradative activity (Strickland, 1980). Indeed, it has been demonstrated that avian

FIG. 3. Possible types of cellular interactions involving mouse fetal germ cells. (A) Germ cell–extracellular matrix. (B) Germ cell–germ cell. (C) Germ cell–somatic cells.

neural crest cells, by the time of their separation from the neural tube and during migration, produce high levels of PA (Valinsky and Le Douarin, 1985). Immunological studies and enzymatic assays recently carried out in our laboratory (R. Canipari, S. Dolci, and M. De Felici, unpublished observations) indicate that mouse PGCs possess proteolytic activity ascribable to PA. In these studies we have found that germ cells isolated from urogenital ridges (mesonephros plus gonadal ridge) of 11.5-dpc mouse embryos react positively to antibodies against PA and show proteolytic activity that is probably due to PA.

The migration route of PGCs goes from the hindgut, up the dorsal mesentery, around the coelomic angle, and finally through the mesonephric region and into the gonadal ridge. It is generally accepted that PGCs cover this relatively short distance (about 10 to 50 μm in the mouse; see Wartenberg, 1983) by ameboid migration. Whatever the molecular events that induce and guide PGC migration (for reviews, see Heath, 1978; Wartenberg, 1983), they need a propitious migratory substrate that allows transient adhesion and progression. Data have now been accumulated on the role of fibronectin (FN), a major ECM component, in promoting adhesion and migration of cells (for reviews, see Le Douarin, 1984; Thiery *et al.*, 1985). In *Xenopus laevis* Heasman *et al.* (1981) reported that FN is present along the pathway of PGC migration; FN also promotes the adhesion and move-ment of PGCs *in vitro*. In the mouse embryo at the peak of PGC migra-tion (from 9.5 to 10.5 days of gestation), FN is present on the surface of somatic cells as well as in the ECM in which PGCs migrate; by 11.5–12.5 days, when most PGCs have arrived in the gonadal ridges, the reaction for FN in these sites weakens or disappears (Fujimoto *et al.*, 1985). In the same study it is also shown that gonadal ridges are always negative to antibodies against FN and that PGCs react posi-tively only at their contact areas with neighboring somatic cells.

We have found (M. De Felici and S. Dolci, unpublished observa-tions) that germ cells isolated *in vitro* from mouse urogenital ridges during the migratory period (at 11 days of gestation) attach preferen-tially to FN substrates and that bovine serum albumin (BSA), collagen type I, and hyaluronic acid are very poor adhesive substrates. Germ cells attached to FN substrate do not spread during 2–3 hours but frequently show pseudopodialike protrusions (Fig. 4). Oocytes obtained from ovaries of 15.5-dpc embryos adhere to FN to a lesser extent, and very little to all other substrates tested. Although these results do not prove that FN promotes or guides PGC migration *in vivo*, they support

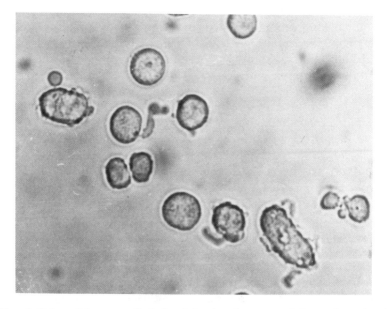

FIG. 4. Primordial germ cells isolated *in vitro* from an 11.5-dpc embryo showing pseudopodialike protrusions on fibronectin substrate. ×550.

the hypothesis that germ cells can interact with FN during the migratory period and that such ability is modified after the completion of gonad colonization.

B. GERM CELL–SOMATIC CELL INTERACTIONS

Although PGCs are not closely associated with any particular cell type during migration, indirect interactions with the surrounding somatic cells via diffusible substances may occur. Morphological evidence suggests that somatic cells supply PGCs with nutritive substances (Clark and Eddy, 1975). It is also possible that PGCs receive from the somatic environment inductive signals conditioning their differentiation. Once PGCs are settled in the gonadal ridges, more close contacts with somatic cells probably favor more direct cell–cell interactions. Histological studies have shown that the undifferentiated gonad contains, besides germ cells, three types of somatic cells: mesenchymal cells, cells derived from the mesonephros, and cells originating in the coelomic epithelium. Associations between germ cells and one or two types of somatic cells are established at this very early period (Gondos, 1978) and are the most characteristic feature during the entire gonad development. Nothing is known about the molecular mechanisms of these associations and whether they may form the basis of metabolic and/or informational exchanges between germ and somatic cells in the fetal gonad. Gonadal somatic cells are thought to support germ cells by providing essential metabolites and to control germ cell differentiation by local signals. According to Wartenberg's hypothesis (1980), based on morphological evidence, a dual system of supporting somatic cells ("dark" cells of mesonephric origin and "light" cells from the coelomic epithelium) might antagonistically stimulate or prevent mitotic proliferation of gonia, respectively. The stimulus to enter meiosis has also been attributed to the action of a meiosis-inducing substance (MIS) secreted by cells derived from the mesonephros, and the reason why meiosis does not occur in male germ cells until puberty has been explained by the action of a postulated meiotic-preventing substance (MPS) produced within the seminiferous cords (for a review, see Byskov, 1978). The dispute concerning whether these signals exist, and if so whether they involve diffusible substances or cell-contact interactions, is still open.

To clarify the nature and the molecular mechanisms of the interactive systems established between germ and somatic cells in the fetal gonad, we are utilizing two *in vitro* culture methods: culture of fetal gonad fragments and reaggregation of fetal germ cells with somatic cells of various origins.

1. Culture of Fetal Ovary Fragments

Studies by Blandau and Odor (1972) and Buehr and McLaren (1985) have demonstrated that mouse oocytes can survive and differentiate *in vitro* from cultured fetal ovary fragments. The latter authors have also shown that oocyte-specific gene expression occurs in this culture system. The results obtained by us using this culture technique can be briefly summarized as follows: during the first 2–3 days of culture somatic cells attach and migrate on the plastic surface to form a cell layer, while germ cells remain loosely attached in clumps on top of the layer, or are free-floating in the medium (Fig. 5A); after 3–4 days viable germ cells are no longer visible, but around 5 to 7 days in some fragments of ovaries obtained from 13.5-dpc or older embryos (but not from earlier embryos), groups of diplotene oocytes are recognizable, scattered among somatic cells. Within 10–15 days of culture the oocytes, varying in size from 30 to 70 μm, develop zonalike investments (Fig. 5B, C). A maximum of 40–50 growing oocytes are obtained from each cultured ovary. M. Buehr and A. McLaren (personal communication) have recently found that entry and progression through meiosis to the growing oocyte stage can occur with fragments of female genital ridges as young as 10.5 dpc, provided special gas-permeable Petriperm dishes are employed. This technical improvement makes the culture of fetal ovary fragments suitable to study early stages of gonad differentiation *in vitro*.

2. Germ Cell–Somatic Cell Reaggregations

A number of studies have demonstrated that cells of the same type can specifically recognize each other and homotypically reaggregate by cell surface adhesion molecules (CAMs) (for reviews, see Edelman, 1985; Obrink, 1986). Similarly, preferential heterotypic adhesion can occur between differing cell types (neurons to myoblasts: Grumet *et al.*, 1982; neurons to glia: Grumet *et al.*, 1983; granulocytes to endothelial cells: Boogaerts *et al.*, 1982; lymphocytes to endothelial cells: Stoolman *et al.*, 1984; spermatocytes to Sertoli cells: Ziparo *et al.*, 1980). Heterotypic adhesion between germ cells and somatic cells may play a prime role during the early stages of gonad development, and might be a necessary step for formation of specialized junctions between germ and somatic cells.

3. Adhesion of Fetal Germ Cells to Somatic Cell Monolayers

To study whether fetal germ cells are able to adhere heterotypically to somatic cells from gonads or to other cell types, we have carried out

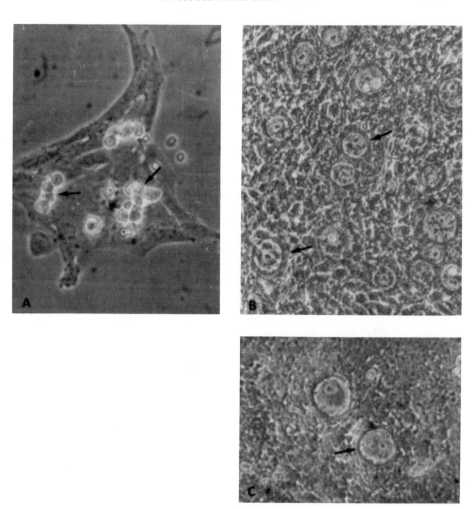

FIG. 5. Stages of *in vitro* culture of fetal mouse ovary fragments. Fragments were obtained by mechanical and enzymatic (1 mg ml^{-1} Pronase, 15 minutes, 37°C) treatment of ovaries of 13.5-dpc or older embryos. Cultures were carried out in medium 199 supplemented with 10% fetal calf serum (modified according to De Felici and McLaren, 1983), at 37°C in 5% CO_2 in air. (A) 1-Day culture: germ cells (arrow) appear attached or free-floating on top of the layer of somatic cells. ×128. (B) 6-Day culture: growing oocytes scattered among somatic cells, some oocytes appear enclosed by follicular cells (arrows). ×165. (C) The same as (B) showing two oocytes surrounded by zonalike investment (arrow). ×225.

in vitro experiments in which germ cells isolated from fetal gonads of different ages were seeded on monolayers of somatic cells of various origins (De Felici and Siracusa, 1985). A schematic representation of the adhesion assay is shown in Fig. 6.

A first observation that arises from these studies is that fetal germ cells obtained from 13.5-dpc or older embryos appear unable to adhere to monolayers of somatic cells obtained from fetal gonads of the same age or from other embryonic tissues, whereas they rapidly (within 30–40 minutes) adhere to somatic cells from pubertal gonads. Moreover, male germ cells adhere to Sertoli cells in a significantly higher percentage than to follicular cells (Fig. 7). Donovan *et al.* (1986) have shown that migratory mouse PGCs (obtained from the dorsal mesentery of 10.5-dpc embryos) are able to spread and move on monolayers of an embryo-derived cell line, while this ability is no longer present in germ cells isolated from the gonads of 13.5-dpc embryos. This suggests that PGCs might change their adhesive properties to somatic cells after entering the gonadal ridges. The lack of adhesion of fetal germ cells to their own somatic cells is in line with previous observations (Heath, 1978; O, 1978); it does not necessarily imply absence of recog-

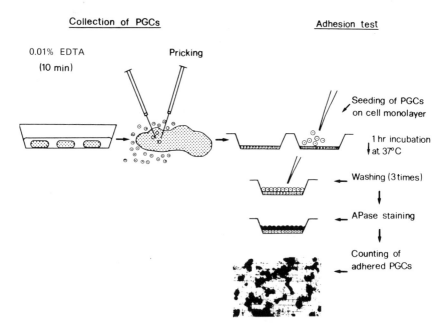

FIG. 6. Schematic representation of the assay used to test germ cell–somatic cell adhesion. (For experimental details, see De Felici and Siracusa, 1985.)

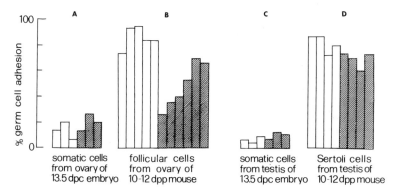

FIG. 7. Adhesiveness of female germ cells (empty columns) and male germ cells (hatched columns) obtained from 13.5-dpc embryos to somatic cells from fetal ovary or testis of the same age (A, C) and to follicular or Sertoli cells from prepubertal (10–12 days postpartum, dpp) gonads (B, D). The columns show single replicates, obtained in two or three experiments.

nition systems but might simply indicate that fetal somatic cells are unable to interact with germ cells by adhesive forces of sufficient strength to be detected by our adhesion assay. Also, the identity of the somatic cells from fetal gonads that form a monolayer in culture is uncertain.

A second observation that emerges from our adhesion studies is the "specificity" of germ cell adhesion: we were unable to detect significant adhesion between germ cells and various other cell types of nongonadal origin (Table I).

4. Formation of Permeable Channels between Germ Cell and Follicular Cells

Having demonstrated that short-term adhesion occurs between fetal germ cells and follicle cells, we have studied whether adhesion was followed by the establishment of more complex cellular interactions between these two cell types (De Felici and Dolci, unpublished observations). A very general type of cellular interaction is cell–cell communication via specialized low-resistance channels, called gap junctions, that allow the transfer of low molecular weight molecules from cell to cell (Loewenstein, 1981). One way to detect the existence of direct communications between cells is to load donor cells with a fluorescent tracer that does not pass through the plasma membrane and to study if dye is transferred to surrounding cells. We have incubated germ cells (from 13- to 15-dpc fetal ovaries) in the presence of 6-car-

TABLE I

ADHESIVENESS OF FEMALE GERM CELLS TO VARIOUS CELL MONOLAYERS[a]

Monolayers	Germ cell treatment	Adhesion[b]
Mesodermal cells from mesonephros	None	−
Dermal fibroblasts	None	−
Kidney cells	None	−
Sertoli cells	None	+++
Follicular cells	None	+++
Follicular cells	Calcium-free medium	−
Follicular cells	Metabolic inhibition (1 mM KCN)	−
Follicular cells	Fixation (1% gluteraldehyde 5 minutes)	−
Follicular cells	Trypsin (0.2%, 10 minutes, 37°C)	±
Follicular cells	Neuraminidase (5 × 10^{-4} IV, 1 hour, 37°C)	+++
Follicular cells	UDP-Galactose (1 mM)	+++

[a] Germ cells obtained from 13.5-dpc embryos. In some experiments in which the adhesion to follicular cells was tested, germ cells were exposed to the specified treatments before the assay. The adhesion was scored after 1 hour incubation at 37°C as described in De Felici and Siracusa (1985).
[b] −, Adhesion <10%; ±, adhesion 20–30%; +++, >70%.

boxyfluorescein diacetate. This compound enters the cells freely, where it is retained following enzymatic conversion to 6-carboxyfluorescein (MW 370, Rotmann and Papermaster, 1966). The labeled cells were then seeded on unlabeled monolayers of follicular cells and the dye transfer checked after various incubation times at 37°C. Significant fluorescence was indeed detected in the surrounding follicular cells after a 3-hour incubation. In contrast, no dye transfer was observed when germ cells were seeded on fibroblast monolayers (to which germ cells do not adhere, De Felici and Siracusa, 1985). This result suggests that intercellular gap junction-like channels may form between fetal germ cells and follicular cells *in vitro* as a consequence of specific cellular adhesion.

5. Influence of Somatic Environment on Germ Cell Differentiation

In vitro reaggregation of germ cells with somatic cells is theoretically the most suitable method to study the influence of somatic cells on the important differentiative events that characterize the development of fetal germ cells, such as their mitotic proliferation, the beginning of meiosis in the female, or the block in the G_1 stage in the male. By this method it would be possible, for instance, to study the fate of germ cells in a somatic environment of the opposite sex (Fig. 8) and to reaggregate germ cells and somatic cells isolated from gonads of different ages. However, methodological difficulties and the inability of isolated fetal germ cells to survive *in vitro* for more than a few hours (De Felici and McLaren, 1982) limit the application of such system. Despite these difficulties, O (1978) found that when hamster fetal germ cells are mixed and reaggregated by centrifugation with somatic cells of the opposite sex, XY germ cells are able to survive in the XX somatic environment and are induced to enter meiosis precociously, while XX germ cells fail to survive in an XY somatic environment. By reaggre-

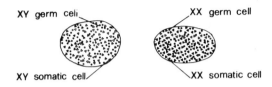

0.01 % EDTA TREATMENT SEPARATE GERM FROM SOMATIC CELLS

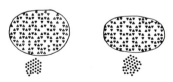

SOMA TRYPSINIZATION AND CULTURE FOR 48-56 hr

REAGGREGATION BY SEEDING GERM ON SOMATIC CELLS OF OPPOSITE SEX

FIG. 8. Schematic representation of a possible method of reaggregating germ cells with somatic cells *in vitro*. This method might allow the fate of fetal germ cells to be studied in the somatic environment of the opposite sex.

gating mouse fetal germ cells from 12.5- to 15.5-dpc embryos with follicular cells obtained from prepubertal ovaries, we have tried to determine the influence of follicle cells on the survival and meiotic progression of female and male germ cells. The adhesion and formation of intercellular communication that rapidly occurs between fetal germ cells and follicular cells (see above) suggested that functional cellular interactions could be established in this system. The results obtained to date (De Felici et al., 1986) have in part failed to fulfill our expectations. Although the survival of germ cells cultured on a follicular cell monolayer tends to be higher than on a plastic surface (Fig. 9), the difference is statistically significant ($p < 0.05$) only for female or male germ cells obtained from 13.5-dpc embryos and cultured at 33°C. Germ cells from 14.5- and 15.5-dpc embryos survive in high percentage (about 60 to 70%) in all culture conditions. The meiotic stage of germ cells isolated from 12.5- to 15.5-dpc embryos was determined at the beginning and after 48 hours of culture both on plastic and on follicular cell monolayers, at 33 and 37°C. Of the few premeiotic female germ cells (obtained from 12.5-dpc fetal ovaries) that were still viable after 48 hours of culture at 33°C or 37°C on follicular cell monolayers, some were in leptotene/zygotene (L/Z). Unfortunately, the viability of germ cells cultured at this stage in the absence of follicular cells was too low to study their meiotic ability and to establish clearly if follicular cells are essential for meiotic entry. However, the results obtained with

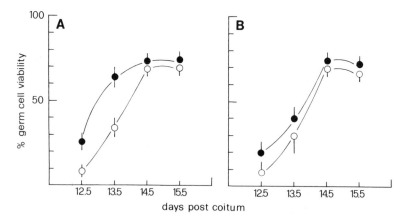

FIG. 9. Viability of female germ cells obtained from 12.5- to 15.5-dpc mouse embryos on a plastic surface (○) and on follicular cell monolayers (●) after 48 hours of culture in medium 199 supplemented with 10% fetal calf serum (modified according to De Felici and McLaren, 1983), at 33°C (A) or 37°C (B) in 5% CO_2 in air. Each point represents the average of at least three experiments (vertical bars, SE).

female germ cells from 13.5-dpc embryos, showing that the percentage of meiotic L/Z nuclei greatly increases during culture independently of the presence of follicular cells, suggest that the latter did not have in such culture conditions any direct inducing action on the beginning of meiosis in female germ cells. On the other hand, nuclei in meiotic prophase were never observed when male germ cells were cultured in any culture condition. Oocytes from 14.5- to 15.5-dpc ovaries were able to progress in culture through meiotic prophase until pachytene or diplotene, and no obvious differences were seen between different culture conditions.

IV. Concluding Remarks

Although some differentiative events may be an autonomous program of the germ cells themselves, there is little doubt that during the early stages of embryogenesis germ cells are involved in a variety of cellular interactions that can modulate their differentiative pattern. By employing *in vitro* systems in which germ cells are cultured isolated or in association with somatic cells, we now begin to have some clue about the nature of such cellular interactions. Evidence is emerging that different interactive systems may characterize the various periods of fetal germ cell development. During migration PGCs appear able to interact with components of ECM and perhaps indirectly with the surrounding somatic cells via diffusible substances. After PGC arrival in the gonadal ridges the appearance of new surface molecules probably allows germ cells to interact more closely and directly with gonadal somatic cells. In this regard, our studies on germ cell adhesion form an encouraging beginning to the investigation of the biological significance and the biochemical mechanisms of germ–somatic cell interactions inside the developing gonad. The search for and characterization of cell surface molecules appearing sequentially during differentiation and involved in different germ cell interactions will be one of the main objectives of our future investigations.

ACKNOWLEDGMENTS

We are grateful to Professor Gregorio Siracusa for helpful suggestions and exchange of ideas and for critical reading of the manuscript. The research of the authors described here was supported by the Ministry of the Public Education (40% and 60% Grants) and by the National Research Council.

REFERENCES

Beaumont, H. M., and Mandl, A. M. (1962). *J. Embryol. Exp. Morphol.* 11, 715–740.
Blandau, R. J., and Odor, D. L. (1972). *In* "Oogenesis" (J. D. Biggers and A. W. Schuetz, eds.), pp. 301–320. Univ. Park Press, Baltimore, Maryland.

Boogaerts, M. A., Yamada, O., Jacob, H. S., and Moldow, G. F. (1982). *Proc. Natl. Acad. Sci. U.S.A.* **79**, 7019–7023.

Buehr, M., and McLaren, A. (1985). *Gamete Res.* **11**, 271–281.

Byskov, A. G. (1978). *Int. J. Androl.* (*Suppl.*) **2**, 29–38.

Clark, J. M., and Eddy, E. M. (1975). *Dev. Biol.* **47**, 136–155.

De Felici, M., and McLaren, A. (1983). *Exp. Cell Res.* **144**, 417–427.

De Felici, M., and Siracusa, G. (1985). *J. Embryol. Exp. Morphol.* **87**, 87–97.

De Felici, M., Boitani, C., and Cossu, G. (1985). *Dev. Biol.* **109**, 375–380.

De Felici, M., Cossu, G., and Siracusa, G. (1986). *In* "Development and Function of the Reproductive Organs" (A. Eshkol, B. Eckstein, N. Dekel, H. Peters, and A. Tsafriri, eds.), pp. 13–22. Ares-Serono Symposia, Rome.

Donovan, P. J., Stott, D., Cairns, L. A., Heasman, L., and Wylie, C. C. (1986). *Cell* **44**, 831–838.

Edelman, G. M. (1985). *Annu. Rev. Biochem.* **54**, 135–169.

Fujimoto, T., Yoshinaga, K., and Kono, I. (1985). *Anat. Rec.* **211**, 271–278.

Gondos, B. (1978). *In* "The Vertebrate Ovary" (R. E. Jones, ed.), pp. 83–120. Plenum, New York.

Grumet, M., Rutishauser, V., and Edelman, G. M. (1982). *Nature (London)* **295**, 693–695.

Grumet, M., Rutishauser, V., and Edelman, G. M. (1983). *Science* **222**, 60–62.

Heasman, J., Hynes, R. O., Swan, A. P., Thomas, V., and Wylie, C. C. (1981). *Cell* **27**, 437–445.

Heath, J. K. (1978). *In* "Development in Mammals" (M. H. Johnson, ed.), Vol. 3, pp. 267–298. Elsevier, Amsterdam.

Hilscher, B. (1981). *Adv. Androl.* **7**, 46–52.

Le Douarin, N. M. (1984). *Cell* **38**, 353–360.

Loewenstein, W. R. (1981). *Physiol. Rev.* **61**, 829–913.

Mintz, B., and Russell, E. S. (1957). *J. Exp. Zool.* **134**, 207–237.

O, N. S. (1978). *In* "Development in Mammals" (M. H. Johnson, ed.), Vol. 3, pp. 299–322. Elsevier, Amsterdam.

Obrink, B. (1986). *Exp. Cell Res.* **163**, 1–21.

Rotmann, B., and Papermaster, B. W. (1966). *Proc. Natl. Acad. Sci. U.S.A.* **55**, 134–136.

Ruby, J. R., Dyer, R. F., and Shalko, R. G. (1969). *J. Morphol.* **127**, 307–340.

Stoolman, T. S., Tenfordl, T. S., and Rosen, S. D. (1984). *J. Cell Biol.* **99**, 1535–1540.

Strickland, S. (1980). *In* "Development in Mammals" (M. H. Johnson, ed.), Vol. 4, pp. 81–100. Elsevier, Amsterdam.

Tam, P. P. L., and Snow, M. H. L. (1981). *J. Embryol. Exp. Morphol.* **64**, 133–147.

Thiery, J. P., Dubaud, J. L., and Tucker, G. C. (1985). *Annu. Rev. Cell Biol.* **1**, 91–113.

Valinsky, J. E., and Le Douarin, N. M. (1985). *EMBO J.* **4**, 1403–1406.

Wartenberg, H. (1980). *Arch. Biol. Med. Exp.* **13**, 321–324.

Wartenberg, H. (1983). *In* "Problems of Keimbahn" (W. Hilscher, ed.), pp. 93–110. Karger, Basel.

Zamboni, L., and Merchant, H. (1973). *Am. J. Anat.* **137**, 299–336.

Ziparo, E., Geremia, R., Russo, A. M., and Stefanini, M. (1980). *Am. J. Anat.* **159**, 385–388.

CHAPTER 8

TESTIS DETERMINATION AND THE H-Y HYPOTHESIS

Anne McLaren

MEDICAL RESEARCH COUNCIL (MRC) MAMMALIAN DEVELOPMENT UNIT
WOLFSON HOUSE, UNIVERSITY COLLEGE LONDON
LONDON NW1 2HE, ENGLAND

I. Introduction

In mammals, formation of the testis is a crucial step in sex determination. From the fetal stage onward, the development of male secondary sexual characteristics, including the masculinization of the hypothalamus and "brain sex," is under the control of androgens secreted from the testes. So potent are these hormonal influences that anatomical, physiological, and behavioral characteristics of both male and female mice can be modified by the sex of their neighbors in the uterus (vom Saal and Bronson, 1978, 1980; vom Saal *et al.*, 1983; Meisel and Ward, 1981). The responsible hormone, testosterone, is produced by the Leydig cells of the fetal testis, and is required to maintain and stimulate the growth of the primordial male sex ducts. One day before testosterone production starts, the pre-Sertoli cells of the mouse and rat testis begin to secrete Müllerian inhibiting substance (anti-Müllerian hormone, Müllerian regression factor), causing the primordial female sex ducts to degenerate. The gene for Müllerian inhibiting substance has been cloned (Cate *et al.*, 1986). One day earlier still, the aggregation of the pre-Sertoli cells into testis cords marks the first indication of sex-specific organogenesis.

II. Testis Formation

In normal embryogenesis, the cytodifferentiation of pre-Sertoli cells from the precursor supporting-cell lineage precedes by some hours their aggregation into testis cords. In the rat (Jost, 1972), this new cell type characterized by abundant clear cytoplasm is first seen in the gonadal blastema in the vicinity of the rete testis; the cells aggregate together in epithelial-like arrays, enclosing within the testis cords the great majority of the primordial germ cells that have entered

163

the genital ridges. Peritubular (myoid) cells form around the cords, and Leydig cells differentiate between them. The same two cell lineages that give rise to pre-Sertoli cells and Leydig cells in a male embryo are thought to differentiate into follicle cells and interstitial cells, respectively, in the ovary. It seems likely that the pre-Sertoli cells induce the subsequent development of peritubular cells and Leydig cells, but this has not yet been demonstrated.

A similar succession of events has been shown to occur in male rat genital ridges cultured *in vitro* in medium lacking serum (Agelopoulou *et al.*, 1984). However, if serum is present in the culture medium, although pre-Sertoli cells differentiate, no testis cords are formed. Such cord-free male gonads undergo normal hormonal development: the pre-Sertoli cells produce Müllerian inhibiting substance at the normal time (Magre and Jost, 1984), and Leydig cell precursors differentiate and become capable of steroidogenesis, secreting testosterone into the culture medium (Patsavoudi *et al.*, 1985). So the key step in sex determination appears to involve cytodifferentiation—that is, differentiation of pre-Sertoli cells and Leydig cell precursors—rather than testis cord formation.

For germ cell sex, the situation is different (McLaren, 1985). Germ cells developing in the female direction enter meiosis before birth and go on to form oocytes: this may occur whether the germ cells are XX or XY in constitution, in a female or a male embryo, in the ovary or testis, or outside the gonad. Whether such germ cells enter meiosis spontaneously (Zamboni and Upadhyay, 1983) or are induced to do so by a hormone ("meiosis-inducing substance"; Byskov, 1978) remains an open question. In contrast, germ cells that do not enter meiosis before birth develop as prospermatogonia, and later take part in spermatogenesis. There is evidence (McLaren, 1984; Francavilla and Zamboni, 1985) that the failure to enter meiosis is due to a factor produced by the testis cords. Genital ridges taken from male mouse embryos 11.5 days *post coitum* form testis cords, with germ cells developing as prospermatogonia; but in ridges taken at 10.5 days *post coitum,* although pre-Sertoli cells differentiate and aggregate into small groups, no testis cords form and all germ cells enter meiosis (A. McLaren and H. Hogg, unpublished observations). Thus in the mouse as in the rat, cytodifferentiation of pre-Sertoli cells precedes and is not dependent on testis cord formation; but differentiation of male germ cells in the male direction, unlike hormonal differentiation, seems to require testis cord formation, perhaps because the cords produce a meiosis-inhibiting factor.

At the protein level (Müller *et al.*, 1984), two-dimensional gel electrophoresis of fetal rat gonads has revealed one male-specific and two female-specific polypeptides at the indifferent gonad stage; after differentiation, three more have been identified in the testis (one in germ cells, one in the tunica albuginea, and one in the remaining somatic tissue), and two more in the fetal ovary (one germinal, one somatic).

As far as sex determination is concerned, it is the differentiation of the somatic part of the gonad, not the germ cells, that is important. Indeed, it seems that testis formation can take place normally even when few or even no germ cells are present. McCoshen (1983) carried out a careful quantitative analysis of prenatal gonadal development in mice homozygous for the White-spotting gene W^v, and in their $W^v/+$ and $+/+$ littermates. The germ cell population is known to be drastically reduced in W^v/W^v mice; McCoshen examined serial sections of fetal gonads and reports that an average of 68 germ cells (range 0–260) entered the gonads, only ~1% of the control value. Yet the growth rate of the somatic component of the W^v/W^v testis was indistinguishable from that of controls, right up to the time of birth. In the ovary, the absence of germ cells started to have an effect on the somatic component shortly before birth, at the time when the follicles start to form around the oocytes. In the absence of oocytes, prefollicular cells are thought not to survive after birth. Merchant (1975) also concluded that germ cells played little or no part in early gonadal organogenesis, on the basis of experiments in which rats were treated with the drug Busulfan to reduce germ cell numbers.

Much of the earlier discussion on gonadal formation has revolved around the question of the origin of the cells that form the initial gonadal blastema. Possible sources are the coelomic epithelium, the adjacent mesenchyme, and the mesonephros. Some authorities have suggested a dual origin, with some tissues derived from one source and others from another, or even two types of progenitor cells contributing to a single tissue. For different views on this controversy, the reader is referred to articles by Witschi (1951), Franchi et al. (1962), Merchant (1975), Zamboni et al. (1981), and Wartenberg (1981). Since the evidence so far consists entirely of static observations (histological and ultrastructural), no definitive conclusion can as yet be reached, and in any case the three candidate tissues themselves have a common origin in the nephrogonadoblastic cells derived from the lateral plate mesoderm. One possible source of confusion is that the studies cited relate to a number of different species, which may differ in the mode of formation of the gonadal blastema, perhaps in relation to whether or not the mesonephros acts as a functional kidney during development. For the mouse, the view put forward by Upadhyay et al. (1981), that the gonadal blastema derives from cells of the nonfunctional mesonephros, provides at least a plausible working hypothesis, and will be used as such in the following discussion.

The issue of the origin of the gonadal blastema is clearly of great interest from the point of view of embryology and comparative anatomy. It is not yet crucial for a consideration of sex determination, although it could become so if we are concerned to locate the point in development at which the precursor supporting-cell lineage becomes committed to form pre-Sertoli rather than follicle cells.

III. Sex Commitment

We know that the sex chromosome constitution of an embryo (XX, XY, XO, XXY) is decided at fertilization, unless as occasionally happens a nondisjunctional event takes place subsequently. We know too that the direction of differentiation of cells outside the gonad (secondary sexual characteristics) is determined by gonadal hormones rather than by their own sex chromosome constitution. If androgen receptors in target tissues are genetically defective, as in Tfm (testicular feminization), XY cells respond to estrogens and a female phenotype is produced in spite of the presence of testes (Lyon and Hawkes, 1970; Ohno and Lyon, 1970; Gehring et al., 1971). Conversely, XX cells can take part in the development of seminal vesicles, since in an XX ↔ XY male mouse chimera the seminal vesicle fluid has been shown to contain proteins characteristic of both component strains (Mintz et al., 1972). This shows that XX cells can secrete a specifically male protein in response to a male environment.

It is important to know how and when the direction of differentiation of the pre-Sertoli/prefollicle cell precursors (the supporting-cell lineage) is determined, since the pre-Sertoli cells are the first to differentiate and may control subsequent gonadal differentiation.

The direction of differentiation of the supporting-cell lineage could be determined entirely cell-autonomously, in accordance with each cell's own sex chromosome constitution. Sex commitment would then in a sense take place at fertilization, when the sex chromosome constitution is established, since no subsequent events could alter the eventual direction of differentiation of the embryo. Although we do not know when the Y chromosome first exerts an effect on development, female and male mouse embryos have been shown to differ from one another long before any gonadal differentiation has taken place. Even at the eight-cell stage, cytotoxic antibodies raised specifically to male cells can kill XY but not XX mouse embryos (Krco and Goldberg, 1976; Epstein et al., 1980; Shelton and Goldberg, 1984; White et al., 1982,

1983). Tsunoda *et al.* (1985) report that male mouse embryos cavitate on average earlier than female, while Burgoyne (unpublished observations) found that XY embryos were developmentally more advanced than their XX littermates at both egg cylinder and somite stages. These differences could be due to either a stimulating effect of the Y chromosome on development, or a retarding effect of having two X chromosomes rather than one. Alternatively, they could be the result of a tendency postulated by James (1983) to explain certain sex ratio effects, namely, that Y-bearing sperm fertilize earlier in the ovulation period than do X-bearing sperm. These observations on developmental stage of XX and XY embryos could affect our interpretation of the findings on eight-cell stages cited above: the antibodies used might detect an antigen present in both XX and XY embryos after a certain stage, e.g., in late eight-cell rather than early eight-cell embryos. Krco and Goldberg (1976) found a cytotoxic effect of their anti-male antisera at the eight-cell but not at the four-cell stage.

Alternatively, the direction of differentiation of the supporting-cell lineage could be determined entirely by exogenous factors, acting either through cell–cell contact or through a diffusible substance. In this case sex commitment could in principle take place at any stage between fertilization and gonadal differentiation. The most likely time would perhaps be when the Sertoli/follicle cell lineage was itself established. Major cell lineages are thought to be laid down shortly after gastrulation, at about 7.5 to 8 days *post coitum* in the mouse (Snow, 1985). The Sertoli/follicle cell lineage would presumably become separated off from other somatic cell lineages of the gonad (e.g., the Leydig/interstitial cell lineage) between 8 days and the time of overt differentiation, perhaps during formation of the genital ridge. Whether or not the Y chromosome had been expressed earlier in development, at this time a Y-controlled gene would be switched on so that XY cells (not necessarily of the lineage) would start to produce a diffusible substance that would determine pre-Sertoli rather than prefollicle cell differentiation in recipient cells whatever their sex chromosome constitution.

A third possibility is that sex commitment involves an interaction between a cell-autonomous and an exogenous factor. We shall see later that recent evidence favors this model.

IV. Is There a "Male-Determining" Substance?

Since development of a male individual depends on the formation of a testis, and since the first step in the formation of a hormonally functional testis appears to be the cytodifferentiation of pre-Sertoli cells, we may interpret the term "male-determining" as shorthand for "pre-Sertoli cell-determining." Whether or not pre-Sertoli cells in turn induce other testicular cell lineages, we do not yet know. What is the evidence that an exogenous factor is involved in pre-Sertoli cell differentiation? In an adult male XX ↔ XY chimera described by Mintz (1969), electrophoretic analysis showed that the XX component contributed at least 95% of the cells, not only in the seminal vesicles and epididymides, but also in the gonads. The report of this mouse, combined with the observation that most XX ↔ XY chimeras develop as males (McLaren, 1976), has led to the widespread belief that primary sex determination involves the production by XY cells of a diffusible male-determining substance that commits both XY and XX cells to testis formation.

However, electrophoretic analyses of whole gonads gives little information on the Sertoli cell population which, as the first to undergo differentiation in the gonadal blastema, is likely to be responsible for organizing the further development of the testis. The observation that at least 95% of the glucose-phosphate isomerase activity in the testis stems from the XX component is not incompatible with all the Sertoli cells being from the XY component, since we do not know how the activity of this enzyme is distributed among the various cell types in the testis. The chimera was sterile, so in the absence of histological analysis it is possible that the gonads of this chimera contained ovarian as well as testicular tissue, or that the seminiferous tubules were devoid of both germ cells and Sertoli cells.

Another source of evidence for an exogenous testis determinant acting on XX as well as on XY cells comes from reports that indifferent XX gonads transplanted adjacent to XY gonads, or transplanted into an adult testis, show testicular rather than ovarian development, with the formation of testis cords rather than ovarian follicles (Turner and Asakawa, 1964; Turner, 1969). However, several carefully controlled attempts to repeat these experiments (Ozdzenski et al., 1976; Burgoyne et al., 1986a) have found no evidence that exogenous factors acting on the indifferent gonad can affect primary sex determination. Burgoyne et al. (1986a) point out that both the embryonic and the adult testis produce a factor that causes XX germ cells in the vicinity to degenerate (perhaps anti-Müllerian hormone; see Vigier et al., 1987), and that in the absence of germ cells no ovarian follicles can form, so a streak gonad results. Ducts from the extraovarian rete persist and may resemble testis cords; but in indifferent XX gonads developing in association with fetal testes or transplanted into an adult testis, they saw no testis cords or prospermatogonia, and the only sign of masculinization was the formation of a slightly thickened capsule resembling a tunica albuginea.

As Burgoyne *et al.* (1986a) have emphasized, the tendency for XX ↔ XY chimeras to develop as males provides no information on the mechanism of primary sex determination. As we have seen, the key cell lineage for testis formation is likely to be the one giving rise to pre-Sertoli cells in a male and follicle cells in a female embryo. If these cells behaved autonomously in an XX ↔ XY chimera, differentiating strictly according to their own chromosome constitution, the result would be a fetal gonad with patches of testis cord formation. Provided that the total mass of these patches exceeded a certain minimum level, there would be enough Müllerian inhibiting substance produced to ensure regression of the female ducts, and enough of the hypothetical meiosis-inhibiting factor to discourage the germ cells from forming oocytes. If Leydig cell development was induced by pre-Sertoli cells (or if the Leydig cells also behaved autonomously), there would be enough androgens to support development of the male ducts. The XX cell population would not participate in testis cord formation, and would become less and less apparent as development proceeded, since in the absence of oocytes it would not give rise to follicle cells, and would not be stimulated to proliferate but would probably degenerate (by analogy with the situation in the W^v/W^v ovary, see above). In accordance with this picture is the observation that ovotestes are relatively common in chimeric or mosaic fetuses, and much less common in the equivalent adult population (see Mystkowska and Tarkowski, 1970; Whitten *et al.*, 1979).

The hypothesis that the Sertoli cell population of an XX ↔ XY chimeric testis is made up indifferently of XX and XY cells has now been refuted by direct experimental test (Burgoyne, Buehr, and McLaren, unpublished observations). Male aggregation chimeras were made between two mouse strains of different glucose-phosphate isomerase (GPI-1) type, Sertoli cells from their testis tubules were then grown *in vitro,* and the GPI-1 isozyme composition of the Sertoli cell populations was ascertained by electrophoretic analysis. In XY ↔ XY chimeras, both isozyme types were represented in the Sertoli cell population, as expected, but in male XX ↔ XY chimeras only the XY component contributed to this cell population. In contrast, in a female XX ↔ XY chimera of the same strain combination, the GPI-1 isozymes of both the XX and the XY component appeared to be represented in the follicle cell population.

In an XX ↔ XY chimera, the sex of the gonads is believed to depend on the proportion of XX and XY cells present at the time of testis formation. Only if the proportion of XY cells is low, say <20%, will both gonads develop as ovaries so that the individual is phenotypically female. If XY cells can then contribute to the follicle cell population, the differentiation of pre-Sertoli cells must be dependent on some exogenous signal. This signal must be controlled directly or indirectly by the Y chromosome: unless it exceeds a certain threshold level (i.e., unless there is more than a certain minimum proportion of XY cells present), pre-Sertoli cell differentiation fails to occur. The capacity to respond to the signal must, however, be a cell-autonomous property of XX cells, since XX cells do not contribute to the Sertoli cell population in male XX ↔ XY chimeras. Thus, from at least the eight-cell stage (when our aggregation chimeras were made) and probably from fertilization, XX cells would be committed to following the prefollicle rather than the pre-Sertoli cell pathway within the supporting-cell lineage; but the direction of development of XY cells would not be determined until the time of the Sertoli cell-inducing signal. This may not occur until after the formation of the genital ridge.

The inducing signal could be a cell contact phenomenon. Alternatively, it could involve a diffusible substance, which could then be regarded as a "male-determining" substance in the sense defined above. We shall now consider what candidates exist for such a substance.

V. Male-Specific Antigen

The observation that female mice of certain inbred strains reject skin grafts from males but not from females of the same strain (Eichwald and Silmser, 1955) led to the recognition that there must exist a male-specific histocompatibility antigen. Because of its association with the presence of a Y chromosome, the antigen was termed H-Y. The same antigen is present in males of all mouse strains; some evidence suggests that it may occur in males of other mammalian species also (Silvers and Yang, 1973; Wiberg, 1985; Wiberg and Günther, 1985). Response to H-Y, as to other minor histocompatibility antigens, is mediated by T lymphocytes, and is controlled by various genetic loci, situated both inside and outside the major histocompatibility complex (MHC) (for review, see Simpson, 1983).

T cells from female mice sensitized against male tissue will also respond to male target cells *in vitro*. The response is H-2 restricted; that is, T lymphocytes of any major histocompatibility (H-2) type can only respond to H-Y on cells belonging to the same H-2 type. Numerous experimental studies using T cell-mediated *in vitro* cytotoxicity tests (Goldberg *et al.*, 1973; Gordon *et al.*, 1975) support the view that the same antigen is involved in both *in vivo* and *in vitro* responses (Simpson, 1982). More recently, proliferation assays based on H-Y-specific T cell clones (Tomonari, 1983) have been developed (see Simpson *et al.*, 1984).

In 1971, antibody responses were detected in female mice grafted with skin from males of the same inbred strain, and it was assumed that these responses too were stimulated by H-Y antigen (Goldberg *et al.*, 1971, 1972). The antibody responses are B cell mediated, and are under separate genetic control from the *in vivo* and *in vitro* T cell-mediated responses. The antibodies are of low titer, and appear to be somewhat unstable. A variety of different serological assay systems have been employed to detect them, including complement-dependent cytotoxicity tests against sperm, lymphoid, epidermal, brain, or Raji cells, binding assays based on fluorescence or peroxidase, *Staphylococcus aureus* and mixed hemadsorption tests, and radioimmunoassays (for review, see Koo, 1981). Unfortunately, none of these assays has proved easily reproducible, perhaps because of variation in the strength and specificity of antisera raised in different females and in different laboratories, as well as possible variation in antigen expression in target tissues. Because of the methodological problems associated with serological typing for male-specific antigen (for critiques, see Zenzes and Reed, 1984; Müller, 1986), the literature contains a number of conflicting reports. For example, female XY wood lemmings with a mutant X chromosome (X*Y) were classified as negative for the serologically detected male antigen by Wachtel *et al.* (1976), but positive by Wiberg *et al.* (1982). XO female mice were found positive by Engel *et al.* (1981), negative by Wiberg and Mayerova (1985). The discrepant findings for XO women (Wolf *et al.*, 1980; Casanova-Bettane and Fellous, 1981; Haseltine *et al.*, 1982) could be explained if some of the women were undetected mosaics. Haseltine *et al.* (1982) reported that women in whom only a 45,X line was detected were serologically negative, but those with an abnormal X chromosome were positive.

Because of the unsatisfactory nature of even the best and most objective assay systems available, the male-specific antigen recognized by B cells has not been well characterized, and we know little as yet of its genetic control. Indeed, we do not yet know whether there is just one such antigen, or several. Nor has it been conclusively shown that the male-specific antigen or antigens recognized by B cells is the same as the H-Y antigen recognized by T cells, although it is often referred to as H-Y antigen. If the earlier reports of Goldberg *et al.* (1971) on wood lemmings and Engel *et al.* (1981) on XO mice are discounted in favor of the subsequent findings of Wiberg *et al.* (1982) and Wiberg and

Mayerova (1985), a complete concordance exists between the results of T cell-mediated assays and those of serological testing; hence there is as yet no necessity to postulate the existence of two male-specific antigens, as did Simpson *et al.* (1982). On the other hand, it is not unexpected to find concordance between different male-specific characteristics, and there is as yet no positive evidence to establish that only a single male-specific antigen exists. Until further evidence comes to light, it seems preferable to adopt a phenomenological terminology, and refer to the antigen recognized by B cells as serologically detectable male (SDM) antigen (Silvers *et al.*, 1982).

VI. The H-Y Hypothesis

In 1975 Wachtel and co-workers put forward the hypothesis that H-Y antigen induces the indifferent mammalian gonad to develop into a testis. In birds, where the heterogametic sex is the female, it would induce the formation of an ovary. Much experimentation (see reviews by Wachtel, 1979, 1982; Stewart, 1983; Ohno, 1985; Müller, 1986) has been carried out during the last decade with the aim of substantiating this hypothesis. None of the results have proved conclusive, yet the hypothesis is by now widely believed to be true, perhaps because of its a priori plausibility. If a male-determining factor was required, no other candidate than H-Y antigen was available, and no other function for H-Y antigen was known.

Since 1975, the initial hypothesis has become more elaborate (see Ohno and Matsunaga, 1981; Wachtel, 1982). Specific receptors for H-Y are postulated on somatic cells of the gonad in both sexes. In an XY embryo, soluble H-Y secreted by Sertoli cell precursors in the indifferent gonad would bind to these receptor sites, and so induce increased production and dissemination of H-Y by pre-Sertoli cells. The antigen would also saturate the β_2-microglobulin (β_2m) anchorage sites of the MHC that are supposed to serve as nonspecific carriers for H-Y, displacing other inducer molecules such as those that could direct ovarian organogenesis. An H-Y molecule attached to the nonspecific carrier site of one pre-Sertoli cell could at the same time bind to the specific receptor site of another such cell, linking the cells together and promoting the aggregation of pre-Sertoli cells into testis cords. Thus soluble H-Y would function as a "cell adhesion molecule" (CAM) for pre-Sertoli cells. The subsequent organogenesis of the testis would follow as a "cascade of differentiative events" (Wachtel, 1982). In an XX embryo, no H-Y antigen would be produced, the specific receptor sites would remain vacant, and the nonspecific β_2m–MHC anchorage sites would be available for ovary-organizing molecules.

In their "H-Y hypothesis," Wachtel *et al.* (1975) assumed that there was only a single male-specific antigen, H-Y. Since it now appears that T cells and B cells could be recognizing different male-specific antigens, we have two potential candidates for a "male-determining" factor, which we shall refer to as H-Y and SDM antigen, respectively. Bearing in mind that the distinction between the two antigens may be an unreal one, we will examine in turn the evidence that either SDM or H-Y may be involved in the determination of "supporting-cell" precursors (XY cells in particular) to develop as pre-Sertoli rather than as prefollicle cells.

VII. Is SDM Antigen a "Male-Determining" Factor in Mammals?

As we have seen, experiments in which female genital ridges at the indifferent stage were exposed to fetal or adult testicular tissue have failed to produce any good evidence that primary testicular differentiation could be induced. Nagai *et al.* (1979) carried out a similar study, using Daudi cell supernate, which has been shown by serological assays to contain SDM antigen and could also contain soluble H-Y. They reported that female calf genital ridges at the indifferent stage, exposed *in vitro* to Daudi cell supernate, showed signs of masculinization. The gonadal epithelium showed some thickening, as in a tunica albuginea, and cordlike structures developed, as seen in male (but also female) calf gonads *in vivo*, but not in female gonads *in vitro* in the absence of Daudi supernate. These findings are suggestive, but in the absence of biochemical or functional studies can hardly be taken as evidence that testicular differentiation was induced. In particular, no evidence of pre-Sertoli cell differentiation was presented. A report of a similar experiment on early human gonads (Ciccarese *et al.*, 1983) is less convincing.

In a related group of experiments, ovaries that were dissociated and reaggregated *in vitro* in the presence of SDM antigen have been reported to form testicular (i.e., tubular) rather than ovarian (i.e., spherical follicle-like) structures (Zenzes *et al.*, 1978a; Müller and Urban, 1981). In other experiments, testes dissociated and reaggregated *in vitro* in the presence of antibody made against SDM antigen formed spherical rather than tubular structures (Ohno *et al.*, 1978; Zenzes *et al.*, 1978b).

These dissociation–reaggregation experiments may differ from those involving intact genital ridges, in that they would detect a testis determinant that acted *in vivo* through cell contact rather than by diffusion, provided that the cells had receptors for the determinant. Specific receptors for SDM antigen have been detected on gonadal cells

(Müller *et al.*, 1978a; Nagai *et al.*, 1979; Wachtel and Hall, 1979). On the other hand, the dissociation–reaggregation experiments seem only indirectly relevant to the question of primary sex determination, since they are carried out on dissociated newborn gonads rather than genital ridges at the indifferent stage. Indeed, Benhaim *et al.* (1982) found that the presence of SDM antigen in the culture medium had no effect on the differentiation of 13-day female rat genital ridges (indifferent stage) but induced the formation of an increased number of cordlike structures in 21-day ovaries. The appearance of cordlike structures was not accompanied by synthesis of testosterone or anti-Müllerian hormone. The only report of functional masculinization is from Müller *et al.* (1978b), who detected luteinizing hormone–human chorionic gonadotrophin (LH–hCG) receptor activity in newborn rat ovaries dissociated and allowed to reaggregate for a few hours in the presence of epididymal fluid, rich in SDM antigen. LH-hCG receptor activity is characteristic of testicular Leydig cells, and need not involve the differentiation of pre-Sertoli cells.

This secondary masculinization may relate to the phenomenon of bovine freemartinism, in which some serum-borne factor [Vigier *et al.* (1976) showed that cellular chimerism was not responsible] emanating from a male twin calf produces degeneration of oocytes and subsequent tubule formation in the female twin's ovaries. Wachtel *et al.* (1980) reported that bovine ovarian cells became positive for absorption in a sperm cytotoxicity test for SDM antigen after exposure to serum from fetal bulls or fetal freemartins but not after exposure to serum from fetal cows. Ovarian cells exposed to serum from fetal bulls or fetal freemartins were inhibited from taking up tritiated male antigen from Daudi cell supernate in a competitive binding radioimmunoassay. They suggest that the masculinization of the freemartin gonad is due to soluble male antigen secreted by the fetal bull, transmitted in the common chorionic vasculature, and bound by gonadal receptors of the fetal cow.

An adverse effect on testicular differentiation of maternal antibodies against SDM antigen has been claimed in mice (Rao *et al.*, 1981). Returning to primary sex determination, the *in vitro* experiments summarized above provide little hard evidence that SDM antigen is causally involved in the primary event of testis differentiation, that is, the development of pre-Sertoli cells. Rather stronger is the circumstantial evidence derived from the association between the presence of SDM antigen and the development of a testis. For example, SDM antigen has been reported to be present both in phenotypically female *Tfm* X/Y mice that possess testes (Bennett *et al.*, 1977) and in sex-reversed

X/X *Sxr* mice (Bennett *et al.*, 1975). No reports have been published of normal male mammals that develop testes in the absence of SDM antigen, although Haseltine *et al.* (1981) and Puck *et al.* (1981) describe two male pseudohermaphrodites and a stillborn XY female who were negative for SDM antigen but possessed testicular tissue.

What about the opposite situation, of female mammals that lack testes yet are positive for SDM antigen? As pointed out earlier, methodological problems have led in the past to contradictory reports on the SDM antigen status of some chromosomally abnormal individuals. In addition, XO women whose single X chromosome is derived from their mother could be positive for SDM antigen by virtue of an undisclosed XY or XYY cell line. Their lack of testes might reflect a level of antigen too low to induce testicular development. A low level of SDM antigen also seems to be characteristic of X*X and XO female wood lemmings, which could also explain their failure to develop testes (Wiberg *et al.*, 1982). On the other hand, the lack of testes in SDM antigen-positive X*Y and X*O female wood lemmings is thought to be due to the deletion from the abnormal X* chromosome of a gene for the gonadal receptor for SDM antigen (Wiberg *et al.*, 1982). The expression of SDM antigen in the absence of a Y chromosome is consistent with the view of Wolf *et al.* (1980) that the structural gene for male-specific antigen is not located on the Y chromosome. An alternative view, which avoids having to postulate either receptor mutations or threshold levels of SDM antigen, holds that an autosomally coded antigenically active precursor substance is produced that may be modified into a "male-determining" substance by a gene on the Y chromosome, or into a substance devoid of both SDM antigenicity and "male-determining" activity by an X-coded gene (Adinolfi *et al.*, 1982).

In birds, the female rather than the male is the heterogametic (ZW) sex, and the "H-Y hypothesis" therefore postulates that ovarian rather than testicular differentiation is induced by H-Y antigen (termed H-W antigen in birds). Nakamura *et al.* (1984) reported that female (ZW) chick tissues showed positive absorption in a sperm cytotoxicity test for SDM antigen, while soluble antigen from mouse testis (termed H-Y) was bound *in vitro* by testicular but not by somatic tissues of male (ZZ) chicks. They suggest that the reaction of "H-Y antigen" and its gonadal receptor may be critical for development of the ZW ovary. However, sex determination is more labile in birds than in mammals, and can be influenced by the administration of hormones; the results of such hormone treatments suggest that the presence of antigen is the consequence rather than the cause of ovarian differentiation. Early treatment of male (ZZ) embryos with estrogen causes the right gonad to regress (as in the female) and the left gonad to differentiate as an ovotestis: Müller *et al.* (1979, 1980) and Zaborski *et al.* (1981) reported that such ovotestes showed positive absorption in a Raji cell cytotoxicity test for SDM antigen, although the somatic tissues remained negative. Conversely, early treatment of female (ZW) embryos with the antiestrogen tamoxifen reduced to male values the level of SDM antigen-absorptive capacity in both liver and gonads (Koo *et al.*, 1985): the right gonad failed to regress and developed testis-like structures, although its steroid output remained ovarian, while the left gonad developed as a normal ovary. If normal ovarian development in the chick can occur in the presence of male levels of the avian equivalent of SDM antigen, either this antigen is not the inducer of ovarian development in birds, or it acts at a very early stage, prior to oviposition (i.e., well before the formation of the genital ridges).

VIII. Is H-Y Antigen a "Male-Determining" Factor in Mammals?

For terminological convenience, we have assumed that the male-specific antigen recognized by T cells (H-Y) is distinct from that recognized by B cells (SDM). Although a histocompatibility antigen recognized by T cells can be shed from the cell surface and exist in the form of soluble antigen, the assay systems devised to measure H-Y antigen are all based on transplantation, T cell-mediated *in vitro* cytotoxicity, or T cell clone proliferation, and are not well suited to the recognition of soluble antigen. The various experimental dissociation–reaggregation studies that have been used to explore the properties of SDM antigen have therefore not been applied specifically to H-Y , although some of the experimental systems do not distinguish between the two antigens.

The arguments in support of a testis-inducing role for H-Y antigen have mainly concentrated on the concordance between presence or absence of testes and presence or absence of H-Y (see Wachtel, 1982; Müller, 1986). XX male mice carrying the sex-reversal factor *Sxr* discovered by Cattanach *et al.* (1971) were found to be positive for H-Y antigen both by skin grafting and by H-2-restricted cytotoxic T cells (Bennett *et al.*, 1977; Simpson *et al.*, 1981). If *Sxr* had proved to consist of a single autosomal mutation, the genetic link between testes and H-Y, though not the direction of the causal association, would have been established. Since XX *Sxr* mice turned out to be carrying a piece of the Y chromosome attached to one of their X chromosomes (for review, see McLaren, 1983), the possibility remained that testis development and H-Y antigen might be controlled by two separate Y-chromosome loci.

The reports of females lacking testes but positive for H-Y antigen are not strong evidence against a role for H-Y in testis determination. Possible explanations for the occurrence of H-Y antigen in XO women (Wiberg, 1985) and female wood lemmings of XO and X*X as well as X*O and X*Y sex chromosome constitution (Wiberg and Fredga, 1985; Wiberg and Gunther, 1985) have been discussed above, in relation to SDM antigen. In the various categories of XY female mice described by Eicher and colleagues and shown to be positive for H-Y antigen by skin grafting, T cell-mediated cytotoxicity, and popliteal lymph node assays (Simpson *et al.*, 1983; Johnson *et al.*, 1983), the failure to develop testes is attributed to mismatching between the Y-linked testis-determining locus (*H-Y* or other) and some autosomal or X-linked locus, perhaps coding for a gonadal receptor molecule.

T16H/X *Sxr* female mice, heterozygous for the preferentially active T(X;16)16H X-autosome translocation and carrying *Sxr* on their silent X chromosome, are thought to be mosaics, with two cell populations of which the one expressing *Sxr* is in the minority (Cattanach *et al.*, 1982; McLaren and Monk, 1982). The observation that they are positive for H-Y antigen (Simpson *et al.*, 1984) would then not be surprising. Their failure to develop testes could be due to a subthreshold concentration of H-Y antigen. On the other hand, Ohno (1985) has postulated that mice of this chromosomal constitution are not mosaics, and that the range of sexual phenotypes that they exhibit (female, intersex, male) is due to some effect of the T16H translocation itself on gonadal development, perhaps on gonad size (see Mittwoch, 1983, 1986). Alternatively, the translocation could be modifying an X-linked locus involved in conferring testis-inducing properties on a precursor H-Y substance (see Adinolfi *et al.*, 1982). Such explanations are not, however, consistent with the finding that the proportion of females, intersexes, and males in mice depends critically on the genotype of the male parent (McLaren, 1986). The presence of the T16H translocation does not in itself reduce gonad size; T16H/X*Sxr* testes are smaller than X/X*Sxr* testes but T16H*Sxr*/X testes are not (McLaren, unpublished observations).

The most cogent evidence against H-Y antigen being responsible for inducing testis formation comes from the existence of male mice that possess testes but do not express H-Y antigen. One such mouse, an XO male, was described by Melvold *et al.* (1977); it was reported to be positive for SDM antigen but negative for H-Y. A variant *Sxr* fragment has since been discovered, termed *Sxr'*, that supports the development of testes in XX *Sxr'* and XO *Sxr'* individuals, but appears not to code for H-Y (McLaren *et al.*, 1984). Not only do the spleens of XX *Sxr'* males type negative for H-Y antigen by both T cell-mediated cytotoxicity tests and T cell clone proliferation assays, but unlike XX *Sxr* males they reject skin grafts from semisyngeneic XY donors (Simpson *et al.*, 1986). XX females accept skin grafts from syngeneic XX*Sxr'* males (Simpson and McLaren, unpublished observations). It is not known whether the event that generated the variant *Sxr'* fragment involved a mutation at the locus coding for H-Y, such that this antigenic determinant was no longer expressed, or whether the locus has been lost from the fragment, for example by unequal crossing over. The first event would be compatible with a single locus coding both for H-Y antigenicity and for testis determination, although the determinant recognized as H-Y by T cells could not itself be involved in inducing the development of testes; the second event would require the existence in normal males of two separate loci, one for H-Y antigen and one for testis determination.

Since H-Y antigenicity appeared not to be involved in testis determination, we made an attempt to discover what other aspect of male-specific function might depend on the presence of this antigen (Burgoyne *et al.*, 1986b). H-Y-negative XX *Sxr'* males proved in no way inferior to H-Y-positive XX *Sxr* males in their coital performance, or in their ability to synchronize estrus in females by testosterone-dependent pheromone production. A striking difference was detected, however, between the ability of XO *Sxr* and XO *Sxr'* mice to support spermatogenesis. Adult XO *Sxr* males have all stages of spermatogenesis represented in their testes, although the later stages are defective and only a few grossly abnormal sperm are produced (Cattanach *et al.*, 1971). In contrast, XO *Sxr'* males have much smaller testes, with almost no spermatogenic cells beyond the spermatogonial stage. Even spermatogonia are rare, and show few divisions; occasional groups of cells enter meiosis, but never progress beyond the pachytene stage.

A very similar situation has recently been reported by Levy and Burgoyne (1986) for patches of XO germ cells in XO/XY mosaic mice. They conclude that there must be a gene on the Y chromosome that is expressed in germ cells, producing a gene product required for spermatogenesis. The presence of normal XY somatic and germ cells in the same testis tubule does not rescue the defective XO germ cells.

IX. Genes on the Y Chromosome

There are thus four possible gene products controlled by the *Sxr* region of the mouse Y chromosome: H-Y antigen, SDM antigen, a substance required for spermatogenesis, and a "male-determining" substance, in the sense of a gene product responsible for the appropriate signal to induce XY cells to differentiate as pre-Sertoli rather than prefollicle cells.

According to the model of sex determination put forward by Chandra (1985), DNA sequences on the Y chromosome do not code for a "male-determining" substance, but rather bind a repressor molecule regulating the activity of an autosomal sex-determining gene. For the purpose of the present argument, however, we will assume a single Y-chromosome locus involved in pre-Sertoli cell determination, rather than a repeated sequence or sequences.

Since the spermatogenesis gene appears to be defective in XO *Sxr'* as well as in XO germ cells, yet is expressed in XO *Sxr* germ cells, it must have been affected by the same event that eliminated expression of H-Y antigenicity in the genesis of the *Sxr'* fragment. Of the two alternative hypotheses considered earlier, the single-locus hypothesis would require a mutational event such that H-Y antigenicity was no longer expressed, and spermatogenesis could no longer proceed. This would argue strongly that H-Y antigen plays an obligate role in spermatogenesis. If the same locus is involved in testis determination, we would have a remarkable example of biological economy, with a single molecule being responsible for the two key processes of male reproductive function. On the second alternative, in which *Sxr'* arose from *Sxr* by a deletion, there is no requirement for H-Y to be involved in spermatogenesis. Its function would remain unknown. Three separate Y-chromosomal loci could be postulated: the lost fragment could have carried two, one (*Hya*) coding for H-Y and another (*Spy*) for a product needed for spermatogenesis, while the third locus (*Tdy*), coding for a hypothetical "male determinant," would remain on the *Sxr'* fragment. If X/X *Sxr'* males prove to be positive for SDM antigen, this could constitute the "male determinant," or yet a fourth locus could exist (*Sdm*), again of unknown function. The most likely alternatives would seem either that H-Y and SDM antigen are the same and are involved in spermatogenesis, with pre-Sertoli cell determination being under the control of a separate locus; or that H-Y is the product of the spermatogenesis gene and SDM antigen is involved in pre-Sertoli cell determination.

X. Conclusions

1. Differentiation of pre-Sertoli cells, the first step in testis formation, appears to be genetically programmed and cell autonomous. Presence of a Y chromosome in the cell is a necessary but perhaps not a sufficient condition for such differentiation.

2.   An inducing signal produced by XY cells may also be required if supporting-cell precursors are to differentiate as pre-Sertoli rather than as follicle cells. The signal could act by cell contact or by diffusion (i.e., a "male-determining" substance), but must exceed a certain threshold level of activity if it is to be effective.

3.   If XX *Sxr'* males prove to be positive for SDM antigen, this antigen will be a strong candidate for some role in testis differentiation, perhaps even the "primary" role of inducing XY supporting-cell precursors to differentiate as pre-Sertoli cells.

4.   It seems unlikely that H-Y antigen, recognized by T cells, is a "male-determining" substance, especially now that a possible alternative function for this antigen has been suggested, in the regulation of spermatogenesis.

5.   If SDM antigen, recognized by B cells, proves to be antigenically identical to H-Y, it too is probably not involved in testis determination.

6.   If the two antigens prove to be different, yet XX *Sxr'* males prove to be negative for SDM as well as for H-Y antigen, SDM antigen will become a rival candidate for the product of the "spermatogenesis" gene. Spermatogonia are the only cells reported not to express SDM antigen in the adult male (Zenzes *et al.,* 1978c).

NOTE ADDED IN PROOF

The conclusion that H-Y antigen is not involved in testis determination has now been confirmed for man. TDF, the human testis-determining factor, maps to the distal end of the short arm of the human Y, while H-Y antigen expression depends on a locus in the proximal part of the short arm (Simpson *et al.,* 1987).

REFERENCES

Adinolfi, M., Polani, P., and Zenthon, J. (1982). *Hum. Genet.* **61,** 1–2.

Agelopoulou, R., Magre, S., Patsavoudi, E., and Jost, A. (1984). *J. Embryol. Exp. Morphol.* **83,** 15–31.

Benhaim, A., Gangnerau, M.-N., Bettane-Casanova, M., Fellous, M., and Picon, R. (1982). *Differentiation* **22,** 53–58.

Bennett, D., Boyse, E. A., Lyon, M. F., Mathieson, B. J., Scheid, M., and Yanagisawa, K. (1975). *Nature (London)* **257,** 236–8.

Bennett, D., Mathieson, B. J., Scheid, M., Yanagisawa, K., Boyse, E. A., Wachtel, S., and Cattanach, B. M. (1977). *Nature (London)* **265,** 255–257.

Burgoyne, P. S., Ansell, J. D., and Tournay, A. (1986a). *Serono Symp. Dev. Funct. Reprod. Organs* **11,** 23–39.

Burgoyne, P. S., Levy, E. R., and McLaren, A. (1986b). *Nature (London)* **320,** 170–172.

Byskov, A. G. (1978). *Int. J. Androl. (Suppl.)* **2,** 29–38.

Casanova-Bettane, M., and Fellous, M. (1981). *C. R. Soc. Biol. (Paris)* **175,** 8–18.

Cate, R. L., Mattaliano, R. J., Hession, C., and Tizard, R. (1986). *Cell* **45,** 685–698.

Cattanach, B. M., Pollard, C. E., and Hawkes, S. G. (1971). *Cytogenetics* **10,** 318–337.

Cattanach, B. M., Evans, E. P., Burtenshaw, M., and Barlow, J. (1982). *Nature (London)* **300**, 445–446.

Chandra, H. S. (1985). *Proc. Natl. Acad. Sci. U.S.A.* **82**, 1165–1169.

Ciccarese, S., Orsini, G., Massari, S., and Guanti, G. (1983). *Cell Differ.* **12**, 185–190.

Eichwald, E. J., and Silmser, C. R. (1955). *Transplant. Bull.* **2**, 148–149.

Engel, W., Klemme, B., and Ebrecht, A. (1981). *Hum. Genet.* **57**, 68–70.

Epstein, C. J., Smith, S., and Travis, B. (1980). *Tissue Antigens* **15**, 63–67.

Francavilla, S., and Zamboni, L. (1985). *J. Exp. Zool.* **233**, 101–109.

Franchi, L. L., Mandl, A. M., and Zuckerman, S. (1962). *In* "The Ovary" (S. Zuckerman, A. M. Mandl, and P. Eckstein, eds.), Vol. 1, pp. 1–88. Academic Press, London.

Gehring, U., Tomkins, G., and Ohno, S. (1971). *Nature (London) New Biol.* **232**, 106–107.

Goldberg, E., Boyse, E. A., Bennett, D., Scheid, M., and Carswell, E. A. (1971). *Nature (London)* **232**, 478–480.

Goldberg, E., Boyse, E. A., Scheid, M., and Bennett, D. (1972). *Nature (London) New Biol.* **238**, 55–56.

Goldberg, E. H., Shen, F. W., and Tokuda, S. (1973). *Transplantation* **15**, 334–336.

Gordon, R. D., Simpson, E., and Samelson, L. (1975). *J. Exp. Med.* **142**, 1108–1120.

Haseltine, F. P., Genel, M., Crawford, J. D., and Breg, W. R. (1981). *Hum. Genet.* **57**, 265–268.

Haseltine, F. P., DePonte, K. K., Breg, W. R., and Genel, M. (1982). *Am. J. Med. Genet.* **11**, 97–107.

James, W. (1983). *In* "Sex Selection of Children" (N. G. Bennett, ed.), pp. 73–99. Academic Press, New York.

Johnson, L. L., Sargent, E. L., Washburn, L. L., and Eicher, E. M. (1983). *Dev. Genet.* **3**, 247–254.

Jost, A. (1972). *Arch. Anat. Microsc. Morphol. Exp.* **61**, 415–438.

Koo, G. C. (1981). *Hum. Genet.* **58**, 18–20.

Koo, G. C., Allen, H. L., Long, R. A., Serio-Dunn, R., Goggin, B., and Weppelman, R. M. (1985). *Differentiation* **29**, 140–144.

Krco, C. J., and Goldberg, E. H. (1976). *Science* **193**, 1134–1135.

Levy, E. R., and Burgoyne, P. S. (1986). *Cytogenet. Cell Genet.* **42**, 208–213.

Lyon, M. F., and Hawkes, S. G. (1970). *Nature (London)* **227**, 1217–1219.

McCoshen, J. A. (1983). *Am. J. Obstet. Gynecol.* **145**, 469–473.

McLaren, A. (1976). "Mammalian Chimaeras." Cambridge Univ. Press, London and New York.

McLaren, A. (1983). *Differentiation* **23** (Suppl.), S93–S98.

McLaren, A. (1984). *Symp. Soc. Exp. Biol., 38th,* pp. 7–23.

McLaren, A. (1985). *In* "The Origin and Evolution of Sex" (H. O. Halvorsen and A. Monroy, eds.), pp. 289–300. Liss, New York.

McLaren, A. (1986). *Dev. Genet.* **7**, 177–185.

McLaren, A., and Monk, M. (1982). *Nature (London)* **300**, 446–448.

McLaren, A., Simpson, E., Tomonari, K., Chandler, P., and Hogg, H. (1984). *Nature (London)* **312**, 552–555.

Magre, S., and Jost, A. (1984). *Proc. Natl. Acad. Sci. U.S.A.* **81**, 7831–7834.

Meisel, R. L., and Ward, I. L. (1981). *Science* **213**, 239–241.

Melvold, R. W., Koln, H. I., Yerganian, G., and Fawcett, D. W. (1977). *Immunogenetics* **5**, 33–41.

Merchant, H. (1975). *Dev. Biol.* **44**, 1–21.

Mintz, B. (1969). *In* "First Conference on the Clinical Delineation of Birth Defects" (D. Bergsma and V. McKusick, eds.). *Birth Defects Orig. Article Ser.* **5**, 11–22.

Mintz, B., Domon, M., Hungerford, D. A., and Morrow, J. (1972). *Science* **175**, 657–659.
Mittwoch, U. (1983). *Am. Nat.* **122**, 159–180.
Mittwoch, U. (1986). *Ann. Hum. Genet.* **50**, 103–121.
Müller, U. (1986). *In* "The Y Chromosome, Part A: Basic Characteristics of the Y Chromosome." Liss, New York.
Müller, U., and Urban, E. (1981). *Cytogenet. Cell Genet.* **31**, 104–107.
Müller, U., Aschmoneit, I., Zenzes, M. T., and Wolf, U. (1978a). *Hum. Genet.* **43**, 151–157.
Müller, U., Zenzes, M. T., Bauknecht, T., Wolf, U., Siebers, J. W., and Engel, W. (1978b). *Hum. Genet.* **45**, 203–207.
Müller, U., Zenzes, M. T., Wolf, U., Engel, W., and Weniger, J. P. (1979). *Nature (London)* **280**, 142–144.
Müller, U., Guichard, A., Reyss-Brion, M., and Scheib, D. (1980). *Differentiation* **16**, 129–133.
Müller, U., Schindler, H., Schempp, W., Schott, K., and Neuhoff, V. (1984). *Dev. Genet.* **5**, 27–42.
Mystkowska, E. T., and Tarkowski, A. K. (1970). *J. Embryol. Exp. Morphol.* **23**, 395–405.
Nagai, Y., Ciccarese, S., and Ohno, S. (1979). *Differentiation* **13**, 155–164.
Nakamura, D., Wachtel, S. S., and Gilmour, D. (1984). *J. Reprod. Immunol.* **6**, 11–17.
Ohno, S. (1985). *Endocr. Rev.* **6**, 421–431.
Ohno, S., and Lyon, M. F. (1970). *Clin. Genet.* **1**, 121–127.
Ohno, S., and Matsunaga, T. (1981). *In* "Levels of Genetic Control in Development," pp. 235–246. Liss, New York.
Ohno, S., Nagai, Y., and Ciccarese, S. (1978). *Cytogenet. Cell Genet.* **20**, 351–364.
Ohno, S., Nagai, Y., Ciccarese, S., and Iwata, H. (1979). *Recent Prog. Horm. Res.* **35**, 449–476.
Ozdzenski, W., Rogulska, T., Balakier, H., Brzozowska, M., Rembiczewska, A., and Stepinska, O. (1976). *Arch. Anat. Microsc.* **65**, 285–294.
Patsavoudi, E., Magre, S., Castanier, M., Scholler, R., and Jost, A. (1985). *J. Endocrinol.* **105**, 235–238.
Puck, S. M., Haseltine, F. P., and Francke, U. (1981). *Hum. Genet.* **57**, 23–27.
Rao, C. S., Vaidya, R. A., and Ambani, L. M. (1981). *J. Reprod. Immunol.* **3**, 175–185.
Shelton, J. A., and Goldberg, E. H. (1984). *Transplantation* **37**, 7–8.
Silvers, W. K., and Yang, S.-L. (1973). *Science* **181**, 570–572.
Silvers, W. K., Gasser, D. L., and Eicher, E. M. (1982). *Cell* **28**, 439–440.
Simpson, E. (1982). *Immunol. Today* **3**, 97–106.
Simpson, E. (1983). *Proc. R. Soc. London Ser. B* **220**, 31–46.
Simpson, E., Edwards, P., Wachtel, S., McLaren, A., and Chandler, P. (1981). *Immunogenetics* **13**, 355–358.
Simpson, E., McLaren, A., and Chandler, P. (1982). *Immunogenetics* **15**, 609–614.
Simpson, E., Chandler, P., Washburn, L. L., Bunker, H. P., and Eicher, E. M. (1983). *Differentiation* **23** (Suppl.), S116–S120.
Simpson, E., McLaren, A., Chandler, P., and Tomonari, K. (1984). *Transplantation* **37**, 17–21.
Simpson, E., Chandler, P., Hunt, R., Hogg, H., Tomonari, K., and McLaren, A. (1986). *Immunology* **57**, 345–349.
Simpson, E., Chandler, P., Goulmy, E., Disteche, C. M., Ferguson-Smith, M. A., and Page, D. C. (1987). *Nature (London)* **326**, 876–878.
Snow, M. H. L. (1985). *UCLA Symp. Mol. Determinants Anim. Form*, pp. 73–98.
Stewart, A. D. (1983). *Dev. Mammals* **5**, 321–367.

Tomonari, K. (1983). *J. Immunol.* **131**, 1641–1645.
Turner, C. D. (1969). *Embryologica* **10**, 206–230.
Turner, C. D., and Asakawa, H. (1964). *Science* **143**, 1344–1345.
Tsunoda, Y., Tokunaga, T., and Sugie, T. (1985). *Gamete Res.* **12**, 301–304.
Upadhyay, S., Luciani, J. M., and Zamboni, L. (1981). In "Development and Function of Reproductive Organs" (A. G. Byskov and H. Peters, eds.), pp. 18–30. Excerpta Medica, Amsterdam.
Vigier, B., Locatelli, A., Prepin, J., du Mesnil du Buisson, F., and Jost, A. (1976). *C. R. Acad. Sci. (Paris)* **282**, 1355–1358.
Vigier, B., Watrin, F., Magre, S., Tran, D., and Josso, N. (1987). *Development* **100**, 43–55.
vom Saal, F. S., and Bronson, F. H. (1978). *Biol. Reprod.* **19**, 842–853.
vom Saal, F. S., and Bronson, F. H. (1980). *Science* **208**, 597–599.
vom Saal, F. S., Grant, W. M., McMullen, C. W., and Laves, K. S. (1983). *Science* **220**, 1306–1309.
Wachtel, S. S. (1979). *Cell* **16**, 691–695.
Wachtel, S. S. (1983). "H-Y Antigen and the Biology of Sex Determination." Academic Press, London.
Wachtel, S. S., and Hall, J. L. (1979). *Cell* **17**, 327–329.
Wachtel, S. S., Ohno, S., Koo, G., and Boyse, E. A. (1975). *Nature (London)* **257**, 235–236.
Wachtel, S. S., Koo, G. C., Ohno, S., Gropp, A., Dev, V. G., Tantravahi, R., Miller, D. A., and Miller, O. J. (1976). *Nature (London)* **264**, 638–639.
Wachtel, S. S., Hall, J. L., Müller, U., and Chaganti, R. S. K. (1980). *Cell* **21**, 917–926.
Wartenberg, H. (1981). In "The Testis" (H. Burger and D. de Kretser, eds.), pp. 39–80. Raven, New York.
White, K. L., Lindner, G. M., Anderson, G. B., and Bon Durant, R. H. (1982). *Theriogenology* **18**, 655–662.
White, K. L., Lindner, G. M., Anderson, G. B., and Bon Durant, R. H. (1983). *Theriogenology* **19**, 701–705.
Whitten, W. K., Beamer, W. G., and Byskov, A. G. (1979). *J. Embryol. Exp. Morphol.* **52**, 63–78.
Wiberg, U. H. (1985). *Hum. Genet.* **69**, 15–18.
Wiberg, U. H., and Fredga, K. (1985). *Immunogenetics* **22**, 495–501.
Wiberg, U. H., and Günther, E. (1985). *Immunogenetics* **21**, 91–96.
Wiberg, U. H., and Mayerova, A. (1985). *J. Immunogenet.* **12**, 55–63.
Wiberg, U., Mayerova, A., Müller, U., Fredga, K., and Wolf, U. (1982). *Hum. Genet.* **60**, 163–166.
Witschi, E. (1951). *Recent Prog. Horm. Res.* **6**, 1–27.
Wolf, U., Fraccaro, M., Mayerova, A., Hecht, T., Zuffardi, O., and Hameister, H. (1980). *Hum. Genet.* **54**, 315–318.
Zaborski, P., Guichard, A., and Scheib, D. (1981). *Biol. Cell* **41**, 113–122.
Zamboni, L., and Upadhyay, S. (1983). *J. Exp. Zool.* **228**, 173–193.
Zamboni, L., Upadhyay, S., Bézard, J., and Mauléon, P. (1981). In "Development and Function of Reproductive Organs" (A. G. Byskov and H. Peters, eds.), pp. 31–40. Excerpta Medica, Amsterdam.
Zenzes, M. T., and Reed, T. E. (1984). *Hum. Genet.* **66**, 103–109.
Zenzes, M. T., Wolf, U., and Engel, W. (1978a). *Hum. Genet.* **44**, 333–338.
Zenzes, M. T., Wolf, U., Günther, E., and Engel, W. (1978b). *Cytogenet. Cell Genet.* **20**, 365–372.
Zenzes, M. T., Müller, U., Aschmoneit, I., and Wolf, U. (1978c). *Hum. Genet.* **45**, 297–303.

CHAPTER 9

CELL HETEROGENEITY IN THE MYOGENIC LINEAGE

Giulio Cossu and Mario Molinaro

INSTITUTE OF HISTOLOGY AND GENERAL EMBRYOLOGY
MEDICAL SCHOOL
I UNIVERSITY OF ROME
00161 ROME, ITALY

I. Introduction

Unlike better known cases of cellular heterogeneity in a defined cell lineage, such as the erythroid lineage (Alter *et al.*, 1983; Beapain *et al.*, 1979; Cudennac *et al.*, 1981; Johnson and Moore, 1975), myogenic cell heterogeneity has received little recognition (for exceptions see Caplan *et al.*, 1983; Stockdale and Miller, 1987).

We believe this to be a classical case where technical difficulties have hampered the production of conclusive data and consequently lowered the attention of the scientific audience to the specific problem. Furthermore, the well-known heterogeneity of muscle fibers with respect to speed of contraction, metabolism, and complement of contractile protein isoforms (Engel, 1974; Kahn, 1976; Buchthal and Schmalbruch, 1980; Whalen, 1985; Bandman, 1985; Barton and Buckingham, 1985) is usually explained on the basis of nerve control and, to a minor extent, response to hormonal signals (for a recent review, see Pette and Vrbova, 1985). Yet several points need to be considered when discussing such an argument. For example, the development of skeletal muscle is a tremendously complex event, which lasts from the somitic period to the end of somatic growth, occupies the majority of the available space in a vertebrate embryo and requires the coordinated migration, interaction, and differentiation of many different cellular populations such as myoblasts, fibroblasts, motoneurons, and endocrine cells. It is possible that different events such as the pattern of muscle formation, the sequential generations of muscle fibers, the proteins expressed by such fibers are all part of the developmental program of a single myogenic cell and are diversified by extracellular cues. Alternatively, such diversifications might imply the existence of specific subpopulations of myoblasts, each of which ap-

185

pears sequentially and expresses its own developmental program. This of course does not imply that a myogenic cell A and a myogenic cell B, or the muscle fibers derived from them, might not be able to respond to an extracellular signal by activating the same set of genes.

It is obvious, however, that nerves and hormones cannot explain these aspects of muscle heterogeneity. Even the expression of fast and slow contractile protein isoforms may not be totally dependent on neural control (Butler *et al.*, 1982; Butler-Brown *et al.*, 1982; Laing and Lamb, 1983a,b; Phillips and Bennett, 1984). On the first line of thinking, people can keep looking for other signals which might instruct either an embryonic or an adult muscle cell on its further program, that is, on the specific timing of differentiation and on the set of proteins to be synthesized.

We will instead discuss the evidence for the existence of different classes of myogenic cells, emerging at different periods during development and embryologically related to specific aspects of muscle differentiation and further maturation.

An additional reason to examine myogenic cell heterogeneity lies in the well-known histopathological picture of primary myopathies (Cullen and Mastaglia, 1980), where certain muscle fibers appear unaffected by the disease while the majority degenerate. The possibility will be discussed that such heterogeneity reflects the existence of different populations of fibers (possibly derived from different populations of myoblasts), which might not express, or express to a different level, the mutated gene.

We will review the literature on early and late myoblasts in somites and limbs and on satellite cells, then briefly discuss possible relationships of these cell types with muscle fiber development and with fiber heterogeneity in primary myopathies.

Since the processes of myogenic differentiation and even more of muscle regeneration are quite distinct in lower vertebrates and invertebrates (Carlson, 1973; Henderson and Spitz, 1985; Nishida and Satoh, 1985), we will limit our discussion to birds and mammals.

II. One or More Myogenic Lineages?

Even though myotubes are formed by fusion of mononucleated cells, which morphologically appear quite similar (Fischman, 1974), these cells are not all alike either in developing muscle tissue or in culture. Besides the obvious presence of nonmyogenic cells, it is known that the cells with competence for fusion do not fuse simultaneously. Rather fusion is a very asynchronous phenomenon *in vivo*, lasting all the postsomitic period of embryonic development and for extended periods after birth. Thus at any given time, an embryonic muscle is composed of myotubes plus a mixture of cells separated from fusion by varying numbers of mitoses. Although it is possible to manipulate this number *in vitro* by simply reducing or increasing the growth factor concentration in the medium (Hauschka *et al.*, 1985), the concentration may be strictly controlled *in vivo*, and thus the number of mitoses that a given cell undergoes before fusion may be relatively constant.

Nameroff and colleagues have recently demonstrated, in an elegant series of experiments, that myogenic cells from 11-day chick embryos will give rise to myogenic clones that are mostly composed of multiples of 2 (i.e., 2, 4, 8, 16 cells). Larger clones are composed of undifferentiated cells and groups of differentiated cells which tend to be multiples of 16 (Smith-Quinn and Nameroff, 1983a,b; Robinson *et al.*, 1984; Smith-Quinn *et al.*, 1984, 1985). Their interpretation of these results is that a precursor muscle cell in the limb of a chick embryo will count four mitoses before differentiating. The smaller clones (2, 4, 8 cells) are therefore generated by cells which have already undergone three, two, or one of their last divisions *in vivo*, and will only divide to complete their number of mitoses. The larger clones may derive from earlier mesenchymal cells, capable of generating *in vitro* more than one muscle precursor cell. The existence of a "developmental clock that counts cell divisions" has been supported by recent studies on oligodendrocyte (Temple and Raff, 1986) and erythroblast (Allen and Dexter, 1982) differentiation.

One interesting point, not analyzed in this work, is the study of very early myogenic cells or very late "satellite" cells under similar experimental conditions.

In other species such as rodents, myogenic cells are extremely sensitive to growth conditions, so that the size of myogenic clones will be largely proportional to the concentration of serum, embryo extract, or other growth factors in the medium. This makes it difficult to know whether a situation similar to that of the chicken occurs in mouse development. In any case, this type of analysis is mainly focused on the duplicative potentialities of precursor muscle cells and would not reveal the existence of other phenotypic differences. The existence of different muscle cell precursors, not related in a mother–daughter but rather in a sister–sister fashion, is based on experimental evidence from several laboratories to be described below.

How does such heterogeneity arise? Holtzer and colleagues (Abbot *et al.*, 1974; Dienstman and Holtzer, 1977; Holtzer *et al.*, 1972, 1975) proposed that, throughout embryonic development, each cell is in a precise compartment of its lineage and is not an "undifferentiated" cell. Whether a blastomere, a somitic cell, or an erythroblast, this cell can give rise to no more than two different cell types and does so by undergoing a mitotic cycle. This mitosis was termed "quantal mitosis," since it gives rise to cells capable of expressing a phenotype not expressed and not expressable in the mother cell. By contrast, proliferative mitoses would generate cells identical to the mother cell and would be necessary to expand the size of a given cellular compartment. One point which is left open in this theory, but is central to our further discussion, is whether a "quantal mitosis" generates two identical (equal mitosis), similar, or different daughter cells (unequal mitosis). For example a "presumptive replicating myoblast" can only give rise through "quantal mitosis" to two postmitotic terminally differentiated myoblasts. On the other hand, a somitic cell is supposed to generate a presumptive myoblast, and a presumptive fibroblast, two obviously different cells. We would like to focus on a third possibility: that the daughter cells of a quantal mitosis might be morphologically indistinguishable, biochemically very similar, yet not identical (Fig. 1).

A myotome cell, already committed to the myogenic lineage, might generate a precursor of early and one of late myogenic cells. The rate of division, the migratory capacity (to the limb), and the number of mitoses that separate the two cells from terminal differentiation might not be the same. As a consequence, early myotubes might derive from the early precursor cell while the other cell progeny was still in its duplicative phase and would not differentiate until days later.

However, many recent reports have questioned the necessity of quantal mitosis; at least of the final one, which generates terminally differentiated postmitotic myoblasts. By using either quail primary myoblasts, rat cell lines, or virally transformed avian cells, many different groups have shown that the transition from a proliferating myoblast to a postmitotic cell is a random event and is a function of the growth factor concentration in the medium (Buckley and Konigsberg,

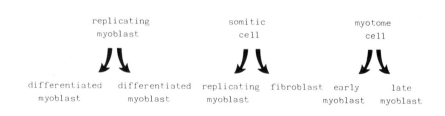

FIG. 1. Daughter cells of a quantal mitosis.

1977; Nadal-Ginard, 1978; Linkhart *et al.*, 1981; Devlin and Konigsberg, 1983; Falcone *et al.*, 1984). According to these authors, a presumptive myoblast has at any given time the option of dividing or differentiating, depending on extracellular cues, such as growth factors, extracellular matrix, and cell–cell interactions.

It is beyond the scope of this review to discuss these hypotheses. Provided that there are mitoses during embryonic development, and that a given cell can generate two different cells, the quantal mitosis theory offers a framework where it is easy to visualize the emergence of diversification within a given lineage. Whether or not a mitosis is obligatory or dispensable in order to express a new set of genes, and whether the number of mitoses is fixed in a program or dependent on the environment, are different problems.

III. Somites and Early Differentiation

The search for heterogeneity within myogenic cells should probably begin with an examination of how precursor cells appear and differentiate as compared to other mesodermal cells in the somite. Relatively few articles have focused on this specific issue. Based on different techniques (electron microscopy, immunofluorescence, organ or cell cultures), the results obtained and their possible interpretation are not always directly comparable.

Early articles described first at the light microscope and then at the ultrastructural level the various phases of somite differentiation and the morphological characters of the cells belonging to the myotome (Allen and Pepe, 1966; Dessauki and Hibbs, 1965; Obinata *et al.*, 1966; Prizblisky and Blumberg, 1966). All agreed that myotome cells, characterized by a pale, round to irregular nucleus with darkly stained nucleolus, derived from the dermatome. No myofilaments were observed in these cells, but an autoradiographic study (Langman and Nelson, 1968) revealed that most did not synthesize DNA. This finding is puzzling if one considers that the few cells of the myotome will give rise to most of the muscles of the body. *In vivo,* cells might slow down their duplicative activity at certain times, without becoming irreversibly postmitotic as one would expect of more mature myogenic cells. At this stage, and for several days thereafter, all myotome cells are mononucleated, and fusion is not observed until stage 24–26 (4–5 days in the chick; 12–13 days in rodent embryos). While these early myotubes, containing cross-striated filaments and stainable with an antimyosin antibody, were clearly identified as differentiated muscle cells, it was evident from immunohistochemical analysis that single myosin-positive cells emerged much earlier both in avian (2.5 days) and rodents (9 days) (Holtzer *et al.,* 1957; Ikeda *et al.,* 1968; Jockush *et al.,* 1984; Bignami and Dahl, 1984). At the time when the first immunohistochemical studies were published, the complexity of myosin isoforms (Bandman, 1985; Barton and Buckingham, 1985; Whalen, 1985) was not yet understood, but the specificity of antibody staining guaranteed that the protein represented a specific differentiated product of muscle, thus unequivocally identifying terminally differentiated mononucleated cells (Fig. 2).

In vitro, fusion and myosin synthesis are independently regulated but simultaneous phenomena (Paterson and Strohman, 1972; Chi *et al.,* 1975); however, *in vivo* these processes do not occur simultaneously, so it might be asked why the synthesis of myosin begins so early if multinucleated myotubes are not formed until days later. An additional problem is that the first attempts to grow somite explants in culture relied on multinucleation as a criterion for identification of differentiated muscle cells (Ellison *et al.,* 1969; Peirone *et al.,* 1977; Swalla and Solursh, 1984). These studies convincingly demonstrated that myotome cells can differentiate *in vitro,* in a cranio–caudal temporal succession as *in vivo* (Ellison *et al.,* 1969), and that different environmental conditions such as coculture with spinal cord (Peirone *et al.,*·1977) or epithelial tissue and cAMP (Swalla and Solursh, 1984) influenced the extent of differentiation. However, lack of immunohistochemical identification of differentiated mononucleated muscle cells

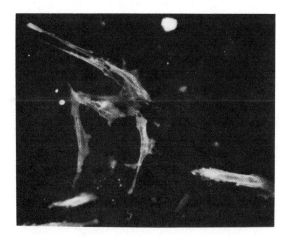

FIG. 2. Immunofluorescent photograph of a culture of somitic cells from 9-day-old mouse embryos, stained with an antimyosin antibody (Biral *et al.,* 1984). Note that only mononucleated cells are stained.

probably resulted in a consistent underestimation of the total extent of muscle differentiation.

In our own experience with cultures of mononucleated cells isolated from mouse somites, nerve cells were required to promote muscle differentiation but only with early somites (8 days). Older somitic cells will differentiate *in vitro* independently from the nerve, probably because they have already received a "signal" *in vivo* (Filogamo and Gabella, 1967). These data are in good agreement with those of Ellison *et al.* (1969), who showed that only late somites were able to differentiate in an *in vitro* aneural situation. The nerve effect must be mediated by soluble factors, as cells without nerve show similar differentiation than cells with nerve if they are cultured in the same dish (Vivarelli and Cossu, 1986).

We have subsequently obtained immunocytochemical evidence of heterogeneity among somitic cells with respect to the expression of myosin heavy-chain (MHC) isoforms. Contrary to what is generally believed (Bandman *et al.*, 1982; Bader *et al.*, 1982), proteins which cross-react with antibodies directed against slow MHC are expressed by a subpopulation of differentiated muscle cells (from 20 to 40% of total myosin-positive cells). This subpopulation apparently migrates to the limb, since it can be observed in cultures of limbs from 10-day and, to a lesser extent, 12-day-old embryos. Reactivity with these antibodies becomes extremely faint at 14 days of development and is no longer detectable at 16 days (Cossu and Whalen, unpublished), the earliest embryonic period from which myoblasts are usually isolated for *in vitro* studies. This would also explain why previous studies failed to detect slow myosins in cultures of myoblasts, with the notable exception of the work of Miller *et al.* (1985), who reported the presence of slow myosin in myotubes derived from early chick embryo myoblasts (see next section).

We also noticed that somitic cells from 10-day-old embryos form few multinucleated myotubes in the absence but practically none in the presence of nerve cells, even though the total extent of muscle differentiation is at this time comparable. Perhaps differences in the extracellular matrix synthesized in the two conditions influence cell movement, preventing the correct cell–cell contact required for fusion. Differentiation of somitic cells occurs only at high density. Attempts to obtain differentiation at low or even clonal density have so far been unsuccessful. Thus the cells of somites cannot differentiate in culture conditions which support differentiation of muscle cells from the limb. Clonal differentiation can be obtained from limbs of chick embryos older than 80 hours (stage 21: Bonner and Hauschka, 1974), and therefore, somitic cells and the first cells which migrate to the limb (before stage 21) require cell–cell contact (or other unidentified factors present in high-density cultures) unnecessary for even CMR I class of early myoblasts (see next section).

IV. Limb Colonization and Limb Cell Heterogeneity

It had long been debated whether or not the muscles of the limb derive from precursor cells which migrate from the somite into the limb bud. The quail–chick transplant experiment answered this question. Because of the different size of the nucleolus it is possible to distinguish quail from chick cells in histological sections, and because transplants of one species into the other are generally successful, it is possible to investigate the developmental origin and the migration patterns of different cell populations (Le Douarin, 1985). In 1977, it was reported that in transplants of quail somites to chick embryos, limb muscles were of quail origin, while cartilage and connective tissue were of chick origin (Chevalier et al., 1977, 1978; Christ et al., 1977). Migration of somitic cells to the limb took place after stage 14. In the absence of a similar cell marker, this question cannot be answered in mammals, but it may be that such an important developmental event has been conserved in evolution. What controls the proportion of cells which leave the somite relative to those cells which form the muscles of the body wall is not known. Also unknown is whether the cells which migrate to the limb differ from those which do not, or whether they are those which receive a chemotactic signal due to their more marginal position in the myotome.

The central role that the apical ectodermal ridge (AER) plays in this event is now well established (Saunders, 1948). This thick layer of ectoderm, present at the edge of the limb bud, is required in order to achieve correct development of the limb. Its early removal will stop further migration of myogenic cells and muscle pattern formation in the distal regions of the limb (Rutz and Hauschka, 1983). The situation may, however, be more complex: Grumpel-Pinot et al. (1984) have demonstrated, by quail–chicken transplant experiments, that only cells already in the limb will positively respond to the presence of the AER (i.e., they migrate) but somitic cells will not, suggesting that other signals, not provided by the AER, are required for migration from the somite to the proximal region of the limb.

Although our current understanding of the mechanisms which control limb colonization is very rudimentary (Jacob et al., 1982; Turner et al., 1983), we do know that the myogenic cells in the limb are not homogeneous. Bonner and Hauschka reported in 1974 that the morphology of the myogenic clones developed *in vitro* from early limb buds differs from those obtained from limbs of older embryos (see also Hauschka, 1974). No myotubes could be detected in clones of cells derived from embryos younger than stage 21 (3.5 days of development). After this stage, a few clones contained some flat oligonucleated small myotubes. From stage 25 these clones were progressively replaced by myogenic clones containing many large multinucleated myotubes, which by 11 days represented the great majority of all clonable cells of the limb. The early muscle colony-forming (MCF) cells required medium conditioned from muscle cell cultures, while the late MCF did not (White *et al.*, 1975).

Evidence that early-MCF cells are not the precursor of late-MCF cells came from a series of experiments which proved that (1) transplants of quail limb (at a stage when only early myogenic cells had migrated into it) into the flank or chorioallantoic membrane of chick embryos, fail to give rise to late myogenic cells; (2) successive subclones of early myogenic cells give only colonies with morphological characters of early muscle cells (Rutz and Hauschka, 1982; Seed and Hauschka, 1984). Thus at least two classes of myogenic cell precursors enter the limb and will generate a population of muscle cells which in turn will develop into the different limb muscles.

More recently, Fiszman and co-workers showed that myotubes derived from "early" myoblasts (6 days *in ovo*) synthesize high levels of myosin light-chain 2 of slow type and low levels of myosin light-chain 2 of fast type, whereas the situation is reversed in "late" myoblasts (9 days *in ovo*). Moreover, the myotubes obtained from early myoblasts synthesize a tropomyosin which consists of b^1, b^2, and a^2 (fast) subunits, while late myoblasts develop into myotubes which synthesize a tropomyosin made of b^1, b^2, a^1, and a^2 fast subunits (Toutant *et al.*, 1984; Mouly *et al.*, 1986).

Miller *et al.* (1985) reported the presence of slow myosin in some myotubes derived from "early" myoblasts but not in myotubes derived from "late" myoblasts.

Finally, in a recent series of experiments we have obtained preliminary evidence of differential sensitivity to tumor promoters among early and late myoblasts. Tumor promoters reversibly inhibit terminal differentiation of myoblasts (Cohen *et al.*, 1977), but not of satellite cells (Cossu *et al.*, 1983). This is described in detail in Section V on satellite cells. Unexpectedly, we have now observed that early myoblasts from both somites and limbs of 10- to 12-day-old mouse embryos are completely insensitive to tumor promoters. Cultures obtained from 14-day-old mouse embryos show increasing proportions of cells which do not differentiate in the presence of such drugs. At 16 days of embryonic development, >90% of cells appear sensitive to tumor promoters, as reported previously (Cossu *et al.*, 1983). Therefore, it appears that early myoblasts and satellite cells are resistant to these molecules, whereas only late myoblasts are inhibited to differentiate.

In conclusion, morphology, growth requirements, expression of slow isoforms of myosin, and differential sensitivity to tumor promoters clearly demonstrate that early myoblasts are a group of myogenic precursors distinct from late myoblasts. Moreover, they are probably not a single class of cells but show further heterogeneity. White *et al.* (1975) reported that while some clones derived from early myoblasts required continuous exposure to conditioned medium (CM) in order to differentiate, others needed only a transient exposure. Later Bonner reported that a third type, CMR (conditioned medium-requiring) III cells, required a contact with nerve in order to differentiate *in vitro* (Bonner, 1978, 1980; Bonner and Adams, 1982). In 1986, Miller and Stockdale reported that early myoblasts give rise to three types of clones: the myotubes developed in the first type of clones synthesize only fast myosin, those developed in the second type synthesize both fast and slow myosins, whereas those of the third type synthesize only slow myosin. As expected, clones derived from late myoblasts contained only fast myosin. They concluded that "myoblasts in the early embryo are an heterogeneous population committed to three myogenic lineages: fast, mixed and slow, whereas myoblasts in the later embryo are only in the fast myogenic lineage." We do not yet know whether these three classes of early myoblasts correspond to those described by White *et al.* (1975).

Inasmuch as these results were obtained in an *in vitro* aneural environment, they conclusively prove the existence of biochemical heterogeneity among different populations of myoblasts.

V. The Emergence and Differentiation of Satellite Cells

Since their discovery (Mauro, 1961), satellite cells have been the subject of intense investigation, inasmuch as these cells were recognized as possible stem cells in skeletal muscle after birth. They are usually identified by their typical location between the basal lamina and the sarcolemma of the contiguous muscle fiber. They possess a heterochromatic nucleus, and sparse cytoplasm with typical organelles (including centrioles) but not myofilaments. The morphological characteristics of satellite cells have been reviewed (Campion, 1984) and will not be discussed here.

In adult healthy animals, satellite cells are mitotically quiescent

(Schultz *et al.*, 1978). If explanted in tissue culture, they recapitulate myogenesis by undergoing a duplicative period followed by withdrawal from the cell cycle, fusion into multinucleated contractile myotubes, and activation of the synthesis of specific muscle gene products (Bischoff, 1974; Witkowski and Dubowitz, 1975; Yasin *et al.*, 1976; Jones, 1977; Kagawa *et al.*, 1978; Yaffe and Sazel, 1977; Cossu *et al.*, 1980). Since satellite cells behave in culture as "bona fide" myoblasts, we may ask the following questions: (1) Are satellite cells and myoblasts the same cells and, if so, what prevents satellite cells from fusing with a forming muscle fiber? (2) If satellite cells represent a different cell type, what is the biochemical basis of this difference and when do satellite cells segregate from the common myogenic lineage?

Work done in this laboratory during the past few years has provided answers to some of these questions. In 1977, Holtzer and his co-workers (Cohen *et al.*, 1977) reported that the tumor promoter tetradecanoyl phorbol acetate (TPA), reversibly inhibits differentiation of chick embryo skeletal myoblasts. However, we reported that satellite cells were capable of differentiating in the presence of concentrations of TPA which would block differentiation of myoblasts (Cossu *et al.*, 1983, 1985a). Since the mechanism of action of TPA has been partially elucidated in the last few years (Nishizuka, 1984; Berridge, 1984), we tried to understand the biochemical basis of the differential TPA sensitivity of myoblasts and satellite cells which is the first reported biochemical difference between these two cell types. TPA binds to and activates the calcium–phospholipid dependent protein kinase (protein kinase C), by substituting for diacylglycerol, the physiological activator of the enzyme, which is released by phosphoinositide turnover, following agonist binding to specific receptors. We reasoned that either Ca^{2+} or phosphatidylserine (PS), the phospholipid required for protein kinase C activation, might not be available to the enzyme in satellite cells, thus preventing activation by TPA. In fact, by increasing the PS concentration of satellite cell membranes by liposome-delivered PS, we found that sensitivity to TPA was restored. Ca^{2+} ionophores had no effect (Cossu *et al.*, 1986b). Thus at a certain developmental stage, when satellite cells diverge from other myogenic cells, some change in their phospholipid metabolism might reduce the PS concentration in the plasma membrane (or even domains thereof), thus preventing activation of protein kinase C by tumor promoters.

A different set of experiments led us to discover a second biochemical difference between satellite cells and myoblasts, namely, the expression of functional acetylcholine receptors (AChR) in undifferentiated satellite cells *in vitro*. During differentiation of chick embryonic myoblasts, AChR are first synthesized in postmitotic differentiated myoblasts and early myotubes (Fambrough and Rash, 1971). We reported, however, that dividing mouse satellite cells respond to iontophoretically applied ACh and bind iodinated bungarotoxin while embryonic myoblasts of the same species do not (Eusebi and Molinaro, 1984). In the same year, Siegelbaum *et al.* (1984) reported that "undifferentiated" myoblasts express functional ACh-dependent channels. These authors did not provide any evidence as to the "undifferentiated" state of the myoblasts. By a combination of immunocytochemical and electrophysiological techniques, we have now conclusively demonstrated that essentially all satellite cells express ACh channels while none of them bind antimyosin antibodies. On the contrary, the same percentage of embryonic myoblasts which expressed ACh channels also stained brightly with the antimyosin antibody, thus representing that fraction of the embryonic muscle cell population which was already differentiating *in vivo,* at the time of *in vitro* explantation. Since, on the other hand, all satellite cells of an adult healthy animal (see below) are quiescent *in vivo* (Schultz *et al.*, 1978), no differentiated cells are present on the first day of culture. Therefore, satellite cells express a differentiated muscle product (AChR) in an uncoordinated fashion with respect to contractile proteins (Cossu *et al.*, 1987). Preliminary data suggest that desmin might also be expressed in dividing cells from 18-day-old chick embryos (probably satellite cells: see below) and not in myoblasts from 10-day-old embryos (Yablonka-Rauveni and Nameroff, 1985).

As to the time of appearance of satellite cells during embryonic development, we assumed that, if satellite cells are TPA-resistant and myoblasts TPA-sensitive, the percentage of differentiation *in vitro* in the presence of TPA would reflect the emergence of TPA-resistant satellite cells *in vivo*. Through this indirect method, we showed that satellite cells appear between day 16 and 18 of embryonic development in the mouse (Cossu *et al.*, 1983) and between week 12 and 14 in the human (Cossu *et al.*, 1985a). These periods are earlier than previously believed on the basis of morphological analysis: in this case only mononucleated cells, lying beneath an already formed basal lamina, could be identified as satellite cells (Ontell, 1974; Schultz, 1976; Kelly, 1978), while the identity of single cells in more immature muscle remained uncertain.

Taken together, these data rule out the idea that satellite cells represent the latest differentiating cells of a homogeneous population of myoblasts, that fail to fuse simply because the muscle fiber is no longer competent to accept new cells (see also below). Since fusion is actively proceeding during this period, satellite cells should be a different cell type, whose fusion requirements are probably different from those of other myoblasts. Indeed, satellite cells keep proliferating and fusing, at a much slower rate than myoblasts, until somatic growth is over. By labeling muscle of growing animals with tritiated thymidine, Moss and Leblond (1970) demonstrated that satellite cells do divide *in vivo* and that, with time, they are incorporated into growing muscle fibers. This seems to be the most reasonable mechanism by which the number of nuclei of a growing fiber increases during postnatal development (Cardanis and Cooper, 1977; Ontell and Dunn, 1978), even though the nuclei of the fiber cannot themselves divide (Okazaki and Holtzer, 1966). It has been suggested by these authors that after a mitotic division of a satellite cell, one daughter cell would fuse with the muscle fiber, while the other would retain mitotic capacity and would contribute to the maintenance of a steady-state level of stem cells. With time, however, the equilibrium would shift toward a reduction of this stem cell compartment, since in aging animals satellite cells, though still capable of differentiation *in vitro,* are reduced both in number and in mitotic capacity (Allen *et al.,* 1982; Schultz and Lipton, 1982).

Besides their role in postnatal muscle development, satellite cells have been considered responsible for regeneration after different injuries such as trauma, denervation, and workload (Aloisi *et al.,* 1973; Schiaffino *et al.,* 1976; Snow, 1977; Ontell, 1974; Schultz, 1978; Hanzlikova *et al.,* 1975), or following degeneration in primary myopathies (Carlson, 1973; Snow, 1979). In these cases, histological examination of diseased muscle has revealed the presence of numerous mononucleated cells of different origins (satellite cells, granulocytes, macrophages, adipocytes, etc.) together with small immature myotubes, characterized by centrally located nuclei (Cullen and Mastaglia, 1980). These myotubes are considered to be derived from fusion of satellite cells and with time they would mature to normal muscle fibers. Formal proof of this fact was provided by several investigators who injected thymidine-labeled satellite cells into the muscle of healthy animals and demonstrated that these cells localize beneath the basal lamina of the muscle fibers and form new myotubes if the preexisting muscle is injured (Jones, 1979; Lipton and Schultz, 1979; Watt *et al.,* 1984).

Immunohistochemical analysis with antibodies against the different myosin isoforms has confirmed that the same isoform transition which occurs during development (Whalen *et al.,* 1981) is repeated during muscle regeneration (Sartore *et al.,* 1982). Eventually, in the case of primary myopathies, the newly formed fibers would express the same genetic defect of the previously degenerated fibers and follow the same fate, so that the process would continue until the proliferative capacity of satellite cells is exhausted and no further muscle cells are produced.

From these data it follows that satellite cells play two different roles: (1) as long as postnatal growth continues, they are a source of nuclei for the growing muscle fiber; (2) every time the muscle tissue is damaged they form new muscle fibers "*ex novo,*" this second function being performed from birth to senility. It should be noted that these two functions are quite different: in (1) satellite cells divide slowly, once a week in the period of maximal growth rate (Cardasis and Cooper, 1977), and part of the progeny would fuse with preexisting healthy muscle fiber; in (2), cells should divide quickly (Linkhart *et al.,* 1981), to prevent outgrowth of other nonmuscle cells, and part of the progeny should fuse with each other rather than with neighboring preexisting muscle fibers which might have survived degeneration.

At the moment we can speculate about two possible explanations: it may be that satellite cells respond to normal growth factors or hormones *in vivo* (Allen *et al.,* 1984; Kardami *et al.,* 1985; Bischoff, 1986a) by dividing at a slow rate and by producing fusion-competent cells which, in the absence of other myoblasts or early myotubes, would fuse with a muscle fiber. The same cell might respond to other factors, present in the injured tissue (Bischoff, 1986b), by dividing at a fast rate, thus producing a high number of fusion-competent myoblasts which would therefore fuse together to form new myotubes. An alternative explanation might reside in the existence of two populations of satellite cells, one capable of responding only to growth factors, the other also to "inflammatory" factors. The first population (growth satellite cells) would last until the end of somatic growth, the second (repair satellite cells) until senility.

The only indirect evidence for the existence of a possible biochemical heterogeneity between these two populations is represented by the fact that myotubes derived from adult satellite cells synthesize lower levels of α-actin than myotubes derived from satellite cells from newborn animals (Allen *et al.,* 1980).

It is difficult to envision direct experiments to solve this problem. Explanting and cloning satellite cells from adult animals should result in a population of "repair" cells only, while the same protocol should yield both "growth" and "repair" cells when applied to young animals. Unfortunately, cloning of these cells still requires very complex media (with serum and embryo extract), so that identification of specific responses to different mitogens might be very difficult. An alternative approach is the production of monoclonal antibodies that might recognize antigenic differences between these two populations and therefore allow their separation and characterization. A similar approach has already given preliminary but encouraging results in other laboratories (Walsh and Ritter, 1981; Wakshull et al., 1983; Lee et al., 1984). The fact that satellite cells are the only natural resource of dystrophic patients against muscle degeneration seems a sufficient reason to concentrate efforts to understand in detail the biochemistry and physiology of these cells.

VI. How Many Different Precursor Muscle Cells?

Hauschka and colleagues conclude their studies on the different precursors of muscle cells in the limb by hypothesizing that the early myogenic cells (which first migrate to the limb) act as positional cues for both fibroblasts and the successive late myogenic cells. It is known that the shaping of the limb into different muscle units is imposed by the connective tissue, that is, fibroblasts which create compartments in which the early muscle fibers develop. It remains to be explained what controls the organization of the fibroblast-derived extracellular matrix (Chiquet et al., 1981; Turner et al., 1983; Carrino and Caplan, 1986) to obtain the correct three-dimensional compartments necessary for the formation of the different muscles. The early myogenic cells may play this role as well as attracting late myogenic cells to form aggregates which will later develop into a muscle primordium. That would explain why relatively few early myogenic cells are needed, as compared to late myogenic cells which will give rise to the bulk of muscle tissue. As detailed in the next section, a first generation of fibers is later surrounded by a second generation of smaller fibers (Kelly and Zachs, 1969). During the development of the early muscle fibers, a third type of myogenic cell appears in the limb: the satellite cell. Early myogenic cells are not the precursor of late myogenic cells (Rutz and Hauschka, 1983), but the latter may generate satellite cells. However, because these cells show unequivocal biochemical differences from late myoblasts (i.e., TPA resistance and ACh sensitivity), they must be considered as a third, separate muscle cell precursor. In addition to these three major types of myogenic cells, further heterogeneity may be suspected on the basis of the data reported above.

Somitic cells show several peculiar features which set them apart from early myogenic cells: (1) in vivo these cells are mainly mononucleated myosin-positive differentiated cells, and their fusion capacity is extremely low in vitro; (2) none of these cells will give rise to muscle colonies upon cloning. We are presently investigating the differentiation pattern of these somitic cells in comparison to early myogenic cells of the limb to identify similarities and possible differences. Three subclasses of early myogenic cells are suggested by morphology, nerve, and CM requirements. The evidence for the existence of these three subclasses (with the exception of the nerve dependence of CMR III) was not conclusive; however, the recent report by Miller and Stockdale (1986) that different clones derived from early myoblasts express slow, slow-fast, or fast myosins clearly shows the existence of three subclasses of these cells. It is not yet known whether they correspond to the subclasses previously identified on the basis of the cultural parameters described above.

Finally, on a purely speculative basis, we would like to propose the existence of two classes of satellite cells: "growth" satellite cells, present only in the muscle of growing animals, and "repair" satellite cells, present throughout all postnatal life (see Section V on satellite cells). While the physiological significance of these two classes of satellite cells is obvious, the interpretation of the different developmental roles of different precursors of somite and early limb cells is difficult to envisage (see also Stockdale and Miller, 1987). Yet the complexity of the spatial and temporal events required to produce the correct patterns of skeletal muscles in higher vertebrates is such that this heterogeneity would not be surprising.

In conclusion we present a scheme of muscle cell precursor heterogeneity which holds true on present evidence (with the exception of the two classes of satellite cells) and might be corrected or expanded by further investigation.

1. *Somitic Cells:* Differentiated, mononucleated (Holtzer *et al.*, 1957), nonclonable, resistant to tumor promoters (Cossu *et al.*, unpublished observations).
2. *Early Myoblasts:* Require CM in order to differentiate at clonal density (White *et al.*, 1975); form small oligonucleated myotubes (Bonner and Hauschka, 1974); resistant to tumor promoters (Cossu *et al.*, unpublished observations). They can be divided thus:
   CMR I (require continuous presence of CM)
   CMR II (require brief exposure to CM)
   CMR III (require nerve contact: Bonner and Adams, 1982)
   ALSO
   Fast (synthesize only fast myosin)
   Mixed (synthesize both types of myosin)
   Slow (synthesize only slow myosin: Miller and Stockdale, 1986)
3. *Late Myoblasts:* Differentiate in fresh medium at clonal density (White *et al.*, 1975); form large multinucleated myotubes (Bonner

and Hauschka, 1974) which synthesize exclusively fast myosin (Miller and Stockdale, 1986). Differentiation is inhibited by tumor promoters (Cohen et al., 1977). Express AChR after differentiation (Fambrough and Rash, 1971).

4. *Satellite Cells:* Differentiate in fresh medium at clonal density (Schultz and Lipton, 1982); form large multinucleated myotubes (Witkowski, 1977). They are resistant to tumor promoters (Cossu *et al.*, 1983); express functional AChR while still duplicating and undifferentiated (Cossu et al., 1986b). They might consist of two specialized classes:

Growth (slow division, fuse with growing healthy muscle fibers)

AND

Repair (fast division, fuse mainly only with other satellite cells)

VII. Muscle Cell Heterogeneity and Primary Myopathies

Skeletal muscle of patients or animals affected by primary myopathies is characterized by the coexistence of apparently healthy, normal-looking fibers and of other fibers showing, to a various extent, the signs of a degenerative process (Cullen and Mastaglia, 1980). Even when the disease is in an advanced state, severely impairing the movements and the life of the subject, a number of muscle fibers seem unaffected by the disease. Each of the muscle cells carries the mutated gene responsible for the disease, and yet some apparently do not express it. It is difficult to explain why such a gene should be expressed only in a subpopulation of muscle fibers, and at the same time alter the phenotype of cells other than muscle such as lymphocytes, erythrocytes, and fibroblasts (Lucy, 1980).

Theories relating muscle degeneration to vascularization or innervation abnormalities have been almost completely abandoned (Rowland, 1980), and it is therefore very unlikely that certain fibers degenerate because of problems in their blood vessels or nerves. Consequently, fibers must differ from each other in ways which correlate with the differential involvement in muscular dystrophy but not with known metabolic and physiological heterogeneity of muscle tissue.

Different populations of myogenic cells may contribute in variable proportions to the histogenesis of each fiber within a developing muscle. Muscle fibers do not form simultaneously, but rather in successive periods of embryogenesis. In rodents, for example, a first generation of myotubes develops at about 15 or 16 days *post coitum,* whereas secondary myotubes, surrounding the first ones, form in the following days (Kelly and Zachs, 1969). It has been reported by Kelly and Rubinstein (1980) that these first fibers contract slowly and indeed possess a slow-type complement of myosins (note, however, that slow contraction

mainly depends on a poorly developed sarcoplasmic reticulum: Boland
et al., 1974), at least until innervation is established and dictates its
own program to the muscle fiber. Slow myosin is found in subpopulations of early myoblasts in the limbs (Miller *et al.*, 1985) and even in
the somite (Cossu and Whalen, unpublished). If "slow" is a "nerve-
independent" character of some early myoblasts and of the first generation of fibers, it may be that these cells do indeed fuse into such fibers.
Let us suppose that certain fibers are mainly formed by early
myoblasts, whereas others mostly derive from late myoblasts and still
others (i.e., the ones which are still very small at birth: Ontell and
Dunn, 1978) are predominantly made from satellite cells. Inasmuch as
these different cell types express a different genetic program, some
might express or depend on high levels of the product of the mutated
gene, while others might possess alternative biochemical pathways
which render the product of the mutated gene more dispensable. In
consequence, fibers mainly composed of the former cells would be more
severely affected by the mutation than fibers derived from the latter
cells. An important corollary of this argument is that satellite cells and
no other myogenic cells should be the ones more severely affected. In
fact muscle tissue is apparently normal at birth and for a short period
thereafter, when the contribution of satellite cells to muscle development is still minimal. After this period most satellite cells proliferate
and fuse with growing muscle fibers to reach (in certain cases) up to
90% of the total nuclei within a fiber. It is at this point that the disease
first appears and, furthermore, since regeneration is completely in the
charge of satellite cells, the process would become irreversible. In other
words, only the fibers composed mainly of myoblasts would survive
degeneration and in time would become the apparently healthy fibers
of dystrophic muscle.

Here again, lack of suitable biochemical or immunological markers
leaves this discussion at a purely speculative level. One approach to
this problem was represented by the analysis of cultured satellite cells
from dystrophic muscle. However, it was long believed that, since dystrophic muscle cells appear quite normal *in vitro,* they would not represent a useful model for studying the pathogenesis of these diseases.
Muscle cells do not mature *in vitro* up to a stage when the disease is
expressed *in vivo*; also, it was postulated that factors required for the
expression of the disease (e.g., nerve supply and work overload) would
not be present in culture (Witkowski, 1977).

However, in the last years, several laboratories have shown clear
abnormalities in dystrophic myotubes developed *in vitro* from satellite
cells isolated from dystrophic patients, chickens, and mice (Yasin *et al.*,

1979; Thompson, 1980; Meril et al., 1981; Ettienne et al., 1981; Ionas-escu et al., 1981; Young et al., 1981; Hutchinson et al., 1984; Miranda et al., 1985; Cossu et al., 1984, 1985b, 1986a). So far, it has not been established if and how these abnormalities relate to the expression of the mutated genes (for a recent review, see Witkowski, 1986).

So far, only satellite cells from diseased muscle have been investigated: studies on myotubes derived from dystrophic myoblasts have not been performed, due to technical difficulties of culturing cells from embryos which do not show phenotypic differences from their normal siblings. Cloning satellite cells from Duchenne dystrophic muscle (Blau et al., 1983) revealed that a percentage (increasing with patient's age) of myogenic clones was formed by cells showing altered morphology and lower mitotic activity. The possibility therefore exists that only a subpopulation of myogenic cell precursors is affected in Duchenne muscular dystrophy. Obviously, other investigations on different developmental stages or on different forms of muscular dystrophy will be necessary in order to understand how general this phenomenon may be.

As one of the many possible alternative approaches, single fibers can be isolated and studied (Bekoff and Betz, 1977a,b; Zuurveld et al., 1984), but these studies have focused on physiological analysis or biochemical characterization of contractile proteins. Total proteins of individual normal fibers could also be analyzed on two-dimensional gels. While studies on diseased tissues are often misleading because of secondary degenerative events, identification of biochemical heterogeneity, independent from contractile proteins, might represent an informative approach (Young and Davey, 1981).

Biochemical definition of affected and resistant fibers would constitute a valuable result in the effort to elucidate the pathogenesis of these diseases.

VIII. Conclusions and Future Perspectives

In this chapter we have focused on two main objectives: (1) to show that heterogeneity exists among myogenic cells and (2) to suggest that this heterogeneity may play an important role in both muscle histogenesis and pathology.

Knowledge of the molecular nature of factors influencing muscle cell proliferation and differentiation is still very preliminary. Specific mitogens are now being characterized (Kardami et al., 1985; Bischoff, 1986b), and myogenic cells have been shown to respond to known growth factors such as fibroblast growth factor or somatomedins (Linkhart et al., 1981; Ewton and Florini, 1980), but the regulation of proliferation in these cells is far from being understood. Therefore, response to specific growth factors cannot yet be used to evaluate myogenic cell heterogeneity. Similarly, no differentiation factors such as nerve growth factor have been conclusively identified, and even the trophic role of nerve in molecular terms is far from clear.

Nevertheless, we hope that putting together most of the available data might suggest other experiments to fill the existing gaps. For example the production of monoclonal antibodies which might recognize certain myogenic cells but not others, and the analysis by two-dimensional gel electrophoresis of total proteins synthesized by myogenic clones from different developmental stages (including satellite cells). These approaches, as well as many others which are presently tried in other laboratories (e.g., transformation of different myogenic cells with temperature-sensitive mutants of retroviruses: M. Fiszman, personal communication), may give us biochemical and immunological markers to define fibers derived from certain myogenic cells, and thus show which cells form which fibers and how and when this process occurs *in vivo*. The same markers will tell us whether or not any embryological relationships exist between different myogenic cells and healthy and affected fibers in muscular dystrophies. If this is indeed the case, then simple comparison of different biochemical pathways in normal muscle fibers derived from different myoblasts might shed new light on the biochemical defects of muscular dystrophies.

ACKNOWLEDGMENTS

We wish to thank Drs. Marc Y. Fiszman, Donald A. Fischman, and Stefano Alemà for helpful discussions and critical reading of the manuscript. The work done in this laboratory was partially supported by M.P.I. 40% (Gruppo Citomorfologia) and by Progetto d'Ateneo "Neuromuscular development *in vivo* and *in vitro*."

REFERENCES

Abbot, J., Schiltz, J., Dienstman, S., and Holtzer, H. (1974). *Proc. Natl. Acad. Sci. U.S.A.* **71,** 1506–1510.
Allen, E., and Pepe, F. (1966). *Am. J. Anat.* **116,** 115–148.
Allen, R. E., McAllister, P. K., and Masak, K. C. (1980). *Mech. Ageing Dev.* **13,** 105–109.
Allen, R. E., McAlister, P. K., Masak, K. C., and Anderson, G. R. (1982). *Mech. Ageing Dev.* **20,** 377–383.
Allen, R. E., Dodson, M. V., and Luten, L. J. (1984). *Exp. Cell Res.* **152,** 154–160.
Allen, T. D., and Dexter, T. M. (1982). *Differentiation* **21,** 86–94.
Aloisi, M., Mussini, I., and Schiaffino, S. (1973). *Basic Res. Myol.* **292,** 338–345.
Alter, B. P., Weinberg, R. S., Golberg, J. D., Jackson, B. T., Piasecki, G. J., Lipton, J. M., and Nathan, D. G. (1983). *In* "Globin Gene Expression and Hemopoietic Differentiation" (G. Stomatoyapoulos and A. W. Nieuhis, eds.), pp. 431–442. Liss, New York.
Bader, D., Masaki, T., and Fischman, D. A. (1982). *J. Cell Biol.* **95,** 763–770.
Bandman, E. (1985). *Int. Rev. Cytol.* **97,** 97–131.

Bandman, E., Matsuda, R., and Strohman, R. C. (1982). *Dev. Biol.* **93**, 508–518.

Barton, P. J., and Buckingham, M. E. (1985). *Biochem. J.* **231**, 249–261.

Beapain, D., Martin, D., and Dieteleu-lievre, F. (1979). *Blood* **53**, 212–225.

Bekoff, A., and Betz, W. J. (1977a). *J. Physiol. (London)* **271**, 25–40.

Bekoff, A., and Betz, W. J. (1977b). *J. Physiol. (London)* **271**, 537–547.

Berridge, M. J. (1984). *Biochem. J.* **220**, 345–360.

Bignami, A., and Dahl, D. (1984). *J. Histochem. Cytochem.* **32**, 473–476.

Biral, D., Damiani, E., Margreth, A., and Scarpino, E. (1984). *Biochem. J.* **224**, 923–931.

Bischoff, R. (1974). *Anat. Rec.* **180**, 645–657.

Bischoff, R. (1986a). *Dev. Biol.* **115**, 129–139.

Bischoff, R. (1986b). *Dev. Biol.* **115**, 140–147.

Blau, H. M., Webster, C., and Pavlath, R. (1983). *Proc. Natl. Acad. Sci. U.S.A.* **80**, 4856–4860.

Boland, R., Martonosi, A., and Tillack, T. (1974). *J. Biol. Chem.* **249**, 612–623.

Bonner, P. H. (1978). *Dev. Biol.* **66**, 207–219.

Bonner, P. H. (1980). *Dev. Biol.* **76**, 79–86.

Bonner, P. H., and Adams, T. R. (1982). *Dev. Biol.* **90**, 175–184.

Bonner, P. H., and Hauschka, S. D. (1974). *Dev. Biol.* **37**, 317–328.

Buchthal, F., and Schmalbruch, H. (1980). *Physiol. Rev.* **60**, 90–143.

Buckley, P. A., and Konigsberg, I. R. (1977). *Proc. Natl. Acad. Sci. U.S.A.* **74**, 2031–2035.

Butler, J., Cosmos, E., and Brierley, J. (1982). *J. Exp. Zool.* **224**, 65–80.

Butler-Brown, G. S., Bugainski, L. B., Cuonloud, S., Schwartz, K., and Whalen, R. G. (1982). *Nature (London)* **299**, 830–833.

Campion, D. R. (1984). *Int. Rev. Cytol.* **87**, 221–225.

Caplan, A. I., Fiszman, M. Y., and Eppenberger, H. M. (1983). *Science* **221**, 921–927.

Cardasis, C. A., and Cooper, G. W. (1977). *J. Exp. Zool.* **191**, 347–358.

Carlson, B. M. (1973). *Am. J. Anat.* **37**, 119–150.

Carrino, D. A., and Caplan, A. I. (1986). *In* "Molecular Biology of Muscle Development" (C. Emerson *et al.*, eds.), pp. 117–131. Liss, New York.

Chevallier, A., Kieny, M., and Mauger, A. (1977). *J. Embryol. Exp. Morphol.* **41**, 245–258.

Chevallier, A., Kieny, M., and Mauger, A. (1978). *J. Embryol. Exp. Morphol.* **43**, 263–278.

Chi, J. C. H., Rubinstein, N. A., Strah, K., and Holtzer, H. (1975). *J. Cell Biol.* **67**, 523–530.

Chiquet, M., Eppenberger, H. M., and Turner, D. C. (1981). *Dev. Biol.* **88**, 220–235.

Christ, B., Jacob, H. J., and Jacob, M. (1977). *Anat. Embryol.* **150**, 87–101.

Cohen, R., Pacifici, M., Rubinstein, N., Biehl, J., and Holtzer, H. (1977). *Nature (London)* **266**, 538–539.

Cossu, G., Zani, B., Coletta, M., Bouchè, M., Pacifici, M., and Molinaro, M. (1980). *Cell Differ.* **9**, 357–368.

Cossu, G., Molinaro, M., and Pacifici, M. (1983). *Dev. Biol.* **98**, 520–524.

Cossu, G., Eusebi, F., and Molinaro, M. (1984). *Muscle Nerve* **7**, 73–76.

Cossu, G., Cicinelli, P., Fieri, C., Coletta, M., and Molinaro, M. (1985a). *Exp. Cell Res.* **160**, 403–411.

Cossu, G., Eusebi, F., Senni, M. I., and Molinaro, M. (1985b). *Dev. Biol.* **110**, 362–368.

Cossu, G., Adamo, S., Senni, M. I., Caporale, C., and Molinaro, M. (1986a). *Biochem. Biophys. Res. Commun.* **137**, 752–758.

Cossu, G., Senni, M. I., Eusebi, F., Giacomoni, D., and Molinaro, M. (1986b). *Dev. Biol.* **118**, 182–189.

Cossu, G., Eusebi, F., Grassi, F., and Wanke, E. (1987). *Dev. Biol.,* in press.
Cudennec, C. A., Thiery, J. P., and LeDouarin, N. (1981). *Proc. Natl. Acad. Sci. U.S.A.* **78,** 2412–2416.
Cullen, M. J., and Mastaglia, F. L. (1980). *Br. Med. Bull.* **36,** 145–152.
Dessauki, D. A., and Hibbs, R. G. (1965). *Am. J. Anat.* **116,** 525–566.
Devlin, B. H., and Konigsberg, I. R. (1983). *Dev. Biol.* **95,** 175–192.
Dienstman, S. R., and Holtzer, H. (1977). *Exp. Cell Res.* **107,** 355–364.
Ellison, M. L., Ambrose, E. J., and Easty, G. C. (1969). *J. Embryol. Exp. Morphol.* **21,** 341–346.
Engel, W. K. (1974). *Neurology* **24,** 344–348.
Ettienne, E. M., Swartz, K., and Singer, R. H. (1981). *J. Biol. Chem.* **256,** 6408–6412.
Eusebi, F., and Molinaro, M. (1984). *Muscle Nerve* **7,** 488–492.
Ewton, D. Z., and Florini, J. R. (1980). *Endocrinology* **106,** 577–583.
Falcone, G., Alemà, S., and Tatò, F. (1984). *EMBO J.* **3,** 1327–1331.
Fambrough, D. M., and Rash, J. E. (1971). *Dev. Biol.* **26,** 55–68.
Filogamo, G., and Gabella, G. (1967). *Arch. Biol.* **78,** 9–16.
Fischman, D. A. (1974). *Curr. Top. Dev. Biol.* **5,** 235–256.
Gumpel-Pinot, M., Ede, D. A., and Flint, O. P. (1984). *J. Embryol. Exp. Morphol.* **80,** 105–125.
Hanzlikova, V., Machova, E. V., and Anik, P. C. (1975). *Cell Tissue Res.* **160,** 411–428.
Hauschka, S. D. (1974). *Dev. Biol.* **37,** 345–358.
Hauschka, S. D., Lim, R., Clegg, C., Chamberlain, J., Bulinski, L., and Linkhart, T. (1985). *In* "Gene Expression" (R. Strohman and S. Wolf, eds.), Vol. 182, pp. 113–122.
Henderson, L. P., and Spitz, N. C. (1985). *Dev. Biol.* **113,** 381–387.
Holtzer, H., Marshall, J. M., and Finch, H. (1957). *J. Biophys. Biochem. Cytol.* **3,** 705–724.
Holtzer, H., Weintraub, H., Mayne, R., and Mochan. B. (1972). *Curr. Top. Dev. Biol.* **7,** 229–256.
Holtzer, H., Rubinstein, N. A., Yeoh, G., Chi, J., Birnbaum, J., and Okaiama, M. (1975). *Q. Rev. Biophys.* **8,** 523–577.
Hutchinson, C. J., Desmon, A., and Yasin, R. (1984). *Exp. Biol. Med.* **9,** 108–114.
Ikeda, A., Abbott, R. L., and Langman, J. (1968). *J. Embryol. Exp. Morphol.* **19,** 193–202.
Ionasescu, V., Monaco, L., Sandra, A., Ionasescu, R., Burneister, L., Depasse, C., and Stern, L. Z. (1981). *J. Neurol. Sci.* **50,** 249–257.
Jacob, M., Jacob, H. J., and Christ, B. (1982). *In* "Limb Development and Regeneration" (R. O. Kelley, P. F. Goetinck, and J. A. McCabe, eds.), pp. 313–322. Liss, New York.
Jockush, H., Muller, U., Jockush, B. M., and Deschner, H. (1984). *Exp. Biol. Med.* **9,** 121–125.
Johnson, G. R., and Moore, M. A. S. (1975). *Nature (London)* **258,** 726–728.
Jones, H. (1977). *Exp. Cell Res.* **107,** 111–117.
Jones, H. (1979). *Exp. Neurol.* **66,** 602–610.
Kagawa, T. E., Chikata, J., Tani, J., and Tsutamme, T. (1978). *Dev. Biol.* **65,** 526–530.
Kardami, E., Spector, D., and Strohman, R. C. (1985). *Dev. Biol.* **112,** 353–358.
Kahn, M. A. (1976). *Prog. Histochem. Cytochem.* **8,** 1–48.
Kelly, A. M. (1978). *Dev. Biol.* **65,** 1–10.
Kelly, A. M., and Rubinstein, N. A. (1980). *Nature (London)* **288,** 266–269.
Kelly, A. M., and Zachs, S. I. (1969). *J. Cell Biol.* **224,** 123–169.
Laing, N. G., and Lamb, A. H. (1983a). *J. Embryol. Exp. Morphol.* **78,** 53–66.
Laing, N. G., and Lamb, A. H. (1983b). *J. Embryol. Exp. Morphol.* **78,** 67–82.
Langman, J., and Nelson, G. R. (1968). *J. Embryol. Exp. Morphol.* **19,** 217–226.
Le Douarin, N. A. (1985). *Cell* **38,** 353–360.

Lee, H. U., Kaufman, S. A., and Coleman, J. R. (1984). *Exp. Cell Res.* **152,** 341–347.
Linkhart, T., Clegg, C., and Hauschka, S. J. (1981). *J. Supramol. Struct.* **14,** 483–497.
Lipton, B. H., and Schultz, E. (1979). *Science* **205,** 1292–1294.
Lucy, J. A. (1980). *Br. Med. Bull.* **36,** 187–192.
Mauro, A. (1961). *J. Biophys. Biochem. Cytol.* **9,** 493–495.
Meril, M., Grey, R., Chauvin, P., and Appell, S. (1981). *Proc. Natl. Acad. Sci. U.S.A.* **78,** 648–652.
Miller, J. B., and Stockdale, F. E. (1986). *Proc. Natl. Acad. Sci. U.S.A.* **83,** 3860–3864.
Miller, J. B., Crow, M. T., and Stockdale, F. E. (1985). *J. Cell Biol.* **101,** 1643–1650.
Miranda, A. F., Mongini, T., and Di Mauro, S. (1985). *Adv. Cell Cult.* **4,** 1–45.
Moss, F. P., and Leblond, C. P. (1970). *J. Cell Biol.* **44,** 459–462.
Mouly, V., Toutant, M., and Fiszman, M. Y. (1987). *Cell Differ.* **20,** 17–25.
Nadal-Ginard, B. (1978). *Cell* **15,** 855.
Nishida, H., and Satoh, N. (1985). *Dev. Biol.* **110,** 450–454.
Nishizuka, Y. (1984). *Nature (London)* **308,** 693–698.
Obinata, T., Yamamoto, M., and Muruyaka, K. (1966). *Dev. Biol.* **14,** 192–213.
Okazaki, K., and Holtzer, H. (1966). *Proc. Natl. Acad. Sci. U.S.A.* **56,** 1484–1488.
Ontell, M. (1974). *Anat. Rec.* **178,** 211–228.
Ontell, M., and Dunn, R. F. (1978). *Am. J. Anat.* **152,** 539–556.
Paterson, B., and Strohman, R. (1972). *Dev. Biol.* **29,** 113–138.
Peirone, S., Sisto-Daneo, L., and Filogamo, G. (1977). *J. Submicrosc. Cytol.* **9,** 311–314.
Pette, D., and Vrbova, G. (1985). *Muscle Nerve* **8,** 676–689.
Phillips, W. D., and Bennett, M. R. (1984). *Dev. Biol.* **106,** 457–468.
Prizblisky, R. J., and Blumberg, J. M. (1966). *Lab. Invest.* **15,** 863–872.
Robinson, M. K., Smith-Quinn, L. B., and Nameroff, M. (1984). *Differentiation* **26,** 112–120.
Rowland, L. P. (1980). *Muscle Nerve* **3,** 3–20.
Rutz, R., and Hauschka, S. D. (1982). *Dev. Biol.* **91,** 103–110.
Rutz, R., and Hauschka, S. D. (1983). *Dev. Biol.* **96,** 366–374.
Sartore, S., Gorza, L., and Schiaffino, S. (1982). *Nature (London)* **298,** 294–296.
Saunders, J. W., Jr. (1948). *J. Exp. Zool.* **108,** 363–404.
Schiaffino, S., Pierobon-Bormioli, S., and Aloisi, M. (1976). *Virchows Arch. B Cell Biol.* **21,** 113–118.
Schultz, E. (1976). *Am. J. Anat.* **147,** 49–70.
Schultz, E. (1978). *Anat. Rec.* **190,** 299–312.
Schultz, E., and Lipton, B. H. (1982). *Mech. Ageing Dev.* **20,** 378–383.
Schultz, E., Gibson, M. C., and Champion, T. (1978). *J. Exp. Zool.* **206,** 451–456.
Seed, J., and Hauschka, S. D. (1984). *Dev. Biol.* **106,** 389–394.
Siegelbaum, S. A., Trautman, A., and Koenig, J. (1984). *Dev. Biol.* **104,** 366–379.
Smith-Quinn, L. B., and Nameroff, M. (1983a). *Differentiation* **24,** 111–123.
Smith-Quinn, L. B., and Nameroff, M. (1983b). *Differentiation* **24,** 124–130.
Smith-Quinn, L. B., Nameroff, M., and Holtzer, H. (1984). *Exp. Cell Res.* **154,** 65–82.
Smith-Quinn, L. B., Holtzer, H., and Nameroff, M. (1985). *Nature (London)* **313,** 692–694.
Snow, M. K. (1977). *Cell Tissue Res.* **185,** 399–408.
Snow, M. K. (1979). *In* "Muscle Regeneration" (A. Mauro, ed.), pp. 91–100. Raven, New York.
Stockdale, F. E., and Miller, J. B. (1987). *Dev. Biol.,* in press.
Swalla, B. J., and Solursh, M. (1984). *J. Embryol. Exp. Morphol.* **79,** 243– 265.
Temple, S., and Raff, M. C. (1986). *Cell* **44,** 773–779.
Thompson, E. J. (1980). *Br. Med. Bull.* **36,** 181–185.

Toutant, M., Montarras, J., and Fiszman, M. Y. (1984). *Exp. Biol. Med.* **9,** 10–15.
Turner, D., Lawton, J., Dollenmaier, P., Ehrismann, R., and Chiquet, M. (1983). *Dev. Biol.* **95,** 497–504.
Vivarelli, E., and Cossu, G. (1986). *Dev. Biol.* **117,** 319–325.
Wakshull, E., Bayne, E. K., Chiquet, M., and Fambrough, D. M. (1983). *Dev. Biol.* **100,** 464–477.
Walsh, F. S., and Ritter, M. A. (1981). *Nature (London)* **289,** 60–64.
Watt, D. J., Morgan, J. E., and Partridge, T. A. (1984). *Muscle Nerve* **7,** 741–750.
Whalen, R. G. (1985). *J. Exp. Biol.* **115,** 43–53.
Whalen, R. G., Sell, M., Butler-Brown, G. S., Schwartz, K., Bouver, P., and Pinset-Harmstrom, I. (1981). *Nature (London)* **292,** 805–810.
White, N. K., Bonner, P. H., Nelson, R., and Hauschka, S. D. (1975). *Dev. Biol.* **44,** 346–357.
Witkowski, J. A. (1977). *Biol. Rev.* **52,** 431–476.
Witkowski, J. A. (1986). *Muscle Nerve* **9,** 283–298.
Witkowski, J. A., and Dubowitz, V. (1975). *J. Neurol. Sci.* **26,** 203–220.
Yablonka-Rauveni, Z., and Nameroff, M. (1985). *J. Cell Biochem. Suppl.* **9B,** 43.
Yaffe, D., and Saxel, O. (1977). *Nature (London)* **270,** 725–727.
Yasin, R., Van Beers, G., Bulien, D., and Thompson, E. J. (1976). *Exp. Cell Res.* **102,** 405–408.
Yasin, R., Van Beers, G., Riddle, P. N., Brown, D., Widdowson, G., and Thompson, E. J. (1979). *J. Cell Sci.* **38,** 201–210.
Young, O. W., and Davey, C. L. (1981). *Biochem. J.* **195,** 317–327.
Young, R. B., McConnell, D. G., Snelter, C. M., and Phillips, T. A. (1981). *Muscle Nerve* **185,** 399–408.
Zuurveld, J. G. E., Veerkamp, J. H., and Wirtz, P. (1984). *J. Biochem.* **16,** 1107–1124.

CHAPTER 10

IMMUNOLOGICAL ASPECTS OF IMPLANTATION AND FETAL SURVIVAL: THE CENTRAL ROLE OF TROPHOBLAST

W. D. Billington

REPRODUCTIVE IMMUNOLOGY GROUP
DEPARTMENT OF PATHOLOGY
UNIVERSITY OF BRISTOL
THE MEDICAL SCHOOL
BRISTOL BS8 1TD, ENGLAND

I. Introduction

The attachment of the blastocyst to the wall of the uterus represents the beginning of a unique association between two genetically disparate organisms. Foremost among the many problems that this association brings is that of avoiding the induction of a maternal immune response against any embryonic cell surface molecules not shared by the female host. These are primarily either embryo-specific molecules, expressed at one or more particular stages of differentiation, or those encoded by the paternally inherited genes of the embryo. The maternal immune system has the potential to recognize these foreign antigens and to mount a destructive immunological attack, predominantly of a cell-mediated nature through its effector T-lymphocyte populations. It is the study of the expression of cell surface antigens on the developing embryo and the extent of the maternal immune reaction to them that has occupied the main attentions of several workers in our laboratory in recent years.

Because the immunological rejection of experimentally and clinically transplanted allogeneic (genetically disparate) tissues has been recognized to be due largely to responses against the major histocompatibility complex (MHC) antigens, it is these antigens that have been studied in the context of the fetomaternal relationship. There is, however, a certain amount of evidence to implicate other antigen systems, and these will be considered later in this review.

209

II. MHC Antigen Expression on the Developing Embryo

Although there have been many studies on a variety of embryonic cells at different stages of gestation (see Kirkwood and Billington, 1981), it is relevant here to consider only the trophectoderm of the blastocyst and its descendant trophoblast populations. Apart from certain extraembryonic membranes (see later), trophoblast is the only fetal tissue in direct, unbroken, and continual contact with the maternal environment throughout gestation. During this time it undergoes extensive proliferation and differentiation, leading to the formation of biologically differing subpopulations in the mature placenta and placental bed.

It is widely accepted that few, if any, maternal immunocompetent cells are able to penetrate the placental (trophoblastic) barrier and gain entry to the developing fetus during normal pregnancy (see Adinolfi, 1975). There is no vascular continuity between mother and fetus, their circulatory systems remaining entirely independent. The central issue is whether the trophoblastic barrier tissues express MHC or other antigens capable of being recognized and reacted against. Current immunological dogma implies that recognition of *any* foreign cell surface antigen requires this to be in association with self-MHC (class I) antigen(s). If this holds true for maternal recognition of foreign antigens on trophoblast, then an absence of class I MHC antigens on this fetal tissue would prevent its destruction by immune responses directed against any antigen system. It is therefore crucial to establish whether or not class I MHC antigens are present on the cell surface of each form of trophoblast throughout its development and differentiation. This has not proved to be an easy task and has depended on the availability of congenic strains of animals, highly specific immunological reagents, appropriate and sensitive assays, and a detailed knowledge of placental morphogenesis.

A. MOUSE TROPHOBLAST

Early studies in this laboratory and elsewhere employed polyspecific reagents and strains of mice differing at multiple histocompatibility loci. These are of historical interest only and have been documented in a recent review (Billington and Bell, 1983a; see also Table I). Although the advent of monoclonal antibodies (mAb) has provided the means of overcoming most (but not all) of the problems of specificity, there are still some difficulties in relation to the unequivocal identification of some of the minor populations of trophoblast. In the absence of definitive trophoblast-specific cell markers, reliance has for long been placed

TABLE I

HISTOCOMPATIBILITY ANTIGENS ON MOUSE TROPHOBLAST

Developmental stage	Class I MHC	Class II MHC	Non-MHC
Trophectoderm	$-^a$	−	+
Ectoplacental cone			
Giant cells	−	−	+
Diploid core	+	ND^b	+
Early differentiating placental trophoblast	+	ND^b	ND^b
Nonplacental trophoblastic giant cells	−	ND^b	ND^b
Mature placenta			
Labyrinthine trophoblast	$-^c$	−	ND^b
Spongiotrophoblast	+	−	ND^b
Trophoblastic giant cells	−	ND^b	ND^b

^{a} There is a transient expression of class I MHC antigens on the trophectoderm which is lost following blastocyst activation.
^{b} Not determined.
^{c} Conflicting evidence (see text).

upon morphological and tinctorial properties of this tissue. There are now mAb with apparent specificity for human trophoblast (Johnson *et al.*, 1981; Sunderland *et al.*, 1981a) but none as yet for the mouse. Those for human trophoblast still have certain limitations and require careful double-labeling procedures with anti-MHC mAb.

Current understanding of MHC antigen expression on mouse trophoblast has been derived from two different experimental approaches. The first involves the short-term culture (usually 12–72 hours) of early embryos or placental cell suspensions *in vitro*. The second is the autoradiographic localization of the binding sites of radiolabeled mAb injected into the pregnant female. The main conclusions to have emerged are that non-MHC antigens are probably expressed throughout the developmental history of trophoblast (Sellens *et al.*, 1978), class II MHC (Ia) antigens are not expressed at any stage on any trophoblastic population (Jenkinson and Searle, 1979; Chatterjee-Hasrouni and Lala, 1981), and class I MHC (H-2) antigens appear on diploid trophoblast cells of the early postimplantation embryo and are expressed on certain trophoblast cells in the mature placenta (Sellens *et al.*, 1978; Jenkinson and Owen, 1980). The trophoblastic giant cell populations (primary, secondary, and tertiary) have no expression of class I, nor probably class II, MHC antigens (Table I).

The most important finding has been the detection of paternally inherited H-2 specificities on the surface of defined placental trophoblast populations. This was first reported by Jenkinson and Owen (1980), using both polyspecific and monoclonal antipaternal antibodies as probes on cultures of dissected fragments of spongiotrophoblast and labyrinthine trophoblast. The former is a compact cellular trophoblastic tissue in direct contact with maternal decidual cells, while the latter is a thin trilaminar membranous component separating the fetal blood vessels and mesenchymal tissues from the maternal blood sinuses and constituting the major site of fetomaternal physiological exchange. Jenkinson and Owen identified significant levels of labeling only on the spongiotrophoblast cultures. This differential expression was also reported by Wegmann and colleagues (Wegmann, 1981; Singh et al., 1983), who demonstrated localization of injected radiolabeled monoclonal anti-H-2K^k (antipaternal strain) antibody on the spongiotrophoblast. Similar radiolabeled antibody-binding studies by Lala and co-workers have produced somewhat conflicting results. Their early report (Chatterjee-Hasrouni and Lala, 1982) claimed that localization was restricted to the labyrinthine region and not on the spongiotrophoblast. Later studies, however, indicated that binding could be identified on both spongiotrophoblast and labyrinthine trophoblast (Colavincenzo and Lala, 1984, 1985). Differences in the experimental protocols and particularly in the timing of the autoradiographic evaluation may explain these discrepancies. It is conceivable that the failure of Jenkinson and Owen to detect antigen expression on the labyrinthine trophoblast may be related to much lower epitope densities in this region and the lower sensitivity of the mixed hemadsorption (red cell binding) and immunofluorescence assays that they employed.

Whatever the precise level of the differential expression of class I MHC antigens on the mouse placental trophoblast subpopulations proves to be, the studies summarized above have demonstrated that these antigens are present and accessible to the maternal circulation in vivo. There had previously existed the possibility that antigens detectable on cells in vitro may not be represented on the apical surface of the same cells in vivo (Jenkinson and Billington, 1974a), as seen in the polarization of H-2 antigens on various adult epithelial lining cells (Parr and Kirby, 1979). The implications of these findings are that trophoblast nonantigenicity is no longer an acceptable hypothesis to explain the lack of immunological rejection of the murine allogeneic conceptus and that there must exist some other mechanism(s) to counteract any potentially deleterious maternal immune reponse (see below).

B. RAT TROPHOBLAST

We have demonstrated that MHC antigen expression on rat placental trophoblast mirrors closely that seen in the mouse (Billington and Burrows, 1986). Using an allospecific mouse antirat class I MHC monoclonal antibody in an indirect immunoperoxidase labeling assay on cryostat sections, strong specific staining was obtained on the spongy-zone trophoblast in direct contact with maternal decidual cells. In contrast, no staining was observed on the labyrinthine trophoblast nor on the trophoblastic giant cells (Fig. 1). None of the trophoblastic cell populations at any stage of gestation were reactive with a mAb against class II antigens. The use of a monoclonal xenoantibody directed against rat RT1[a] molecules allowed the unequivocal detection of paternally inherited class I antigens on the spongy-zone trophoblast, identified histologically by counterstaining the sections. This immunohistological approach had been attempted previously on mouse placen-

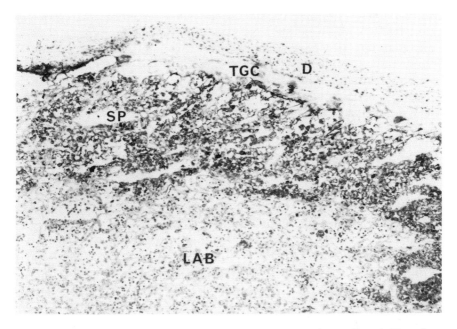

FIG. 1. Paternal class I MHC antigen expression on rat placental trophoblast. Immunoperoxidase staining of cryostat section of rat placenta with a mouse monoclonal antibody to rat RT1[a] antigen reveals strong specific labeling of spongy-zone trophoblast (SP) and no reaction on either labyrinthine trophoblast (LAB) or trophoblast giant cells (TGC) adjacent to maternal decidua (D). For details see Billington and Burrows (1986).

tal tissues. However, despite numerous technical modifications, it proved impossible to overcome the problems of nonspecific staining with mouse mAb and high endogenous immunoglobulin levels in the mouse placenta.

C. HUMAN TROPHOBLAST

There is wide agreement that the syncytiotrophoblast of the human placental chorionic villus is devoid of MHC antigens. The earlier reports of Goodfellow et al. (1976) and Faulk et al. (1977) have been confirmed repeatedly, using mAb in immunoperoxidase or immunofluorescence labeling studies on cryostat sections of term placentas (see Sunderland et al., 1981a; Faulk and McIntyre, 1983). This is a crucial feature, since the syncytiotrophoblast provides a major fetal interface and is continuously bathed by maternal blood. From this finding stemmed the belief that nonexpression of class I antigens alone could explain the survival of the fetal allograft (Barnstable and Bodmer, 1978). However, Sunderland and his colleagues (1981b) reported the detection of HLA-A, B, and C antigens on the proliferating extravillous cytotrophoblast of the 6-week chorionic sac. Several workers have subsequently examined the nonvillous cytotrophoblast populations of the placenta, placental bed, and amniochorionic membrane, and have also detected HLA antigen expression. The definitive identification of these human trophoblastic populations has been assisted by the use in immunohistology of mouse mAb against syncytiotrophoblast microvillous membrane preparations (Bulmer et al., 1984), although we still lack an antibody capable of reacting with all trophoblastic cells.

At first sight it would appear that there is a differential expression of MHC antigens on different human trophoblast populations comparable to that seen in the mouse and rat placenta. However, the situation is not so clear-cut. First, those immunohistological studies that have led to HLA antigen detection have employed mAb (mainly W6/-32) directed only against the monomorphic (framework) determinants of the class I molecule (Sunderland et al., 1981b; Faulk and McIntyre, 1983; Bulmer and Johnson, 1985). Second, not all mAb directed against monomorphic determinants are reactive on cytotrophoblast cells (Hsi et al., 1984; Wells et al., 1984). Third, there is a report that four different mAb directed against polymorphic determinants of the class I molecule specific for the fetal allotype showed no reactivity against trophoblast (Redman et al., 1984). It may therefore be that W6/-32 identifies an incomplete or aberrant class I molecular structure on the trophoblast, as suggested by recent preliminary biochemical characterization of the antigen on the trophoblast cells of the amniochorion

(Sargent et al., 1986). This could result from genetic deletion of part of the molecule, such as the terminal α_1 domain of the HLA-A, B, C heavy-chain structures. Alternatively, the molecule may be some form of differentiation antigen analogous to those encoded by the mouse Qa complex. It is an important task to determine the precise nature of the molecular structure identified by W6/32. Should it be confirmed that nonvillous trophoblast fails to express class I antigens of paternal specificity or expresses only a differentiation antigen that is not recognized by the maternal immune system, this would provide a simple explanation for placental and thus fetal survival, at least in humans. It is likely that the question will only be answered with the application of the techniques of molecular genetics, enabling gene sequencing and mapping.

In this context it is noteworthy that a unique class I (Pa) antigen has been identified on the rat placenta (Ghani et al., 1984).

III. Trophoblast Susceptibility to Immune Attack

The evidence cited above implies that mouse trophoblast should provide a target for immune-mediated attack in vivo. This patently does not occur in normal pregnancy. Although this is almost certainly because the pregnant female does not generate an effective antipaternal MHC response (Billington et al., 1983), owing to the inhibitory influence of immunomodulating agents (see below), it cannot provide a complete explanation for the survival of the trophoblast. This is evident from the observation that pregnancy is unaffected by the experimental induction of a strong specific sensitization directed against the paternal alloantigens of the fetus (Mitchison, 1953; Taylor, 1973).

It is difficult to design suitable experiments to assess trophoblast susceptibility in vitro owing to the problems associated with the isolation and purification of trophoblast cells (see Loke, 1983). These have defeated the efforts of countless workers for more than three decades and arise from the fact that there are different subpopulations in intimate and complex cellular association with maternal tissues. The existence of a substantial trophoblast population in the form of a tortuous sheet of multinucleate syncytium is obviously a major obstacle to obtaining satisfactory target cells for in vitro assays, especially since this is a terminally differentiated population incapable of cell division. The chorionic plate of the term placenta may provide a more fruitful source of separated trophoblast cells (Khalaf et al., 1985). From the evidence available, it is clear that human trophoblast is extremely resistant to both antibody and cell-mediated immune lysis. Only by pretreatment with neuraminidase and incubation with experimentally sensitized effector cells, such as interferon-boosted natural killer (NK) cells, has trophoblast been shown to exhibit any significant susceptibility (Paul and Jailkhani, 1982; Pross *et al.*, 1985). This could well be an important factor in its *in vivo* survival.

Although fewer studies have been carried out to determine the *in vitro* susceptibility of mouse trophoblast, a relatively clear picture has emerged. The early proliferating ectoplacental cone trophoblast is resistant to immune attack (Jenkinson and Billington, 1974b), but populations of trophoblast that develop subsequently express histocompatibility antigens and become susceptible. Significant antipaternal cytotoxic cell killing of cultures obtained from the placenta during the later stages of its morphogenesis has been demonstrated (Smith, 1983a; Table II). Dissected populations of spongiotrophoblast from the mature placenta are especially susceptible. Immune cell lysis of the labyrinthine trophoblast occurs to a lesser degree and could be due to contaminating fetal mesenchymal cells (Smith, 1983a). These studies employed mouse strain combinations differing at both *H-2* and non-*H-2* loci and require confirmation using H-2 congenic strains. It is, however, likely that the killing is directed against paternal H-2 antigens, since the onset of susceptibility correlates precisely with the time of first appearance of MHC antigens on the trophoblast (Jenkinson and Owen, 1980). In addition, strong cytotoxic cell killing primarily re-

TABLE II

In Vitro SUSCEPTIBILITY OF MOUSE TROPHOBLAST TO
IMMUNE CELL LYSIS[a]

Target tissue[b]	Number of cultures	Cytotoxicity (% ± 1 SD)
Whole placenta	10	28.1 ± 17.5
Spongiotrophoblast	10	34.3 ± 11.8
Labyrinthine trophoblast	7[c]	30.2 ± 18.6
Fetal fibroblasts	10	65.1 ± 19.5

[a] Data from Smith (1983a).
[b] All target cells prepared from 13-day conceptus and incubated for 48 hours (after overnight plating out) with spleen cells from H-2 + non-H-2 incompatible immunized donor.
[c] Of 10 cultures, 3 showed no cytotoxic killing, hence the overall mean for the 10 labyrinthine trophoblast cultures is significantly lower than this 30% level.

quires recognition of H-$2D$ and H-$2K$ regions of the MHC rather than non-H-2 antigens, which normally evoke weak cytotoxic activity (Bach et al., 1976).

Taken together, studies on mouse trophoblast indicate that it should present a recognizable and potentially susceptible target in vivo in the later stages of pregnancy. It must therefore be assumed that its survival in presensitized females is assured by some factor(s) that interferes with the maternal effector cell–trophoblast membrane interactions necessary for target cell damage. This issue is considered below.

IV. Pregnancy-Induced Maternal Immune Responses

It is necessary to establish the precise nature and extent of the maternal immune responses to the developing embryo. This will provide information on the differences that must exist between the pregnant female and the recipient of a tissue or organ allograft where classical rejection reactions involving cytotoxic (T_c) cells and cytotoxic alloantibodies are generated. The salient point to emerge from innumerable studies is that pregnancy is not consistently associated with the elicitation of either humoral or cellular immunity against paternally inherited fetal transplantation antigens. There are therefore immunoregulatory factors operating to divert the maternal immune responses away from the expected forms.

A. ANTIPATERNAL ALLOANTIBODIES

Our own detailed analysis of the alloantibody response in murine pregnancy has shown that this has several characteristic features (Bell and Billington, 1980, 1981, 1983; Roe and Bell, 1982; Bell, 1984). The antipaternal antibodies are (1) present only in a few inbred strains, either H-2^b or H-2^b derived; (2) induced only in second or later pregnancies; (3) predominantly non-complement-fixing IgG_1 subclass; (4) directed against a very restricted number of potentially immunogenic H-2 specificities; and (5) unable to inhibit allogeneic mixed-lymphocyte reactions or T_c killing of allogeneic fibroblast targets. Many of these features have subsequently been reported for rat pregnancy sera, although the precise nature of the antibodies varies according to the particular strain combinations examined (Smith et al., 1982). Human pregnancy sera contain anti-HLA lymphocytotoxic antibodies but only in a minority of primiparous women and in no more than about half of all pregnancies (Jonker et al., 1977).

B. CELL-MEDIATED IMMUNITY

Numerous reports have documented changes in maternal lymphocyte reactivity both during and after allogeneic pregnancy. The picture is a rather confusing one, since the information has accumulated from different species and a wide variety of *in vivo* and *in vitro* assays using lymphocytes from spleen, regional lymph nodes, and peripheral blood. The most important feature is that there is no convincing evidence for the generation of antipaternal cytotoxic T cells either in mouse (Billington *et al.*, 1983; Smith and Chappell, 1984) or in human pregnancy (Sargent and Redman, 1985).

V. Immunogenic Stimulus in Pregnancy

What is the source of the immunogenic material that induces pregnancy-associated immune responses? For many years it was assumed that fetal lymphocyte leakage was the explanation for the presence of anti-HLA antibodies in human maternal sera. However, only the use of the fluorescence-activated cell sorter (FACS) has provided acceptable evidence for this phenomenon (Herzenberg *et al.*, 1979). No such evidence has been obtained for any other species, so transplacental lymphocyte traffic in species other than human is generally believed to be minimal or nonexistent.

Since transfer of soluble fetal MHC antigen, even if shown to occur, is unlikely to lead to the observed maternal responses, it is possible that the alloantigen-bearing trophoblast may be involved. In the mouse, the spongiotrophoblast lies adjacent to the maternal decidua basalis, where populations of maternal Ia antigen-bearing dendritic cells have been identified (Jenkinson and Searle, 1979; Searle *et al.*, 1983). These dendritic cells appear to be in a favorable position for the presentation of paternal alloantigens to the maternal immune system.

Experimental evidence has been provided for the immunogenicity of the placenta (Billington and Bell, 1983b; Bell and Billington, 1986). Recipient virgin female mice have been challenged by injections of cell suspensions prepared from the placenta or the fetus and the responses compared to those produced by adult spleen cells (Table III). While both fetal and placental cells induced alloantibodies, only the placental cells elicited antibodies with all the characteristics of those seen in normal pregnancy. This suggests that the spongiotrophoblast is the effective immunogen, although this needs to be confirmed using injections of the specific subpopulation dissected from the placenta. Other studies have shown that spongiotrophoblast, unlike labyrinthine trophoblast and fetal fibroblasts, is incapable of inducing primary cyto-

TABLE III

COMPARISON OF ALLOANTIBODIES INDUCED BY PREGNANCY AND BY
ADULT AND FETAL CELL IMMUNIZATION OF VIRGIN FEMALE MICE[a,b]

Immunogenic stimulus	Total alloantibody[c]: titer[e] (range)	Cytotoxic antibody[d] (% target cell kill)
Pregnancy	1/1819 (1513–2188)	Undetectable
Adult spleen cells	1/5763 (4402–7545)	83 ± 6%
Fetal cells	1/4080 (2822–5897)	74 ± 5%
Placental cells	1/1445 (946–2208)	Undetectable

[a] Data from Bell and Billington (1986).
[b] C57BL mice challenged with (C57BL × CBA) F_1 cells.
[c] Determined by mixed hemadsorption assay.
[d] Complement-dependent spleen cell cytotoxicity assay.
[e] Logarithmic transformation of data.

toxic effector cell activity in an *in vitro*-sensitization system (Smith, 1983b). There are two possible explanations for this result. There is either an absence of maternal antigen-presenting cells in these preparations (indeed every effort is made to avoid decidual cell contamination), or there is some form of inhibition by soluble immunosuppressive agents liberated by the trophoblast itself, as indicated in other studies (Kouttab *et al.*, 1976; Pavia and Stites, 1981).

It may be tentatively concluded that spongiotrophoblast provides the immunogenic challenge in normal mouse pregnancy. The anatomically analogous extravillous cytotrophoblast of the human placenta may provide a stimulus additional to that of the fetal lymphocytes. The absence of class II MHC antigens from trophoblast is relevant in this context, since it is known that pretreatment with allogeneic cells lacking these antigens renders recipients less responsive to stimulation by normally strongly immunogenic cells from the same source (Welsh *et al.*, 1977).

VI. Immunoregulatory Mechanisms for Maternal Responses

Numerous immunoregulatory factors have been proposed for a role in the control of the maternal antifetal immune responses of pregnancy. If, as suggested above, spongiotrophoblast alone is able to elicit all the characteristics of the maternal response, it would obviate the need for any factors other than those of trophoblastic origin. The literature on this subject is extensive, conflicting, and confusing. To a considerable extent, this is because few workers have asked themselves whether the experimental systems that they have employed are relevant to the question of the regulation of the inductive or the effector phase of the maternal immune response. The issues at stake are the way in which the female is prevented from generating a rejection response in normal pregnancy and the reason for the nonrejection of the trophoblast in a presensitized female. The first must involve agents that modify afferent and/or central immune responses, whereas the second concerns those that inhibit effector actions. Although there are appropriate assays to distinguish between these two levels of response, many of them involve *in vitro* analysis and their relevance to events *in vivo* can always be questioned.

The early hypotheses on maternal immunoregulation related to the suppression of cell-mediated effector cells by a wide variety of "blocking factors" in the maternal serum, including antipaternal alloantibodies, steroid and protein hormones, and other pregnancy-associated macromolecules. Since anti-class I antibodies occur in a minority of pregnancies, these clearly cannot have an essential function. Nor indeed might any antibodies, since agammaglobulinemic (B-cell-depleted) mice are able to reproduce normally (Rodger, 1985). Since cytotoxic cells are not generated in normal pregnancy, none of these so-called blocking agents can in this situation be relevant in the inhibition of effector cell activity. Only in the experimentally presensitized female would it be necessary to invoke this form of efferent inhibition.

A. REGULATION OF INDUCTIVE PHASE OF MATERNAL IMMUNE RESPONSE

Current hypotheses on the mechanisms responsible for the suppression or diversion of potentially deleterious antifetal immunity revolve largely around the activity of soluble factors elaborated by the placenta (more specifically, the trophoblast) or of lymphocytic cells within the maternal decidual tissues. Studies on the mouse placenta have revealed the ability of different soluble factors to influence a wide variety of *in vitro* and *in vivo* responses against MHC and other antigen systems (Chaouat *et al.*, 1985; Duc *et al.*, 1985; Chaouat, 1987). Chaouat and colleagues are currently attempting the purification and biochemical characterization of these regulatory molecules. Conclusive proof that they are of trophoblastic origin is, however, still required.

There has been, appropriately, a move away from the idea that regulation of the maternal immune response occurs at the systemic level. It would not make evolutionary sense for the pregnant female to be systemically immunosuppressed and therefore unduly susceptible to infections at the very time when the perpetuation of the species is at stake.

A second form of local intrauterine immunoregulation has been proposed by Clark (1985). It involves the accumulation of a novel type of non-T-lymphocyte suppressor cell population at the implantation site. These cells are reported to be capable of inhibiting both the induction and expression of maternal antipaternal cytotoxic lymphocyte (CTL) responses through the action of a soluble suppressor factor that blocks the response of T cells to interleukin 2. Our earlier studies showing that mouse decidual cell cultures and supernatants exert a regulatory effect on lymphocyte responses *in vitro* (Kirkwood and Bell, 1981; Badet *et al.*, 1983) could be at least partially interpreted on the basis of a low level of such suppressor cell "contamination" of the decidual tissue.

B. REGULATION OF EFFECTOR CELL ACTIVITY

In addition to the placentally derived and suppressor lymphocyte factors described above, there are many of the pregnancy-associated maternal serum molecules that can inhibit cytotoxic effector cell activity. Of these, the molecules that occur in all pregnant females (and in every species examined) and are non-antigen specific are likely to prove of most relevance. It would appear to be a better evolutionary ploy to link the production of an essential immunoregulatory molecule to the physiological state of pregnancy irrespective of the genetic status of the individual fetus. In these terms, the steroid hormone progesterone or the serum protein α_2-macroglobulin have much to commend them. Both have been shown to be capable of inhibiting the killing of fetal cells *in vitro* by CTL (Szekeres-Bartho *et al.*, 1985; Badet, 1984). Both occur in all mammalian species.

The proposed immunoregulatory pathways in the maternofetal relationship are illustrated diagrammatically in Fig. 2.

VII. Are Immunoregulatory Factors Essential for Successful Pregnancy?

Both local and systemic regulatory molecules clearly occur in the pregnant female. One or more of these must be responsible for the diversion of the maternal immune response away from a classical rejection reaction toward what Voisin (1980) refers to as an enhancing or facilitatory reaction. This is an interesting pregnancy-related phenomenon that could prove of considerable importance for the manipulation of the immune response to human tissue and organ allografts, for example by the treatment of patients with the purified regulatory agents. However, since it is known that experimentally induced classical effector elements have no deleterious effect on the survival of the embryo, the prevention of their generation in normal pregnancy can-

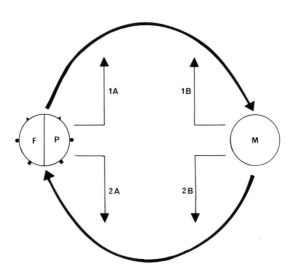

FIG. 2. Hypothetical immunoregulatory controls in the maternofetal relationship. M, Mother; F, fetus; P, placenta. (1) Regulatory factors of placental (1A) or maternal (1B) origin inhibiting induction of maternal antifetal rejection reaction (afferent modulation). (2) Regulatory factors of placental (2A) or maternal (2B) origin blocking the effect of any cell-mediated immune reaction against fetoplacental target antigens (efferent blocking).

not be regarded as an essential phenomenon. One is then forced to return to a consideration of those factors preventing the recognition and/or destruction of the potentially vulnerable fetal target cells. Since maternal lymphocyte traffic across the placenta and into the fetus appears restricted to few, if any, cells, and then only toward the end of gestation, these targets must be the trophoblast populations bearing appropriate antigens, together with certain extraembryonic membranes (see below). The susceptibility of the trophoblast is thus the central issue.

We do not know whether trophoblast represents a susceptible target *in vivo.* As indicated earlier, although some forms of mature mouse trophoblast undergo immune cell lysis *in vitro,* human trophoblast is highly resistant, even when subjected to severe osmotic and thermal stress (Paul *et al.,* 1980). Even though mouse spongiotrophoblast is destroyed by cytotoxic effector cells (Table II), it is a relatively much poorer target (34% cell death) than fibroblasts prepared from the same conceptus (65% cytotoxicity) (Smith, 1983a). The different conditions pertaining *in vivo,* especially in relation to membrane turnover kinetics, may render the trophoblast totally invulnerable to antibody or immune cell lysis. This would be the simplest explanation for the survival of the allogeneic fetus. It would involve no immunoregulatory mechanisms whatsoever or, at most, those related to the self-protecting synthesis of trophoblast factors that might act to inhibit antigen recognition either directly by physical masking or indirectly by interaction with the maternal effector cells. The CTL and NK cell-inhibiting factors isolated from the mouse placenta (Chaouat *et al.,* 1985) would come into this last category.

The reductionist hypothesis, that immunoregulation is not required, may be difficult to disprove. This would be hard to accept for those who are wedded to the dogma that maternal immune recognition of the implanting embryo and the generation of a protective response is essential for successful pregnancy. It would also be impossible to reconcile with the view that failure of immunoregulatory control is causally related to reproductive disorders, especially human recurrent spontaneous abortion (Taylor and Faulk, 1981). The recent evidence that spontaneous embryo resorption in a particular mouse strain combination (CBA/J♀ × DBA/2J♂) can be significantly reduced by active and passive immunization procedures (Wegmann, 1984) would appear to support the theory of immunoregulation, although this experimental animal model requires more detailed investigation. It is in any case not strictly comparable with the human condition since it involves only partial litter loss.

VIII. The Maternofetal Interface: Other Aspects

In addition to the trophoblast populations of the placenta and the placental bed, there are other fetal elements that have direct contact with maternal tissues. These are certain extraembryonic fetal membranes, exemplified by the human amniochorion and the mouse yolk sac, that are potentially capable of being recognized and reacted against by maternal effector cells.

The chorionic cells of the human amniochorion are cytotrophoblastic and lie between the fetal amniotic mesenchymal cells and the maternal decidua parietalis. The cytotrophoblastic cells appear from immunohistological observations to be heterogeneous as judged by their reactivities with a panel of mAb (Bulmer and Johnson, 1985). Although some of these cells bind W6/32, none of them appear to stain with 61/D2, a mAb directed against a different monomorphic determinant on class I molecules (Hsi *et al.*, 1984). As with the placental extravillous trophoblast, this indicates the presence of a truncated or aberrant class I molecule rather than a classical HLA-A, B, or C antigen. The W6/32-positive cells are unlikely to prove susceptible to immune cell lysis *in vitro*: there seems no reason to invoke any immunoregulatory mechanism to explain their survival in close association with maternal decidual tissue.

In the second half of gestation in the mouse, the layer of trophoblast cells surrounding the conceptus in the nonplacental region degenerates, together with the acellular Reichert's membrane, to expose the outer (endodermal) surface of the yolk sac to the uterine wall. These yolk sac endodermal cells have been isolated as a purified population and used as targets in antibody and cell-mediated cytotoxicity assays (Jenkinson and Billington, 1974a; Jenkinson *et al.*, 1975). They showed significant susceptibility *in vitro*, but *in vivo* they appear to lack expression of MHC antigens on their apical surface (Parr *et al.*, 1980). It is also unclear whether maternal effector cells are able to gain access to the uterine lumen across the re-formed uterine epithelium in the vicinity of the yolk sac membrane.

In summary, the available evidence indicates that whatever the nature of the fetal cells providing the interface with the maternal tissues, trophoblastic or endodermal in the two most extensively studied species of human and mouse, they commonly, but not invariably, exhibit some degree of resistance to lysis *in vitro* and may be completely nonsusceptible *in vivo*.

IX. Relevance of Nonhistocompatibility Antigen Systems

All of the studies reviewed so far have been carried out within the framework of a consideration of the relevance of classical transplantation, and especially the class I and class II MHC, antigen systems. This is to be expected in view of the known role of the MHC in allogeneic cell recognition and rejection mechanisms. In the mouse, the non-H-2 antigens are relevant, since tissue rejection occurs between MHC-compatible strains with minor histocompatibility antigen differences. However, there is also a body of evidence implicating other cell surface antigen systems in rejection phenomena.

In situations of MHC compatibility or where tissues are devoid of MHC antigens, other antigen systems can be recognized (Matsunaga and Ohno, 1980). The MHC antigen-deficient human syncytiotrophoblast and very likely the rodent labyrinthine trophoblast could come into this category. There is also increasing evidence that organ-specific and tissue-specific molecules are involved in allograft rejection reactions (Lalezari, 1980; Lordon *et al.*, 1981), so trophoblast-specific antigens could play a role.

A. TROPHOBLAST-SPECIFIC ANTIGENS

The existence of trophoblast-specific antigens was first suggested by the finding that heterologous antisera to placental tissues induced abortion when administered to pregnant animals. More convincing evidence has been provided by the production of heterologous and, more recently, monoclonal antibodies to separated trophoblastic cell populations or trophoblast plasma membrane preparations. A rabbit antimouse ectoplacental cone trophoblast antiserum has been used in immunoperoxidase and immunofluorescence assays to demonstrate the presence of antigen(s) restricted to the pre- and early postimplantation mouse trophoblast and the two major trophoblast populations of the mature placenta (Searle and Jenkinson, 1978; Searle *et al.*, 1981). There does not yet appear to be a mAb specific for mouse trophoblast. Numerous groups have raised polyclonal or monoclonal antibodies against human syncytiotrophoblast plasma membranes and studied their patterns of reactivity in immunohistology (see Searle *et al.*, 1981; Faulk and Hsi, 1983; Johnson, 1984). A few of the membrane antigens have been characterized biochemically (Brown *et al.*, 1983; Davies and Browne, 1985a; Webb *et al.*, 1985).

B. ANTITROPHOBLAST ANTIBODY FORMATION IN PREGNANCY

There is evidence that the human trophoblast membrane antigens are recognized by the maternal immune system. This was first claimed by Hulka and his colleagues (1961, 1963), although the immunofluorescence assay employed did not provide convincing evidence of trophoblast-specific antibodies in maternal serum. Davies (1985a) has now developed a novel enzyme-linked immunosorbent assay (ELISA) for the detection of these antibodies using immobilized syncytiotrophoblast membrane vesicles as antigen. This assay is able to detect IgG and IgM antitrophoblast antibodies in normal human pregnancy. IgG antibody is detectable in the earliest serum samples obtained (5 weeks after the last menstrual period), is maximal during the first trimester, and declines progressively thereafter. IgM antibody peaks early and disappears by the tenth week of gestation. The kinetics of the responses are comparable in second pregnancies, but the mean antibody levels are substantially lower than in primiparous women (Davies and Browne, 1985b,c). The decline in antibody levels during the second and third trimesters of pregnancy has been shown to be due to the formation of immune complexes (Davies, 1985b,c). Preincubation of the maternal serum with protein A–Sepharose followed by treatment with 1 M glycine and neutralization with NaOH allows isolation and dissociation of the complexes and determination of the total antitrophoblast antibody activity in the ELISA. The levels of immune complexes remain fairly constant throughout pregnancy, indicating the continued formation of antitrophoblast antibody. Analysis of the immune complexes revealed the presence of five major proteins (M_r 2 × 10^6, 400,000, 150,000, 13,000, <10,000). That they were of trophoblastic origin was shown by their reactivity in the ELISA with affinity-purified antitrophoblast antibody and their similarities to the proteins obtained following nonionic detergent solubilization of the syncytiotrophoblast plasma membrane. Although trophoblast antigen shedding has been claimed previously (O'Sullivan et al., 1982), this is the first demonstration that this leads to immune complex formation.

What are the possible implications of the induction of maternal antitrophoblast antibodies? They are detectable in most human pregnancies and contribute to the formation of immune complexes. Both, however, occur chiefly during the first pregnancy and early in the second. This suggests that some form of suppression takes place, perhaps mediated by suppressor memory cells or by the regulatory influence of the immune complexes, or even the development of an autoanti-idiotypic antibody control (see Singal et al., 1984). The antitrophoblast antibodies could act as blocking agents for the protection of the placenta but this is open to the same criticisms as those leveled at alloantibodies. It would be necessary to demonstrate that the trophoblast membrane antigens were capable of stimulating cytotoxic T-cell formation in vivo and of rendering the syncytiotrophoblast potentially susceptible to their lytic activity. The first would require class II MHC-bearing antigen-presenting cells and T-helper cell differentiation, and the second, a form of trophoblast–cytotoxic cell interaction not necessitating class I MHC recognition.

An immunoregulatory system based on non-MHC trophoblast antigens, as originally proposed by Faulk and colleagues (1978) on the basis of an identified trophoblast–lymphocyte cross-reactive (TLX) antigen system, has, however, still to be considered. The TLX antigens are suggested to be polymorphic (McIntyre and Faulk, 1982), but there is as yet no evidence that they stimulate a maternal immune response. They appear to be different from those described by Davies and Browne (1985a); the latter elicit maternal antibodies that show no diminution of activity after absorption with pooled peripheral blood lymphocytes (Davies, 1985a). Further information is clearly required on trophoblast

membrane-associated molecules and their involvement in fetomaternal immunological interactions.

X. Immunological Aspects of Pregnancy Failure

As mentioned earlier, there is a long-standing hypothesis that maternal recognition of foreign antigens on the implanting embryo is an
essential requirement for successful pregnancy. This has usually been
formulated in rather vague terms and with stated or implied reference
to histocompatibility antigens. The successful implantation and development of embryos in matings between syngeneic mice would then
require an extension of the concept to tissue-specific or embryo stage-
specific (differentiation) antigens. Unless maternal antibodies were in
some way necessary for the regulation of embryonic cell differentiation
and development, for which there is little or no evidence, the hypothesis must be considered in terms of a protective immune (blocking)
response against another potentially damaging one. But it must be
appreciated that there would be no need for the first response in the
absence of the second!

Faulk and colleagues have developed the concept in a more defined
way to offer an explanation for the important clinical problem of recurrent spontaneous abortion (see Faulk and McIntyre, 1983). They postulate that it is maternal recognition of trophoblast, not classical histocompatibility antigens, that is the key feature. If these antigens (the
TLX antigens mentioned earlier) are common to the lymphocytes of
both husband and wife, then for this system the embryo would be
compatible with the mother. This could result in lack of recognition
and subsequent spontaneous abortion, presumably mediated by conventional immunological effector pathways elicited by the inevitable
HLA incompatibilities between mother and embryo. Their reasoning
led to the first immunotherapeutic treatment of recurrent spontaneous
abortion based on immunization of mothers with incompatible (third
party) leukocytes (Taylor and Faulk, 1981). Other groups employing
an immunotherapeutic approach have used only the husband's leukocytes (Beer et al., 1981; Mowbray et al., 1985). The fact that comparable
levels of success have been achieved makes it difficult to sustain a
uniform hypothesis. The use of syncytiotrophoblast plasma membranes (which lack MHC antigens) as the immunogen would enable a
clear distinction to be made between the possible involvement of TLX
or HLA antigens.

An alternative explanation has been proposed for the success of
leukocyte treatment of abortion-prone women (Davies, 1986). This is
based upon the detection of two nonspecific immunosuppressive factors

that are present in normal serum but maintained in an inactive state by association with a third molecule, a novel protein termed pregnancy-depleted immunoregulatory factor (pdIRF) (Davies and Browne, 1985d,e). Depletion of pdIRF in normal pregnancy results in activation of the immunosuppressive factors, which are then presumed to play an important, but as yet undefined, role in preventing rejection of the embryo. The failure of the abortion-prone woman to initiate depletion of pdIRF would lead to lack of activation of the immunosuppressive factors and subsequent pregnancy failure. Leukocyte infusions could then be seen as a stimulus for pdIRF depletion and hence maintenance of the pregnancy. This hypothesis, though speculative, reconciles several conflicting aspects of the interpretation of the immunological basis of spontaneous abortion and of the different immunotherapeutic regimes currently employed. However, recurrent pregnancy failure could still prove to have largely an underlying genetic rather than an immunological cause (Gill, 1987).

XI. Concluding Remarks

There is at present no convincing evidence that blastocyst attachment and implantation depend on maternal immunological recognition of any of the antigen systems so far described, including the male-specific Y antigen (Adinolfi et al., 1985). The survival of the postimplantation embryo is ensured by the encapsulating barrier of trophoblastic cells and outer extraembryonic membranes that prevent the entry of maternal immunocompetent cells. The survival of the fetal barrier tissues themselves is primarily due to the failure of the pregnant female to mount a classical rejection response, possibly owing to the production of one or more immunomodulating factors by the trophoblast or soluble suppressor factors by maternal lymphocytes.

Since pregnancy is unaffected even after experimental induction of cytotoxic antibody and effector cells with specificity for the fetal antigens, there must be a secondary mechanism to provide protection against immune attack. This may lie in the failure of the trophoblast to express cell surface antigenic determinants of a type recognizable by the effector elements, as could prove to be the case for human trophoblast, or in the ability of the trophoblast to secrete, or cause to be secreted, molecules capable of inhibiting cytolytic interactions, as appears to occur in the mouse. Other forms of immunoregulation, particularly those involving alloantibodies or a wide variety of pregnancy-associated serum proteins, may not be essential for fetal survival. It is a matter of current controversy whether human recurrent spontaneous abortion and other pregnancy disorders have an immunological basis.

There is still an abundance of hypotheses and a dearth of established facts in this scientifically and clinically important field of reproductive immunology. Some of the conflicting data undoubtedly stem from the use of different assay systems and different species. We do not know whether a single mechanism operates to permit fetal survival in all mammalian species, or whether the evolution of viviparity on numerous independent occasions has led to different solutions that have of necessity been conserved. In either case, the central role is played by the trophoblast. A combined approach utilizing immunological and molecular genetic techniques may reveal that the architecture of the cell surface and the nature of the immunoregulatory factors secreted by this fetal tissue endow it with unique properties, allowing it to withstand development and differentiation in a genetically alien environment.

ACKNOWLEDGMENTS

This review is based on studies carried out in collaboration with the following past or present members of the Reproductive Immunology Group: Eric Jenkinson, Roger Searle, Georgina Smith, Martin Sellens, Katrina Kirkwood, Steve Bell, Martin Davies, Judith Bulmer, and Francis Burrows. I am indebted to The Rockefeller Foundation, The Medical Research Council, The Wellcome Trust, and Birthright (Royal College of Obstetricians and Gynaecologists) for financial support.

REFERENCES

Adinolfi, M. (1975). *In* "Immunobiology of Trophoblast" (R. G. Edwards, C. W. S. Howe, and M. H. Johnson, eds.), pp. 193–215. Cambridge Univ. Press, London and New York.

Adinolfi, M., Polani, P. E., and Crolla, J. A. (1985). *Exp. Clin. Immunogenet.* **2**, 54–64.

Bach, F. H., Bach, M. L., and Sondel, P. M. (1976). *Nature (London)* **259**, 273–281.

Badet, M.-T. (1984). *J. Reprod. Immunol.* **6**, 299–311.

Badet, M.-T., Bell, S. C., and Billington, W. D. (1983). *J. Reprod. Fertil.* **68**, 351–358.

Barnstable, C. J., and Bodmer, W. F. (1978). *Lancet* **1**, 326.

Beer, A. E., Quebbeman, J. F., Ayers, J. W. T., and Haines, R. F. (1981). *Am. J. Obstet. Gynecol.* **141**, 987–999.

Bell, S. C. (1984). *J. Immunogenet.* **11**, 21–31.

Bell, S. C., and Billington, W. D. (1980). *Nature (London)* **288**, 387–388.

Bell, S. C., and Billington, W. D. (1981). *J. Reprod. Immunol.* **3**, 3–13.

Bell, S. C., and Billington, W. D. (1983). *J. Reprod. Immunol.* **5**, 299–310.

Bell, S. C., and Billington, W. D. (1986). *J. Reprod. Immunol.* **9**, 289–302.

Billington, W. D., and Bell, S. C. (1983a). *In* "Biology of Trophoblast" (Y. W. Loke and A. Whyte, eds.), pp. 571–595. Elsevier, Amsterdam.

Billington, W. D., and Bell, S. C. (1983b). *In* "Fetal Antigens and Cancer." *Ciba Found. Symp.* **96**, 69–88.

Billington, W. D., and Burrows, F. J. (1986). *J. Reprod. Immunol.* **9**, 155–160.

Billington, W. D., Bell, S. C., and Smith, G. (1983). *In* "Immunology of Reproduction" (T. G. Wegmann and T. J. Gill, eds.), pp. 205–227. Oxford Univ. Press, London and New York.

Brown, P. J., Molloy, C. M., and Johnson, P. M. (1983). *J. Reprod. Immunol.* **5**, 351–361.

Bulmer, J. N., and Johnson, P. M. (1985). *Placenta* **6**, 127–140.

Bulmer, J. N., Billington, W. D., and Johnson, P. M. (1984). *Am. J. Obstet. Gynecol.* **148**, 19–26.

Chaouat, G. (1987). *J. Reprod. Immunol.* **10**, 179–188.

Chaouat, G., Kolb, J. P., and Rivière, M. (1984). *Ann. Immunol.* **135D**, 302–306.

Chaouat, G., Kolb, J. P., Rivière, M., and Chaffaux, S. (1985). *Contrib. Gynecol. Obstet.* **14**, 54–65.

Chatterjee-Hasrouni, S., and Lala, P. K. (1981). *J. Immunol.* **127**, 2070–2073.

Chatterjee-Hasrouni, S., and Lala, P. K. (1982). *J. Exp. Med.* **155**, 1679–1682.

Clark, D. A. (1985). *Immunol. Lett.* **9**, 239–247.

Colavincenzo, V., and Lala, P. K. (1984). *Anat. Rec.* **208**, 33A.

Colavincenzo, V., and Lala, P. K. (1985). *Anat. Rec.* **211**, 42A.

Davies, M. (1985a). *J. Immunol. Methods* **77**, 109–118.

Davies, M. (1985b). *Immunol. Lett.* **10**, 199–205.

Davies, M. (1985c). *Clin. Exp. Immunol.* **61**, 406–415.

Davies, M. (1986). *Am. J. Reprod. Immunol. Microbiol.* **10**, 58–63.

Davies, M., and Browne, C. M. (1985a). *J. Reprod. Immunol.* **8**, 33–44.

Davies, M., and Browne, C. M. (1985b). *J. Reprod. Immunol.* **7**, 285–297.

Davies, M., and Browne, C. M. (1985c). *J. Dev. Physiol.* **7**, 269–280.

Davies, M., and Browne, C. M. (1985d). *Am. J. Reprod. Immunol. Microbiol.* **9**, 77–83.

Davies, M., and Browne, C. M. (1985e). *Am. J. Reprod. Immunol. Microbiol.* **9**, 84–90.

Duc, H. T., Massé, A., Bobé, P., Kinsky, R. G., and Voisin, G. A. (1985). *J. Reprod. Immunol.* **7**, 27–39.

Faulk, W. P., and Hsi, B.-L. (1983). In "Biology of Trophoblast" (Y. W. Loke and A. Whyte, eds.), pp. 535–570. Elsevier, Amsterdam.

Faulk, W. P., and McIntyre, J. A. (1983). *Immunol. Rev.* **75**, 139–175.

Faulk, W. P., Sanderson, A. R., and Temple, A. (1977). *Transplant. Proc.* **9**, 1379–1384.

Faulk, W. P., Temple, A., Lovins, R. E., and Smith, N. C. (1978). *Proc. Natl. Acad. Sci. U.S.A.* **75**, 1947–1951.

Ghani, A. M., Gill, T. J., Kunz, H. W., and Misra, D. N. (1984). *Transplantation* **37**, 187–194.

Gill, T. J. (1987). In "Physiology of Reproduction" (E. Knobil and J. D. Neill, eds.). Raven, New York, in press.

Goodfellow, P. N., Barnstable, C. J., Bodmer, W. F., Snary, D., and Crumpton, M. J. (1976). *Transplantation* **22**, 595–603.

Herzenberg, L. A., Bianchi, D. W., Schroder, J., Cann, H. M., and Iverson, G. M. (1979). *Proc. Natl. Acad. Sci. U.S.A.* **76**, 1453–1455.

Hsi, B.-L., Yeh, C. J. G., and Faulk, W. P. (1984). *Immunology* **52**, 621–629.

Hulka, J. F., Hsu, K. C., and Beiser, S. M. (1961). *Nature (London)* **191**, 510–511.

Hulka, J. F., Brinton, V., Schaaf, J., and Baney, C. (1963). *Nature (London)* **198**, 501–502.

Jenkinson, E. J., and Billington, W. D. (1974a). *J. Reprod. Fertil.* **41**, 403–412.

Jenkinson, E. J., and Billington, W. D. (1974b). *Transplantation* **18**, 286–289.

Jenkinson, E. J., and Owen, V. (1980). *J. Reprod. Immunol.* **2**, 173–181.

Jenkinson, E. J., and Searle, R. F. (1979). *J. Reprod. Immunol.* **1**, 3–10.

Jenkinson, E. J., Billington, W. D., and Elson, J. (1975). In "Maternofetal Transmission of Immunoglobulins" (W. A. Hemmings, ed.), pp. 225–232. Cambridge Univ. Press, London and New York.

Johnson, P. M. (1984). In "Immunological Aspects of Reproduction in Mammals" (D. B. Crighton, ed.), pp. 109–131. Butterworths, London.

Johnson, P. M., Cheng, H. M., Molloy, C. M., Stern, C. M. M., and Slade, M. B. (1981). *Am. J. Reprod. Immunol.* **1**, 246–254.

Jonker, M., van Leeuwen, A., and van Rood, J. J. (1977). *Tissue Antigens* **9**, 246–258.

Khalaf, S. A., Livingstone, J. C., Nickson, D. A., Henderson, S. J., and Sutcliffe, R. G. (1985). In "Early Pregnancy Factors" (F. Ellendorff and E. Koch, eds.), pp. 141–151. Perinatology Press, Ithaca, New York.

Kirkwood, K. J., and Bell, S. C. (1981). *J. Reprod. Immunol.* **3**, 243–252.

Kirkwood, K. J., and Billington, W. D. (1981). *J. Embryol. Exp. Morphol.* **61**, 207–219.

Kouttab, N. M., Fowler, A. K., Strickland, J. E., and Hellman, A. (1976). *J. Immunol.* **117**, 1644–1650.

Lalezari, P. (1980). *Transplant. Proc.* **12**, 12–21.

Loke, Y. W. (1983). In "Biology of Trophoblast" (Y. W. Loke and A. Whyte, eds.), pp. 663–701. Elsevier, Amsterdam.

Lordon, R. E., Wilson, R. L., Shield, C. F., and Ferrone, S. (1981). *Transplantation* **32**, 286–290.

McIntyre, J. A., and Faulk, W. P. (1982). *Hum. Immunol.* **4**, 27–35.

Matsunaga, T., and Ohno, S. (1980). *Transplant. Proc.* **12**, 135–140.

Mitchison, N. A. (1953). *J. Genet.* **51**, 406–420.

Mowbray, J. F., Liddell, H., Underwood, J. L., Gibbings, C., Reginald, P. W., and Beard, R. W. (1985). *Lancet* **1**, 941–943.

O'Sullivan, M. J., McIntyre, J. A., Prior, M., Warriner, G. A., and Faulk, W. P. (1982). *Clin. Exp. Immunol.* **48**, 279–287.

Parr, E. L., and Kirby, W. N. (1979). *J. Histochem. Cytochem.* **27**, 1327–1336.

Parr, E. L., Blanden, R. V., and Tulsi, R. S. (1980). *J. Exp. Med.* **152**, 945–955.

Paul, S., and Jailkhani, B. (1982). *Am. J. Reprod. Immunol.* **2**, 204–207.

Paul, S., Gupta, P. D., Jailkhani, B. L., and Talwar, G. P. (1980). *J. Reprod. Fertil.* **58**, 183–187.

Pavia, C. S., and Stites, D. P. (1981). *Cell. Immunol.* **58**, 202–208.

Pross, H., Mitchell, H., and Werkmeister, J. (1985). *Am. J. Reprod. Immunol. Microbiol.* **8**, 1–9.

Redman, C. W. G., McMichael, A. J., Stirrat, G. M., Sunderland, C. A., and Ting, A. (1984). *Immunology* **52**, 457–468.

Rodger, J. C. (1985). *Transplantation* **40**, 372–375.

Roe, R., and Bell, S. C. (1982). *Immunology* **46**, 23–30.

Sargent, I. L., and Redman, C. W. G. (1985). *J. Reprod. Immunol.* **7**, 95–104.

Sargent, I. L., Ellis, S., McMichael, A., and Redman, C. W. G. (1986). *J. Reprod. Immunol. Suppl.* 33.

Searle, R. F., and Jenkinson, E. J. (1978). *J. Embryol. Exp. Morphol.* **43**, 147–156.

Searle, R. F., Billington, W. D., Whyte, A., and Loke, Y. W. (1981). *Placenta* **2**, 93–104.

Searle, R. F., Bell, S. C., and Billington, W. D. (1983). *Placenta* **4**, 139–148.

Sellens, M. H., Jenkinson, E. J., and Billington, W. D. (1978). *Transplantation* **25**, 173–179.

Singal, D. P., Butler, L., Liao, S.-K., and Joseph, S. (1984). *Am. J. Reprod. Immunol.* **6**, 145–151.

Singh, B., Raghupathy, R., Anderson, D. J., and Wegmann, T. G. (1983). In "Immunology of Reproduction" (T. G. Wegmann and T. J. Gill, eds.), pp. 231–250. Oxford Univ. Press, London and New York.

Smith, G. (1983a). *J. Reprod. Immunol.* **5**, 39–47.

Smith, G. (1983b). *Transplantation* **36**, 224–226.

Smith, G., and Chappell, F. (1984). *Immunology* **52**, 49–54.

Smith, R. N., Margolias, R. T., and Sternlicht, M. (1982). *J. Immunol.* **129**, 777–782.

Sunderland, C. A., Naiem, M., Mason, D. Y., Redman, C. W. G., and Stirrat, G. M. (1981a). *J. Reprod. Immunol.* **3**, 323–331.

Sunderland, C. A., Redman, C. W. G., and Stirrat, G. M. (1981b). *J. Immunol.* **127**, 2614–2615.

Szekeres-Bartho, J., Hadnagy, J., and Pacsa, A. S. (1985). *J. Reprod. Immunol.* **7**, 121–128.

Taylor, C., and Faulk, W. P. (1981). *Lancet* **2**, 68–70.

Taylor, G. M. (1973). *Immunology* **25**, 783–792.

Voisin, G. A. (1980). *Immunol. Rev.* **49**, 3–59.

Webb, P. D., Evans, P. W., Molloy, C. M., and Johnson, P. M. (1985). *Am. J. Reprod. Immunol. Microbiol.* **8**, 113–119.

Wegmann, T. G. (1981). *J. Reprod. Immunol.* **3**, 267–270.

Wegmann, T. G. (1984). *Ann. Immunol.* **135D**, 309–312.

Wells, M., Hsi, B.-L., and Faulk, W. P. (1984). *Am. J. Reprod. Immunol.* **6**, 167–174.

Welsh, K. I., Burgos, H., and Batchelor, J. R. (1977). *Eur. J. Immunol.* **7**, 267–272.

CHAPTER 11

HOMEO BOX GENES IN MURINE DEVELOPMENT

Allen A. Fienberg,* Manuel F. Utset,* Leonard D. Bogarad,†
Charles P. Hart,† Alexander Awgulewitsch,† Anne Ferguson-Smith,†
Abraham Fainsod,† Mark Rabin,† and Frank H. Ruddle*,†

* DEPARTMENT OF HUMAN GENETICS
† DEPARTMENT OF BIOLOGY
YALE UNIVERSITY
NEW HAVEN, CONNECTICUT 06511

I. Introduction

Embryogenesis must result from an interaction of the information emanating from two origins: the genome and the environment. Although mutants tell us that morphogenesis must depend on information contained within the DNA sequence, the rules that govern the multidimensional process of morphogenesis cannot ultimately be predicted from the one-dimensional information contained within the DNA. The underlying rules of development that bridge this gap in information transfer have been termed the "grammar" of development (Lewin, 1984).

The elucidation of the rules that govern the grammar of development is one of the long-standing problems of biology. The success of any theory of development depends, in part, on the degree to which we understand the spatial and temporal relationships that govern how groups of cells are defined into organ and tissue primordia. These relationships can be better defined as an understanding of cell fate, cell determination, and cell movement at all stages of embryogenesis. Some of this information can come from the generation of fate maps, cell and tissue transplantation experiments, and an understanding of cell movement and cell differentiation. The picture is broadened by applying a genetic analysis and it is the synthesis of these endeavors that yields the most cogent analysis of developmental processes.

Based on the pioneering work of Sturtevant (1929) and Stern (1936), experiments using *Drosophila* led the way in our understanding of developmental genetics. Powerful genetic and recombinant

233

DNA tools have enabled *Drosophila* geneticists to identify many of the genes involved in morphogenesis and to correlate their patterns of expression at the molecular level with normal and abnormal patterns of development. It will not be long before an analysis of the gene products will give us insight into the molecular mechanisms of the rules of *Drosophila* development.

The information obtained from systems such as *Drosophila* is impressive. Two schools of thought have been generated on how to apply this information to mammals. First, there are those that see few parallels between invertebrate and vertebrate patterns of embryogenesis. This viewpoint implies that the rules of mammalian development must be discovered anew, using what is learned about *Drosophila* development as only a formal example of one possible solution to the problem of pattern formation. Conversely, there are those who propose that although the final structures and tissues formed are very different among different phyla, the molecular mechanisms underlying the decision-making processes might be fundamentally similar. In other words, the "grammar" might be basically the same. This school has set out to use the advances of *Drosophila* genetics as a practical tool for the isolation of vertebrate morphogenetic loci.

Over the past several years, our laboratory and those of others have shown that sequences homologous to *Drosophila* morphogenetic loci exist in a wide range of animals. In order to determine whether these genes play developmentally important roles in mammalian development, we have begun to analyze their chromosomal organization in mouse and human and their spatial and temporal patterns of expression. We review the data accumulated from our laboratory and from others and compare it to information gained from *Drosophila*. In addition we try to point out the similarities and differences between invertebrate and vertebrate development and speculate on the possible functions of homeotic genes in vertebrates.

II. The Genetics of Homeosis in *Drosophila* and the Homeo Box

The process of embryogenesis in any organism can be thought of as a progressive expression of information that subdivides the embryo into ever finer units of determination. In *Drosophila* this process can be roughly divided into three steps: (1) the maternal establishment of the anteroposterior and dorsoventral coordinates of the embryo, (2) the segmentation of the embryo, and (3) the assignment of identities to each of the segments. The genetic analysis of each of these processes has proceeded more or less independently. However, recent findings suggest that they share common molecular mechanisms.

The genetic analysis of the assignment of segment identity is most advanced, taking advantage of spontaneous mutations causing what Bateson (1894) termed a homeotic phenotype. Homeosis refers to the substitution of one organ for another belonging to the same group of serially homologous structures, and provides an important clue that early developmental decisions may take place in a binary fashion. A detailed examination of homeosis was begun by Edward Lewis in 1946 when he initiated his study of the *bithorax* gene complex *(BX-C)* on chromosome 3. At the time three alleles of the *bithorax* gene already existed: *bx* found by Bridges in 1915, bx^3 of Stern (1935), and bx^{34e} of Schultz (1935). Each of these mutations caused, to a different degree, a transformation of structures of the anterior portion of the third thoracic segment into structures found on the corresponding portion of the second thoracic segment. The bithorax complex is now known to contain genes that control the segment identity of the mesothoracic and metathoracic segments and all eight abdominal segments. Genetic analyses divide the BX-C into three lethal complementation groups: *Ubx, abd-A,* and *Abd-B* (Sanchez-Herrero *et al.,* 1985). Each gene is primarily responsible for determining segment identity within a distinct region of the fly. *Ubx* determines the segment identity of the second and third thoracic and first abdominal segments, *abd-A* controls the identity of abdominal segments A2–A4, and the *Abd-B* gene controls segments A5–A8 and the genitalia. The *Antennapedia* gene complex *(ANT-C),* which is located on the same chromosome as the *bithorax* complex, controls the identity of more anterior regions of the fly (Kaufman *et al.,* 1980; Kaufman, 1983). To a first approximation, the proximodistal order of homeotic genes on the chromosome corresponds to the order of their functional domains along the anteroposterior axis of the fly (Lewis, 1978). This colinearity may be related to the evolution of these genes, or it may be indicative of some functional aspect.

The Lewis model (1978) proposes that homeotic genes control segment identity in the following way. First, homeotic genes encode substances which regulate other genes that actually determine segmental structure and function. In short, homeotic genes select specific pathways of development. Second, individual segment identities are imparted by the expression of distinct combinations of homeotic genes. Third, the distinct combinations arise because each homeotic gene has a unique anterior boundary of expression and is expressed in all segments posterior to the boundary. To explain the spatial regulation of homeotic gene expression, Lewis proposed a concentration gradient of a repressor of homeotic gene expression along the anteroposterior axis of the embryo, as well as a proximodistal gradient of affinity for the repressor along the chromosome. While the idea of a gradient may still be valid, current models also invoke cross-regulatory interactions between homeotic genes (Struhl, 1982; Hafen *et al.*, 1984; Harding *et al.*, 1985; Struhl and White, 1985; Wedeen *et al.*, 1986).

Each homeotic gene of the *ANT-C* and *BX-C* complexes contains a short region of DNA sequence homology termed the homeo box (McGinnis *et al.*, 1984a,b; Scott and Weiner, 1984). This region encodes a 60-amino acid domain that has some homology with DNA-binding domains of bacterial and yeast proteins (Shepherd *et al.*, 1984; Laughon and Scott, 1984). This DNA-binding homology suggests that cross-regulatory interactions may occur at the transcriptional level and provides a framework for understanding how each homeotic gene, or combination thereof, can select a particular developmental pathway. The homeo box has been detected at 10 loci in the *Antennapedia* and *bithorax* complexes. These copies are found in the *Antennapedia* complex at the *Deformed* (Regulski *et al.*, 1985), *bicoid* (Frigerio *et al.*, 1986), *F90-2* (Hoey *et al.*, 1986), *sex combs reduced* (Regulski *et al.*, 1985), *zerknüllt* (Doyle *et al.*, 1986), *fushi tarazu*, and *Antennapedia* loci (McGinnis *et al.*, 1984b). In the *bithorax* complex they are found at the *Ubx* (McGinnis *et al.*, 1984b), *abd-A*, and *Abd-B* loci (Regulski *et al.*, 1985). Because of the high conservation of these homeo boxes (except bicoid) to the *Antp* homeo box, they have been termed the *Antennapedia* class (Regulski *et al.*, 1985). Not all genes of the *Antennapedia* class that contain homeo boxes are involved in determining segment identity. The *zerknüllt* gene appears to be involved in pattern specification along the dorsoventral axis of the embryo (Wakimoto *et al.*, 1984; Doyle *et al.*, 1986), while the *ftz* gene is involved in the segmentation process itself (Wakimoto and Kaufman, 1981). Other genes involved in the segmentation process that contain homeo boxes are *paired* (Frigerio *et al.*, 1986), *engrailed* (Fjose *et al.*, 1985), and *even-skipped* (Macdonald *et al.*, 1986; Harding *et al.*, 1985). Furthermore, several genes that may determine global anteroposterior coordinates in the embryo also contain a homeo box. These are *caudal* (Mlodzik *et al.*, 1985), *bicoid* (Frigerio *et al.*, 1986), and *F90-2* (Hoey *et al.*, 1986). The *engrailed* and *invected* genes contain a highly divergent homeo box sequence which has been denoted the *engrailed* class. The discovery of homeo boxes within genes involved in anteroposterior determination broadens the role of the homeo box, suggesting that it may be involved in processes other than segmentation or segment identity. However, the homeo box has still been found only in genes that appear to control fundamental processes of pattern specification during *Drosophila* embryogenesis.

Under the assumption that the homeo box might be found in genes performing similiar functions in other organisms, our laboratory and others have used the homeo box as a probe to screen mouse genomic libraries under low-stringency conditions. Many mouse homeo boxes have been isolated and sequenced. Their homology to *Drosophila* homeo box sequences ranges from 44 to 96% at the amino acid level. Homeo boxes of both the *Antennapedia* and *engrailed* classes have been found, as well as several that cannot be placed in either class.

III. Murine Homeo Box Gene Organization

Two known clusters of genes that contain homeo boxes of the *Antennapedia* class have been mapped in the mouse (see Fig. 1). *Hox-1* spans at least 70 kb and is found on chromosome 6 (McGinnis *et al.*, 1984c) between the κ light chain and the T-cell receptor β gene (Bucan *et al.*, 1986). *Hox-2* spans at least 50 kb and is found on chromosome 11 (Rabin *et al.*, 1985; Joyner *et al.*, 1985a) at bands C–E (Münke *et al.*, 1986), 1 cM proximal to the *Rex* locus (Hart *et al.*, 1987a). From Southern blot hybridizations and sequence data, each cluster is thought to contain at least six genes containing homeo boxes. A single such gene, *Hox 3.1*, has been assigned to chromosome 15 F1–3 (Awgulewitch *et al.*, 1986; Rabin *et al.*, 1986).

Homeo box sequences homologous to the *engrailed* class have also been found in mouse. One locus designated *En-1* has been mapped to within several centimorgans of the murine morphogenetic locus *Dominant hemimelia* on chromosome 1. A second *engrailed*-like homeo box designated *En-2* has been mapped to mouse chromosome 5 in close linkage with *hammertoe* and *hemimelic extra toes (Hx)*. The *engrailed* gene of *Drosophila* and *En-1* display sequence homology over a region of ~120 amino acids. This homology is found not only within the homeo box but also extends 30 amino acids both 5' and 3' of the homeo box (G. Martin, personal communication; Joyner and Martin, 1987). This conservation between *Drosophila* and mouse of sequence homology outside the homeo box is unique so far.

It remains to be seen whether the *En* loci and *Hox-3* also contain clustered homeo box-containing genes. One might speculate that we are approaching the limit of existing genes, since genomic Southern analysis under low-stringency conditions reveals approximately 15 to 20 bands that cross-hybridize with homeo box probes. However, the low-stringency hybridization conditions will only detect sequences with homology >60%. Additional sequences with significant homology to a homeo box may exist, yet escape detection. Most of the genes containing homeo boxes were cloned from libraries using the *Antp* and *Ubx* or *Scr* homeo boxes: this may explain why there is such a strong

ALLEN A. FIENBERG ET AL.

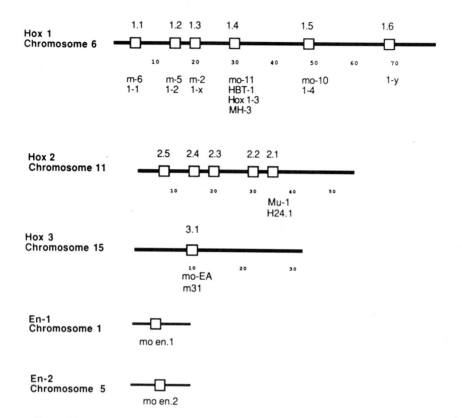

FIG. 1. The murine homeo box gene system. At least five homeo box loci have been identified in the mouse. Their names and chromosomal assignments are shown in the left margin of the figure. Open squares represent homeo box sequences. Above each box is given its name in the standardized Hox nomenclature (Martin *et al.*, 1987). Below each are the original plasmid names. Distances in kilobases are shown below each locus. The *Hox-1* locus on chromosome 6 contains at least six homeo boxes within 70 kb. The *Hox-2* locus contains at least five homeo boxes within 40 kb. Based upon analysis of the human *Hox-2* locus, a sixth homeo box sequence is thought to be present within 10 kb to the right of *Hox 2.1* (Hauser *et al.*, 1985). One homeo box sequence has been identified in the *Hox-3* locus on chromosome 15. The *En-1* locus on chromosome 1 contains at least one *engrailed*-class homeo box, as does the *En-2* locus on chromosome 5.

predominance of homeo boxes with homology to these sequences. Screens with more divergent homeo box sequences may uncover new mouse homeo boxes and expand the homology groups beyond the present *Antp* and *engrailed* classes.

Studies in humans have proceeded in conjunction with those in mouse and have revealed several conserved linkage relationships between these two species (reviewed by Rabin *et al.*, 1986; Ruddle *et al.*, 1986). Within mouse, mapping information has shown that homeo box loci can always be found linked to loci known to be involved in skeletal and limb development or nervous system development. This linkage may be fortuitous, since historically these are genetic markers that are easy to detect and represent a disproportionate number of mapped loci. However, this organization may have some functional significance.

There are several examples of developmentally interesting gene complexes in mouse that span large genetic distances. These are (1) *albino* locus on chromosome 7 (reviewed by Gluecksohn-Waelsch, 1979), (2) *agouti–lethal yellow* on chromosome 2 (Mayer and Fishbane, 1972; Papaioannou and Gardner, 1979; Poole, 1980; Papaioannou and Mardon, 1983), (3) *T complex* on chromosome 17 (reviewed by Bennett, 1980; Lyon, 1981; Silver *et al.*, 1984), (4) *H-2* complex on chromosome 17 (reviewed by Kaufman *et al.*, 1984), (5) *dilute–short ear* complex on chromosome 9 (reviewed by Rinchik *et al.*, 1985). The *Hox-1* and *Hox-2* loci span at least 50–75 kb, which seems small compared to the size of the complexes described above. However, one might hypothesize that either additional homeo box sequences will also be found nearby, or that closely linked morphogenetic mutants are part of a larger complex of which homeo box genes are only a part.

Sequence comparisons between individual members of the two clusters of murine homeo box genes show no evidence of a recent duplication of a single complex. These comparisons have indicated, however, the existence of highly homologous subgroups within the gene family. For example, the nucleotide and amino acid sequence of Hox-3.1 is relatively diverged from most of the other sequenced homeo domains (Awgulewitsch *et al.*, 1986) but is identical at 59 of 60 amino acids with the Hox-2.4 homeo domain (Hart *et al.*, 1987b). The nucleotide sequence homology between these two boxes is only 79%. Similarly, Hox-1.4 shares four of the six differences that distinguish Hox-2.1 from the prototypical Antennapedia homeo domain (Wolgemuth *et al.*, 1986; Hauser *et al.*, 1985). Whether these structural similarities reflect close evolutionary and/or functional relationships between individual homeo box genes remains to be more rigorously tested.

Homeo box sequence comparisons have also indicated apparent cognate relationships between individual homeo domains among different species. For example, the mouse Hox-2.3 (Hart *et al.*, 1987b), the human HuC1 (Boncinelli *et al.*, 1985), and the *Xenopus* MM3 (Müller *et al.*, 1984) share extensive homology. This extends into the 3' flank of the homeo domain, where each ends in a stretch of six glutamic acid residues followed by a stop codon 15 amino acids downstream from the homeo domain. A similar relationship exists among the murine Hox-2.1 (Hauser *et al.*, 1985), the human Hu1 (Levine *et al.*, 1984), and the *Xenopus* Xhox1B (Harvey *et al.*, 1986) homeo domains. Another group includes murine Hox-1.4 (Wolgemuth *et al.*, 1986), human C13 (Boncinelli *et al.*, 1985), and *Xenopus* Xhox1a (Harvey *et al.*, 1986). This latter cognate group may also extend to the *Drosophila* Deformed homeo domain (Regulski *et al.*, 1985), which has similar amino acid substitutions at the same positions as those above.

Questions of the relationship of individual homeo box genes, both evolutionary and functional, will be better addressed through the comparative analyses of the entire proteins in which the homeo domains are found. Detailed analysis of the evolutionary dynamics of the homeo box gene family will require the comparative analysis of species from distinct phylogenetic lineages.

IV. Homeo Box Gene Expression

Many laboratories are currently investigating the expression of mouse homeo box genes. In *Drosophila,* homeo box genes display striking temporal and spatial patterns of expression that reflect their morphogenetic functions. With the hope that the patterns of mouse homeo box gene expression will provide important clues to their function during development, much effort has been put into a search for stage-, cell type-, or region-specific patterns of expression. These efforts have utilized a variety of techniques, including Northern analysis, nuclease protection, *in situ* hybridization, and cDNA cloning.

A. Hox 1 COMPLEX

1. Hox 1.1 and 1.2

Hox 1.1 and *1.2* have been analyzed extensively in embryonal carcinoma (EC) cell lines and during mouse development (Colberg-Poley *et al.*, 1985a,b). These studies have made extensive use of F9 cells, which serve as a model system to study the differentiation of primitive endoderm into visceral or parietal endoderm. This differentiation event can be manipulated reliably by adding retinoic acid and cAMP to induce parietal endoderm, or retinoic acid alone to induce visceral endoderm. Northern analysis of *Hox 1.1* has demonstrated that transcripts of 2.9 and 1.5 kb can be detected in undifferentiated F9 cells. Upon induction of differentiation into parietal endoderm or visceral endoderm, a new transcript of 2.4 kb is transcribed. Using probes specific for the homeo box and flanking sequences, Colberg-Poley *et al.* have demonstrated that the induced transcript contains the homeo box whereas the transcripts seen in uninduced cells do not contain the homeo box. Two simple models explaining how this might occur have been presented (Colberg-Poley *et al.*, 1985c). Northern analysis of mouse embryos (Colberg-Poley *et al.*, 1985b) has revealed *Hox 1.1* transcripts similar in size to those seen in differentiated F9 cells (2.9, 2.4, 1.5 kb). These RNA species peak in abundance at 12 days *post coitum* (dpc). Analysis of various adult tissues demonstrated abundant *Hox 1.1* transcripts of various sizes in testis, brain, and kidney. Transcripts could also be found in bone marrow, macrophages, spleen, and ovary.

Studies with *Hox 1.2* have shown that transcripts of 5.5 kb can be detected that are specific to the differentiated state of F9 cells and that these same RNA species are found in abundant levels during mouse development at 12.5 dpc. Preliminary experiments suggest that *Hox 1.2* are found in fewer adult tissues than *Hox 1.1*.

2. Hox 1.4

Hox 1.4 (*mo-11:* Ruddle *et al.*, 1985; *Hox1-3:* Duboule *et al.*, 1986; *HBT-1:* Wolgemuth *et al.*, 1986; *MH-3:* Rubin *et al.*, 1986) has come under intense study. During embryogenesis *Hox 1.4* expression has been detected as early as 9 dpc. By Northern analysis two transcripts of 2.5 and 1.4 kb are detected (Duboule *et al.*, 1986). Rubin *et al.* and Duboule *et al.* demonstrate that these RNA species decrease progressively as embryogenesis proceeds, and are undetectable after 16 dpc. In the adult mouse *Hox 1.4* expression appears to be limited to the testis. Rubin *et al.* and Wolgemuth *et al.* estimate that the adult testis mRNA is 1.4–1.5 kb in length. However, Duboule *et al.* estimate that this adult testis specific RNA is 1.25 kb. In a detailed S1 analysis Duboule *et al.* demonstrate testis-specific splicing patterns that suggest that the testis-specific RNA is different from the 1.4- to 1.5-kb RNA detected during embryogenesis.

Recently, Wolgemuth and co-workers have shed some light on this confusion by resolving two testis-specific RNA species of 1.35 and 1.45 kb. By looking at purified populations of pachytene spermatocytes, early spermatids, and elongating spermatids, they showed that these mRNA species change in abundance as spermatogenesis proceeds, so that the 1.35-kb species is more abundant during the earlier pachytene stage, while the 1.45-kb species is more abundant at the later spermatid stage (D. Wolgemuth, personal communication).

The initial appearance of *Hox 1.4* transcripts in the postnatal development of the testis has been determined by Rubin *et al.* Northern analysis of RNA from prepuberal mice demonstrated that transcription can first be detected at day 14. Spermatogonia enter into meiosis at day 9 and by day 14 germ cells have progressed to the pachytene stage of meiosis implying that this gene is not specifically associated with germ line determination or the decision to enter meiosis. Rubin *et al.* have confirmed their Northern analysis with *in situ* hybridization experiments, demonstrating that signals could be detected over pachytene spermatocytes and spermatids but not from regions containing spermatogonia. Expression of *Hox 1.4* was not detected in mice with a mutation at the *Sl* (steel) locus, correlating *Hox 1.4* expression with the presence of germ cells in the testis.

3. Hox 1.5

By Northern analysis *Hox 1.5* transcripts have been detected during embryogenesis and in the adult mouse. These transcripts range in size from 3.2 to 5.0 kb and have been detected in the brain, spinal column, testis, and ovary of newborn or adult mice. During embryogenesis this expression has been localized in detail by *in situ* hybridization (see Fig. 2A) on sections prepared from embryos on successive days from 8.5 to 12.5 dpc (Fainsod *et al.*, 1987). At 8.5 days expression is detected in the neural fold with an anterior limit of expression extending into the hindbrain. Expression within the central nervous system (CNS) remains high and the anterior boundary of expression appears to remain constant such that at 12.5 dpc it falls within the myelencephalon, just posterior to the pontine flexure. The spinal ganglia are also labeled at 12.5 days. These studies have mapped the onset of expression to an interval between 7.5 and 8.5 dpc. By 7.5 dpc the anterior–posterior axis is well established, thus it is unlikely that *Hox 1.5* plays a role in this process. However, the interval between 7.5 and 8.5 days marks the onset of neurulation in the mouse embryo.

B. *Hox 2* COMPLEX

1. Hox 2.1

Murine *Hox 2.1* has been shown to be expressed during mouse embryogenesis (Hart *et al.*, 1985; Hauser *et al.*, 1985; Jackson *et al.*, 1985; Utset *et al.*, 1987). In a temporal analysis using whole embryos, *Hox 2.1* was found to be expressed as early as 7.5 dpc with a peak of expression at 12.5 dpc (Jackson *et al.*, 1985). *In situ*-hybridization experiments have shown that in the 13.5-dpc embryo *Hox 2.1* transcripts are found within the CNS in a spatially restricted fashion (see Fig. 2C). The most abundant *Hox 2.1* expression is detected within the presumptive medulla. No expression is detected in more anterior regions of the

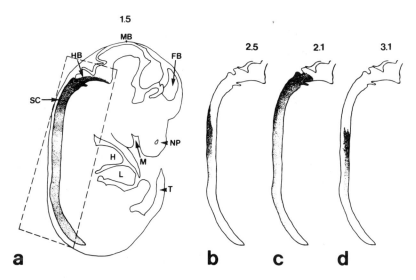

FIG. 2. Region-specific expression of murine homeo box genes within the fetal CNS. Shown are schematic representations of the patterns of transcript accumulation of *Hox 1.5, Hox 2.5, Hox 2.1,* and *Hox 3.1* within the 13.5-dpc CNS. (a) Pattern of *Hox 1.5* expression. The stippling indicates that *Hox 1.5* transcripts are detected within the hindbrain posterior to the pontine flexure and in the spinal cord. FB, Forebrain; MB, midbrain; HB, hindbrain; SC, spinal cord; NP, nasal pit; M, mouth; H, heart; L, liver; T, tail. Box encloses region of CNS schematized in b–d. (b) Pattern of *Hox 2.5* expression. Transcripts accumulate within the dorsal half of the spinal cord posterior to the first cervical vertebra. (c) Pattern of *Hox 2.1* expression. Transcripts accumulate within the medulla and spinal cord. (d) Pattern of *Hox 3.1* expression. Transcripts accumulate within the ventral two-thirds of the spinal cord posterior to the third cervical vertebra.

brain. From the medulla, expression extends into the cervical spinal cord, trailing off caudally within the nerve cord. This spatially restricted pattern of expression is consistent with the RNase protection experiments of Jackson *et al.* (1985) which demonstrated *Hox 2.1* expression within the brain and spinal cord at 12.5 dpc.

Within the newborn CNS, *in situ* hybridization experiments reveal a similiar pattern of *Hox 2.1* expression. In addition, Northern blots at this stage have demonstrated the presence of 1.7- to 1.9-kb *Hox 2.1* transcripts within the newborn brain and the cervical and thoracic regions of the spinal column, but no *Hox 2.1* transcripts have been detected within the lumbar spinal column. These results imply that once the regionally localized pattern of *Hox 2.1* expression is established within the embryonic CNS, it is fixed throughout the final week of prenatal development.

Expression of human *Hox 2.1* was first studied in a human teratocarcinoma cell line NT2-D1, which upon addition of retinoic acid differentiates into a variety of tissues including neurons. Hauser *et al.* showed that human *Hox 2.1* transcripts were not detectable in undifferentiated cells but were detected within 2 days of the initiation of differentiation. Continued expression of this mRNA required the presence of retinoic acid which is not required for the maintenance of the differentiated state. Human *Hox 2.1* has been shown to be expressed in human fetal tissues of 5–8 weeks gestation (Simeone *et al.*, 1986). This expression was demonstrated by Northern analysis to be confined to the brain and spinal cord, as in mice (Utset *et al.*, 1987; Jackson *et al.*, 1985).

2. *Hox 2.2, 2.3, and 2.4*

Transcripts from each of the homeo box regions in *Hox 2.2, 2.3,* and *2.4* have been detected in embryos 13.5 dpc (Hart *et al.*, 1985). Work is now in progress to characterize their spatial patterns of expression.

3. *Hox 2.5*

Recently, the existence of a new homeo box gene, denoted *Hox 2.5,* has been demonstrated in the *Hox-2* cluster (Bogarad *et al.*, in preparation). Northern analysis of RNA from embryos 13.5 dpc demonstrates that *Hox 2.5* codes for two transcripts of 3.0 and 2.3 kb. These transcripts can be detected in the spinal cord but not the brain or liver of newborn and adult mice. By *in situ* hybridization analysis using 13.5-dpc embryos, *Hox 2.5* specifically hybridizes to the spinal cord with an anterior boundary at the level of the first cervical vertebra (see Fig. 2B). Maximal expression is detected at the second cervical vertebra and extends posteriorly. *In situ* hybridization analysis of cross sections of the 13.5-dpc spinal cord localizes *Hox 2.5* transcripts to the dorsal half of the spinal cord.

C. *Hox 3*

Transcription of the *Hox 3.1* gene has been detected in embryonic and adult tissues (Awgulewitsch *et al.*, 1986). An abundant transcript of 2.7 kb can be detected in embryos as early as 11 dpc and persists until birth. Northern analysis of newborn tissues shows that transcripts are found predominantly in the spinal cord with weaker signals found in the kidney. Within the spinal cord the transcripts are asymmetrically distributed, with more in the cervical and thoracic regions than in the lumbar–sacral–caudal region. No transcripts are detected within the newborn brain. In addition to the 2.7-kb transcript detected in intact embryos, an additional, less abundant RNA of 2.1 kb is also detected. The same regional distribution of *Hox 3.1* transcripts can also be observed in the adult spinal cord with two subtle differences. First, the relative abundance of transcripts in the lumbar region of the spinal cord is higher than that observed in the same region of newborn mice. Second, the 2.1-kb transcript appears to be more abundant than the 2.7-kb transcript.

By using *in situ* hybridization, the spatial pattern of *Hox 3.1* transcript accumulation within the CNS has been determined with higher resolution (Awgulewitsch *et al.*, 1986). In sagittal sections of newborn mice, *Hox 3.1* transcripts are detected in the spinal cord with an anterior limit of transcript accumulation at approximately the level of the third cervical vertebra (see Fig. 2D). No morphological transition occurs at this expression boundary. These results have been confirmed using cross sections of the spinal cord which have shown, in addition, that transcripts are localized to the gray matter of the spinal cord and that the spinal ganglia do not show specific labeling. A similiar anterior boundary of expression has been observed within the spinal cord of embryos 13.5 dpc. At this stage, transcripts appear localized to cells within the ventral two-thirds of the spinal cord. Weak labeling of several thoracic vertebrae is also observed.

Hox 3.1 expression has also been studied in F9 cells. Breier *et al.* (1986) have shown that transcription of *Hox 3.1* accompanies the differentiation into parietal endoderm. However, in comparing the pattern of induction with that of *Hox 1.1* described earlier, Breier *et al.* note that *Hox 3.1* peaks ~1 day later than *Hox 1.1*. This delayed appearance of *Hox 3.1* suggests that gene products expressed earlier may be required for *Hox 3.1* expression. Breier *et al.* suggest that one of these gene products may be *Hox 1.1*. This question can now be answered directly by introducing modified *Hox 1.1* constructs into F9 cells.

D. En-1 AND En-2

Studies in *Drosophila* have shown that the *engrailed* gene is involved in the events that subdivide the embryo into compartments. Specifically genetic analysis suggests that the engrailed gene product is required to specify cells as members of posterior compartments. In addition, the gene *invected* has been identified as showing considerable sequence homology with the *engrailed* gene, although no mutations are known that indicate its developmental role (Poole *et al.*, 1985).

Transcripts from En-1 and En-2 have been detected in PSA-1 teratocarcinoma stem cells which serve as a model system for several stages of mouse embryogenesis (Martin, 1980). Stage 1 refers to cells that resemble the inner cell mass of the mouse blastocyst, whereas stages 2 and 3 resemble tissues from 4.5 to 6.5 dpc and 9.5 to 11.5 dpc, respectively. Northern analysis of En-1 using mRNA from each of these stages shows that a 3.1-kb transcript can be detected that is specific to stages 2 and 3. A transcript of 2.0 kb of lower abundance is detected in all stages. Northern analysis of embryos from 9.5 to 17.5 dpc shows that a similar En-1 transcript of 3.1 kb is expressed throughout this time period with a peak of expression between 10.5 and 12.5 dpc (Joyner et al., 1985b).

Northern analysis of RNA from isolated tissues indicates that transcripts from both En-1 and En-2 are expressed abundantly in the posterior portion of the fetal brain and at significantly lower levels in other fetal tissues such as the anterior portion of the fetal brain and the spinal cord.

E. Homeo Box Gene Expression in Xenopus

Four homeo box genes have been characterized in Xenopus: XIH-1 (previously named AC-1: Carrasco et al., 1984), XIH-2 (previously named MM3: Müller et al., 1984), Xhox-1A and Xhox-1B (Harvey et al., 1986). XIH-1 produces three transcripts of 1.2, 1.6, and 2.3 kb, with the earliest transcripts initiating at late gastrulation (Carrasco et al., 1984). XIH-2 transcripts are abundantly expressed in oocytes, disappear during cleavage, and are detectable again after the midblastula transition, though at lower levels (Müller et al., 1984).

Harvey et al. (1986) have isolated and sequenced an almost full-length cDNA for Xhox-1A. The homeo box and flanking sequences suggest that Xhox-1B may be homologous to the mouse and human Hox 2.1. Northern analysis of Xhox-1A and Xhox-1B shows that each produces distinct 1.6-kb transcripts. The Xhox-1A transcript can be detected as early as the gastrula stage whereas the Xhox-1B transcript appears slightly later, in the neurula stage. In addition to the zygotic RNAs, Xhox-1A transcripts are detected at a low level in the ovary and unfertilized eggs.

Under the well-founded assumption that Xhox-1A and Xhox-1B may be expressed in neural tissue, Harvey et al. have examined the expression of these genes in exogastrulated embryos. These result from high-salt culture conditions that inhibit the invagination of the mesoderm and endoderm. In these conditions the neural induction of the ectoderm does not occur. In exogastrulated embryos Xhox-1A and Xhox-1B transcription is reduced but detectable, suggesting that expression of these genes is not dependent on neural induction.

V. The Homeo Box as a
DNA-Binding Domain

The amino acid sequence encoded by the homeo box, called the homeo domain, shows regions similar to well-defined DNA-binding domains of such proteins as the *E. coli lac* repressor, λ cI repressor, and yeast α_2 mating-type protein (Laughon and Scott, 1984; Shepherd *et al.*, 1984). The sequence similarity is between amino acids 31 and 50 of the homeo box and the helix 2–helix 3 region which confers DNA-binding specificity to the DNA-binding proteins. Single conservative changes within either helix of these prokaryotic binding proteins can be detrimental to function (see Pabo and Sauer, 1984, for review). Within all homeo domains the putative recognition helix (amino acids 42–50) is the most highly conserved region of the Hox proteins, while the proposed backbone-binding helix (amino acids 31–38) is more highly divergent.

The DNA-binding capability of homeo domain proteins has been directly demonstrated. Using a β-galactosidase fusion protein, the *Drosophila engrailed* homeo domain has been shown to bind specifically to DNA upstream of the *engrailed* and *ftz* genes (Desplan *et al.*, 1985). Similarly, we have demonstrated that the homeo domain of the mouse *Hox 1.5* protein binds specifically to DNA upstream of its respective homeo box (Fainsod *et al.*, 1987). Specific binding has been demonstrated by gel retardation assays and DNase I protection experiments (Bogarad and Ruddle, unpublished). These studies are consistent with a conserved DNA-binding function for homeo domains.

The binding of homeo domains to the 5′ region of their respective genes in both *Drosophila* and mouse implies that autoregulation of transcription may be a common regulatory strategy for homeo box genes. The binding of the *engrailed* homeo domain to the 5′ region of the *ftz* gene (Desplan *et al.*, 1985) implies a cross-regulatory function as well. The ability of homeo domain proteins to form possible homo- and heterodimers (Laughon *et al.*, 1985) adds another level of complexity to the system. The *in vivo* affinity of *Hox* proteins for their target could be determined by homeo domain–DNA interactions and protein–protein interactions. These interactions could affect affinity directly via heterodomain binding, or indirectly by affecting the conformation of the *Hox* binding domain. We suggest that *Hox* proteins can generate sufficient information to regulate differentially the expression of numerous target genes.

VI. Homeosis and Mammalian Development

Studies in *Drosophila* have shown that the fundamental unit of development is the compartment (Garcia-Bellido *et al.*, 1973; Crick and Lawrence, 1975; Garcia-Bellido and Ripoll, 1978). At an early stage of *Drosophila* development, the embryo is subdivided into a series of founder cells, each small group being termed a polyclone. Thus each compartment is derived from a group of cells, not from a single cell (i.e., it is not a clone). The decision to form a polyclone is based on cell position, not on cell ancestry. Compartments are made up of all the surviving descendants of a polyclone and reflect the segregation of embryonic cells into mosaic groups of defined fates. Each compartment undergoes a series of binary decisions subdividing it into smaller and smaller units (although Brower, 1985, has questioned the extent of this subdivision). It is thought that each compartment is a homologous structure for two reasons. First, the same topographical decisions (i.e., anterior/posterior, dorsal/ventral) occur in each compartment as it subdivides. Second, without the differential expression of homeotic genes, different compartments can give rise to the same or similar structures. Thus homeotic genes act within the realm of compartments.

The elucidation of the compartment as a unit of development uncovers an underlying rule of development, one that is not obvious based on morphology. For example, the eye might appear to be a unit of function but is not a developmental unit. At no time early in development is there a group of "eye cells," an eye primordium that will give rise to the eye only. Rather the eye is, in formal terms, part of the anterior compartment of the antennal segment of the head (Morata and Lawrence, 1978, 1979). The compartment is therefore a restriction of cells to a lineage that is defined by a particular pattern of development rather than a specific cell type.

The presence of genes containing homeo boxes in mammals suggests that homeotic mutations might be found. However, mammalian homeotic mutations if they exist at all are rare. This may be due to (1) technical reasons based on the practical differences of working with vertebrates rather than with invertebrates, or (2) basic differences in the embryological plan of invertebrates and vertebrates, that either preclude homeosis from occurring or result in embryonic lethality in vertebrates.

Our knowledge of *Drosophila* homeotic genes is the product of mutant screens designed specifically to elucidate the genetics of embryo development. Given the small size of a fruit fly, the short generation time and the ability to observe the embryo at all stages in its development, such studies are relatively practical. The full expression of the homeotic phenotype often results in embryonic lethality. However, using the techniques of mitotic recombination (Stern, 1936; Becker, 1957) the homeotic phenotype can be observed at all stages of development. None of these technical characteristics apply to studies in the mouse. Thus homeotic phenotypes may exist but may remain undetected because not enough mutants have been generated in the mouse. Additionally, homeotic phenotypes may have escaped detection owing to the technical difficulties of scoring embryonic lethals.

If homeotic genes perform the same function in mammals as they do in *Drosophila*, then one must consider whether mammals are compartmented. The existence of compartments in *Drosophila* is demonstrated by the use of techniques that allow the genetic marking of individual cells during development. The most versatile of these techniques is that of induced mitotic recombination, as it allows the marking of clones at any stage in development. This technique reveals the number of founder cells for a given primordium and provides information on the spatial patterns of growth. The *Minute* technique (Morata and Ripoll, 1975) is also useful, as it allows the investigator to determine whether observed restrictions of clonal growth are due to trivial reasons such as limited cell division or in fact reflect genuine restrictions of developmental capacity. The combination of these two techniques has identified compartments in *Drosophila* and has allowed the determination of their time of formation and the patterns of their successive binary decisions.

In the mouse, fate-mapping studies have shown that preimplantation development is characterized by decisions that superficially resemble the formation of compartments (Rossant, 1986). These studies (reviewed in Gardner, 1983; Rossant and Papaioannou, 1977) have shown that the initial decisions of the preimplantation embryo serve to segregate the morula into trophectoderm and inner cell mass lineages. Subsequently, the trophectoderm gives rise to mural and polar trophectoderm, while the inner cell mass gives rise to the primitive ectoderm and primitive endoderm. These decisions appear to be binary and are made by groups of cells at each stage based on cell–cell interactions. Thus within each lineage, cell fate is not invariant and cells can be added or removed without any deleterious effect.

The decisions that result in the segregation of the fetal tissue primordia occur during gastrulation in the mouse, after the embryo has implanted in the uterus. This presents formidable obstacles for cell-marking experiments. The embryo can be isolated at any time to mark specific cells but it cannot be sustained *in vitro* for very long (typically,

36–48 hours). While considerable work has been done on assessing the fate of cells in the gastrulating embryo (for review see Beddington, 1983, 1986; Snow, 1985), these analyses have not been precise enough to pinpoint the exact time and location of cell commitment to the different embryonic lineages. The extensive cell mixing that is presumed to occur up until tissue allocation also tends to complicate such analyses (West, 1978; Gardner, 1986). Thus the existence of compartments in mammalian embryos has been neither established nor disproven. Since compartments are the realm of homeotic gene action, their identification is necessary to predict the patterns of homeotic transformations.

Even if compartments did exist, there are properties of mouse development that reduce the chance of detecting a homeotic phenotype. For example, morphogenesis in the mouse relies heavily on inductive events. These inductions may lead developmental mutations to have large-scale, nonautonomous effects, resulting in a lethal phenotype that obscures homeotic transformations. In addition, if lethality occurred during early or midgestation there are relatively few morphological markers that allow the investigator to distinguish between serially homologous structures. For example, at 10 dpc it would be difficult to determine if a homeotic transformation had changed the identity of the sixth somite to that of the ninth somite.

If one assumes that segmentation is a superficial reflection of compartmentation in *Drosophila,* one may ask whether there are any clues in vertebrates to suggest that a similar process occurs. Somite development is one such example, as it involves the progressive condensation of paraxial mesoderm into paired blocks of cells. Are somites the equivalent of compartments? The sclerotome of each somite divides into an anterior and posterior region in the process of forming a vertebra, but there are no known mutations that affect this division. The vertebral column is divided into five regions: cervical, thoracic, lumbar, sacral, and caudal. The vertebrae within each region have a characteristic morphology. If each region was a compartment would a homeotic mutation affect all the vertebrae from each region? Most mutations that affect the skeleton seem to do so in a general way. Abnormalities such as fused vertebrae or fused or missing ribs usually occur throughout the length of the skeleton. Some mutations, however, predominantly affect certain regions. For example in the mouse, the sex-linked mutation, *bent-tail,* produces abnormalities in the caudal vertebrae (Grüneberg, 1955a), while the autosomal recessive mutation *tail kinks* causes abnormalities in the cervical, thoracic, and caudal regions but leaves the lumbosacral region unaffected (Grüneberg, 1955b). Certain mutations such as *rachiterata* (Theiler *et al.,* 1974; Varnum and Stevens,

1974) shift the boundary of the thoracic region by producing a rib articulating to the seventh cervical vertebra.

Limb development is another developmental process that bears a resemblance to compartmentation; it has been best studied in the chick. The limb bud develops by a series of binary decisions that initially determine limb quality (forelimb versus hindlimb), then the limb axes (Hamburger, 1938). In successive decisions the anterior–posterior axis is determined followed by the dorsal–ventral axis. As the limb bud grows in the proximodistal direction there is a condensation of mesenchyme into blastemata that are the primordia for muscle and bone. These blastemata might represent compartments. The condensation of the blastemata follows a spacing mechanism such that the number of skeletal elements is directly proportional to the amount of mesoderm present. The specification of the pattern of the limb along the anterior–posterior axis is influenced by regionally localized areas of morphogen which appear to influence cell division rate. Tissue transplantation experiments and mutants have suggested the presence of such morphogenetic factors. For example, in the *wingless* mutant (Zwilling, 1949, 1956, 1974) the wing buds initially form but then regress, presumably due to the lack of the morphogen termed the apical ectodermal maintenance factor (AEMF). This factor is presumed to be localized in the posterior half of the limb bud. Additional genetic evidence for the existence of this regionally localized morphogen is found in the mutant *duplicate* (Landauer, 1956; Zwilling and Hansborough, 1956). In *duplicate* it is assumed that the AEMF is redistributed in the anterior and posterior regions, so that a mirror-image duplication takes place.

The limb bud also undergoes a shaping process by the formation of posterior and anterior necrotic zones. The genetic basis for such processes is inferred from such mutants as *Ametapodia* (Cole, 1967) and *talpid* (Cole, 1942; Goetinck and Abbott, 1964; Hinchliffe and Ede, 1967; Hinchliffe and Thorogood, 1974). In the *talpid* series of mutants, the anterior necrotic zone and posterior necrotic zones are eliminated, leading to excess mesoderm and hence polydactyly. In the *Ametopodia* mutant the posterior necrotic zone is enlarged, leading to excess cell death and hence elimination of the metacarpal bones. The *Ametapodia* mutant also displays claws on the wing. Such a mutation is clearly atavistic as ancient birds such as Archeopteryx displayed wing claws but such structures have been lost in the evolution of modern birds (Fisher, 1940; Ostrom, 1974). The *Ametapodia* mutant could be classified as homeotic if it could be demonstrated that the claws resembled those normally found on the feet.

The similarity of limb development to the compartmentalization process in *Drosophila* has previously been suggested by Hinchliffe and Johnson (1980). There is an initial patterning of homogeneous cells into regularly spaced condensations, then each condensation acquires an individual identity determined by its position in a morphogenetic field. Perhaps further studies of cell lineage restriction will demonstrate that fore- and hindlimbs are homologous compartments or that each limb is composed of a series of compartments.

The mouse embryo clearly undergoes a segmentation process, although we have endeavored to show that this does not necessarily imply compartmentation. Leaving questions of embryonic lethality aside, the lack of obvious homeotic phenotypes suggests that perhaps the identity of homologous structures is not mediated by a common set of genes analogous to homeo box genes in *Drosophila*. Possibly the hindlimb and forelimb differentiate as such because entirely different combinations of genes "select" each developmental pathway. Given this situation, the mutation of one gene cannot lead to the transformation of one structure to another. The discovery of homeo boxes in genes not directly involved in segmental identity suggests that the homeo box may not necessarily act only within the realm of a compartment. We suggest that homeo box genes in vertebrates may play an active role in regulating hierarchical developmental interactions. Mutations in such systems do not necessarily lead to homeotic transformations but rather to a cessation or derangement of the entire developmental process.

VII. Summary

Considerable information has accumulated on mouse homeo box gene organization and expression. Homeo box genes are expressed in a wide variety of tissues, developmental stages, and cell lines. How can this be interpreted in view of the relationship of these genes to *Drosophila* morphogenetic loci? One view is that homeo box genes control determinative decisions by modulating transcription of as yet unidentified target genes. Proponents of this view are faced with two tasks: to identify developmental processes that are controlled by homeo box genes, and to identify the target genes that mediate this control. Such target genes might be identified on the basis of *in vitro* homeo domain–DNA interactions.

Candidate morphogenetic processes might be identified on the basis of the observed patterns of homeo box gene expression. It must be stressed that finding expression in a given tissue in no way demonstrates that the expression is necessary for the determination of that tissue. The role of *Drosophila* homeo box genes in determinative decisions is based upon analysis of mutants to demonstrate that the pattern of homeo box gene expression determines the morphogenetic outcome. To test whether the expression of a mouse homeo box gene is involved in a determinative decision, one must disrupt the normal pattern of expression of that gene and observe the resulting morphogenetic effect. In mouse this can be approached by looking for allelism with known morphogenetic loci, by isolating mutants in homeo box genes through large-scale mutagenesis screens, or by introducing altered homeo box genes into transgenic mice.

One of the most intriguing possibilities is that homeo box genes are involved in regional specification along the anteroposterior axis. *In situ* hybridization and Northern blot analysis have demonstrated that at least four different homeo box genes display distinct regional patterns of expression along the anteroposterior axis of the developing CNS. The expression of each of these genes has a unique anterior boundary from which expression extends posteriorly within the CNS. *Hox 1.5* expression has an anterior boundary within the hindbrain just posterior to the pontine flexure. The anterior boundary of *Hox 2.1* expression lies more posteriorly within the medulla of the hindbrain. Weak expression of *Hox 2.5* is detected in the spinal cord just posterior to the first cervical vertebra, and maximal expression is found posterior to the second cervical vertebra. *Hox 3.1* expression within the CNS system is restricted to cells posterior to the third cervical vertebra. These patterns of expression resemble the patterns of *Drosophila* homeotic gene expression within the CNS of the developing fly. It remains to be determined whether the similarities in patterns of expression reflect similar morphogenetic roles.

ACKNOWLEDGMENT

We would like to acknowledge the participation of Dr. William McGinnis in the work cited from this laboratory. His continuing advice and encouragement is also greatly appreciated. A.A.F. is the recipient of a Markey Foundation Fellowship. M.F.U. is supported by a Life and Health Insurance Medical Research Fund Scholarship. L.D.B., C.P.H., and A.F.-S. are supported by N.I.H. predoctoral training grants. A.F. is a National Cancer Cytology Center Post-Doctoral Fellow. M.R. was an N.I.H. postdoctoral trainee. We thank Vincent Salerno for excellent technical assistance and Suzy Pafka for photographic assistance. This work was supported by N.I.H. grant GM09966 to F.H.R.

REFERENCES

Awgulewitsch, A., Utset, M. F., Hart, C. P., McGinnis, W., and Ruddle, F. H. (1986). *Nature (London)* **320,** 328–335.

Bateson, W. (1894). "Materials for the Study of Variation." Macmillan, London.

Becker, H. J. (1957). *Vererbungsl.* **88,** 333–373.

Beddington, R. S. P. (1983). *In* "Development in Mammals" (M. H. Johnson, ed.), Vol. 5, pp. 1–32. Elsevier, Amsterdam.

Beddington, R. S. P. (1986). *In* "Experimental Approaches to Mammalian Embryonic Development" (J. Rossant and R. A. Pedersen, eds.). Cambridge Univ. Press, London and New York.

Bennett, D. (1980). *Harvey Lect.* **74**, 1–21.
Boncinelli, E., Simeone, A., La Volpe, A., Faiella, A., Fidanza, V., Acampora, D., and Scotto, L. (1985). *Cold Spring Harbor Symp. Quant. Biol.* **50**, 301–306.
Breier, G., Bucan, M., Francke, U., Colberg-Poley, A. M., and Gruss, P. (1986). *EMBO J.* **5**, 2209–2217.
Brower, D. L. (1985). *Cell* **41**, 361–364.
Bucan, M., Yang-Feng, T., Colberg-Poley, A. M., Wolgemuth, D. J., Guenet, J.-L., Francke, U., and Lehrach, H. (1986). *EMBO J.* **5**, 2899–2905.
Carrasco, A. E., McGinnis, W., Gehring, W. J., and De Robertis, E. M. (1984). *Cell* **37**, 409–414.
Colberg-Poley, A. M., Voss, S. D., Chowdhury, K., and Gruss, P. (1985a). *Nature (London)* **314**, 713–718.
Colberg-Poley, A. M., Voss, S. D., Chowdhury, K., Stewart, C. L., Wagner, E. F., and Gruss, P. (1985b). *Cell* **45**, 39–45.
Colberg-Poley, A. M., Voss, S. D., and Gruss, P. (1985c). *Cold Spring Harbor Symp. Quant Biol.* **50**, 285–290.
Cole, R. K. (1942). *J. Hered.* **33**, 82–86.
Cole, R. K. (1967). *J. Hered.* **58**, 141–146.
Crick, F. H. C., and Lawrence, P. A. (1975). *Science* **189**, 340–347.
Desplan, C., Theis, J., and O'Farrell, P. H. (1985). *Nature (London)* **318**, 630–635.
Doyle, H. J., Harding, K., Hoey, T., and Levine, M. (1986). *Nature (London)* **323**, 76–79.
Duboule, D., Baron, A., Mahl, P., and Galliot, B. (1986). *EMBO J.* **5**, 1973–1980.
Fainsod, A., Awgulewitsch, A., and Ruddle, F. H. (1987a). *Dev. Biol.,* in press.
Fainsod, A., Bogarad, L., Ruusala, T., Crothers, D. M., and Ruddle, F. H. (1987b). *Proc. Natl. Acad. Sci. U.S.A.* **83**, 9532–9536.
Fisher, H. I. (1940). *Am. Midland Nat.* **23**, 234–243.
Fjose, A., McGinnis, W. J., and Gehring, W. J. (1985). *Nature (London)* **313**, 284–289.
Frigerio, G., Burri, M., Bopp, D., Baumgartner, S., and Noll, M. (1986). *Cell* **47**, 735–746.
Garcia-Bellido, A., and Ripoll, P. (1978). *In* "Genetic Mosaics and Cell Differentiation" (W. J. Gehring, ed.), pp. 119–156. Springer-Verlag, Berlin and New York.
Garcia-Bellido, A., Ripoll, P., and Morata, G. (1973). *Nature (London) New Biol.* **245**, 251–253.
Gardner, R. L. (1983). *Int. Rev. Exp. Pathol.* **24**, 63–133.
Gardner, R. L. (1986). *J. Cell Sci. Suppl.* **4**, 337–356.
Gluecksohn-Waelsch, S. (1979). *Cell* **16**, 225–237.
Goetinck, P. F., and Abbott, U. K. (1964). *J. Exp. Zool.* **155**, 161–170.
Grüneberg, H. (1955a). *J. Genet.* **53**, 551–562.
Grüneberg, H. (1955b). *J. Genet.* **53**, 536–550.
Hafen, E., Levine, M., and Gehring, W. J. (1984). *Nature (London)* **307**, 287–289.
Hamburger, V. (1938). *J. Exp. Zool.* **77**, 379–400.
Harding, K., Wedeen, C., McGinnis, W., and Levine, M. (1985). *Science* **229**, 1236–1242.
Harding, K., Rushlow, C., Doyle, H. J., Hoey, T., and Levine, M. (1986). *Science* **233**, 953–959.
Hart, C. P., Awgulewitsch, A., Fainsod, A., McGinnis, W., and Ruddle, F. H. (1985). *Cell* **43**, 9–18.
Hart, C. P., Dalton, D. K., Nichols, L., Hunihan, L., Roderick, T. H., Langley, S. H., Taylor, B. A., and Ruddle, F. H. (1987a). *Genetics,* in press.
Hart, C. P., Fainsod, A., and Ruddle, F. H. (1987b). *Genomics,* in press.
Harvey, R. P., Tabin, C. J., and Melton, D. A. (1986). *EMBO J.* **5**, 1237–1244.
Hauser, C. C., Joyner, A., Klein, R. D., Learned, T., Martin, G., and Tjian, R. (1985). *Cell* **43**, 19–28.

Hinchliffe, J. R., and Ede, D. A. (1967). *J. Embryol. Exp. Morphol.* **17**, 385–404.

Hinchliffe, J. R., and Johnson, D. R. (1980). "The Development of the Vertebrate Limb." Clarendon, Oxford.

Hinchliffe, J. R., and Thorogood, P. V. (1974). *J. Embryol. Exp. Morphol.* **31**, 747–760.

Hoey, T., Doyle, H. J., Harding, K., Wedeen, C., and Levine, M. (1986). *Proc. Natl. Acad. Sci. U.S.A.* **83**, 4809–4813.

Jackson, I. J., Schofield, P., and Hogan, B. (1985). *Nature (London)* **317**, 745–748.

Joyner, A. L., and Martin, G. R. (1987). *Genes Dev.* **1**, 29–38.

Joyner, A. L., Lebo, R. V., Kan, Y. W., Tjian, R., Cox, D. R., and Martin, G. R. (1985a). *Nature (London)* **314**, 173–175.

Joyner, A. L., Kornberg, T., Coleman, K. G., Cox, D. R., and Martin, G. R. (1985b). *Cell* **43**, 29–37.

Kaufman, J. F., Auffray, C., Korman, A. J., Shackelford, D. A., and Strominger, J. (1984). *Cell* **36**, 1–13.

Kaufman, T. C. (1983). In "Time, Space and Pattern in Embryonic Development" (W. R. Jeffry and R. R. Raff, eds.), pp. 365–383. Liss, New York.

Kaufman, T. C., Lewis, R., and Wakimoto, B. (1980). *Genetics* **94**, 115–133.

Landauer, W. (1956). *J. Genet.* **54**, 199–218.

Laughon, A., and Scott, M. P. (1984). *Nature (London)* **310**, 25–31.

Laughon, A., Carroll, S. B., Storfer, F. A., Riley, P. D., and Scott, M. P. (1985). *Cold Spring Harbor Symp. Quant Biol.* **50**, 253–262.

Levine, M., Rubin, G. M., and Tjian, R. (1984). *Cell* **38**, 667–673.

Lewin, R. (1984). *Science* **224**, 1327–1329.

Lewis, E. B. (1978). *Nature (London)* **276**, 565–570.

Lyon, M. F. (1981). *Symp. Zool. Soc. London* **47**, 455–477.

McGinnis, W., Levine, M., Hafen, E., Kuroiwa, A., and Gehring, W. J. (1984a). *Nature (London)* **308**, 428–433.

McGinnis, W., Garber, R. L., Witz, J., Kuroiwa, A., and Gehring, W. J. (1984b). *Cell* **37**, 408–412.

McGinnis, W., Hart, C. P., Gehring, W. J., and Ruddle, F. H. (1984c). *Cell* **38**, 675–680.

Macdonald, P. M., Ingham, P., and Struhl, G. (1986). *Cell* **47**, 721–734.

Martin, G. R. (1980). *Science* **209**, 768–776.

Martin, G. R., Boncinelli, E., Duboule, D., Gruss, P., Jackson, I., Krumlauf, R., Lonai, P., McGinnis, W., Ruddle, F., and Wolgemuth, D. (1987). *Nature (London)* **325**, 21–22.

Mayer, T. C., and Fishbane, J. L. (1972). *Genetics* **71**, 297–303.

Mlodzik, M., Fjose, A., and Gehring, W. J. (1985). *EMBO J.* **4**, 2961–2969.

Morata, G., and Lawrence, P. A. (1978). *Nature (London)* **274**, 473–474.

Morata, G., and Lawrence, P. A. (1979). *Dev. Biol.* **70**, 355–371.

Müller, M. M., Carrasco, A. E., and DeRobertis, E. M. (1984). *Cell* **39**, 157–162.

Münke, M., Cox, D. R., Jackson, I. J., Hogan, B. L. M., and Francke, U. (1986). *Cytogenet. Cell Genet.* **42**, 236–246.

Ostrom, J. H. (1974). *Q. Rev. Biol.* **49**, 27–47.

Pabo, C. O., and Sauer, R. T. (1984). *Annu. Rev. Biochem.* **53**, 293–321.

Papaioannou, V. E., and Gardner, R. L. (1979). *J. Embryol. Exp. Morphol.* **52**, 153–163.

Papaioannou, V. E., and Mardon, H. (1983). *Dev. Genet.* **4**, 21–29.

Poole, S. J., Kauvar, L. M., Drees, B., and Kornberg, T. (1985). *Cell* **40**, 37–43.

Poole, T. W. (1980). *Dev. Biol.* **80**, 495–500.

Rabin, M., Hart, C. P., Ferguson-Smith, A., McGinnis, W., Levine, M., and Ruddle, F. H. (1985). *Nature (London)* **314**, 175–178.

Rabin, M., Ferguson-Smith, A., Hart, C. P., and Ruddle, F. H. (1986). *Proc. Natl. Acad. Sci. U.S.A.* **83**, 9104–9108.

Regulski, M., Harding, K., Kostriken, R., Karch., F., Levine, M., and McGinnis, W. (1985). *Cell* **43**, 71–80.

Rinchik, E. M., Russell, L. B., Copeland, N. G., and Jenkins, N. A. (1985). *Trends Genet.* **1**, 170–176.

Rossant, J. (1986). *In* "Experimental Approaches to Mammalian Embryonic Development" (J. Rossant and R. A. Pedersen, eds.). Cambridge Univ. Press, London and New York.

Rossant, J., and Papaioannou, V. E. (1977). *In* "Concepts in Mammalian Embryogenesis" (M. I. Sherman, ed.), pp. 1–36. MIT Press, Cambridge, Massachusetts.

Rubin, M. R., Toth, L. E., Patel, M. D., D'Eustachio, P. D., and Nguyen-Huu, M. C. (1986). *Science* **233**, 663–667.

Ruddle, F. H., Hart, C. P., Awgulewitsch, A., Fainsod, A., Utset, M., Dalton, D., Kerk, N., Rabin, M., Ferguson-Smith, A., Fienberg, A., and McGinnis, W. (1985). *Cold Spring Harbor Symp. Quant. Biol.* **50**, 277–284.

Ruddle, F. H., Hart, C. P., Rabin, M., Ferguson-Smith, A., and Pravtcheva, D. (1986). *Hum. Genet. Proc. 7th Int. Congr. Berlin,* in press.

Sanchez-Herrero, E., Vernos, I., Marco, R., and Morata, G. (1985). *Nature (London)* **313**, 108–113.

Schultz, J. (1935). *Drosophila Inform. Serv.* **4**, 6.

Scott, M. P., and Weiner, A. J. (1984). *Proc. Natl. Acad. Sci. U.S.A.* **78**, 1095–1099.

Shepherd, J. C. W., McGinnis, W., Carrasco, A. E., De Robertis, E. M., and Gehring, W. J. (1984). *Nature (London)* **310**, 70–72.

Silver, L. M., Garrels, J. I., and Lehrach, H. (1984). *In* "Genetic Engineering—Principles and Methods," Vol. 6, pp. 141–156. Plenum, New York.

Simeone, A., Mavilio, F., Bottero, L., Giampaolo, A., Russo, G., Faiella, A., Boncinelli, E., and Peschle, C. (1986). *Nature (London)* **320**, 763–765.

Snow, M. H. L. (1985). *In* "Molecular Determinants of Animal Form" (G. M. Edelman, ed.), pp. 75–98. Liss, New York.

Stern, C. (1935). *Drosophila Inform. Serv.* **3**, 29.

Stern, C. (1936). *Genetics* **21**, 625–730.

Struhl, G. (1982). *Proc. Natl. Acad. Sci. U.S.A.* **79**, 7380–7384.

Struhl, G., and White, R. A. H. (1985). *Cell* **43**, 507–519.

Sturtevant, A. H. (1929). *Z. Wiss. Zool.* **135**, 323–356.

Theiler, K., Varnum, D., and Stevens, L. C. (1974). *Z. Anat. Entwicklungsgesch.* **145**, 75–80.

Utset, M. F., Awgulewitsch, A., Ruddle, F. H., and McGinnis, W. (1987). *Science* **235**, 1379–1382.

Varnum, D. S., and Stevens, L. C. (1974). *J. Hered.* **65**, 91–93.

Wakimoto, B. T., and Kaufman, T. C. (1981). *Dev. Biol.* **81**, 51–64.

Wakimoto, B. T., Turner, F. R., and Kaufman, T. C. (1984). *Dev. Biol.* **102**, 147–172.

Wedeen, C., Harding, K., and Levine, M. (1986). *Cell* **44**, 739–748.

West, J. D. (1978). *In* "Development in Mammals" (M. H. Johnson, ed.), Vol. 3, pp. 413–460. Elsevier, Amsterdam.

Wolgemuth, D. J., Engelmyer, E., Duggal, R. N., Gizang-Ginsberg, E., Mutter, G. L., Ponzetto, C., Viviano, C., and Zakeri, Z. F. (1986). *EMBO J.* **5**, 1229–1235.

Zwilling, E. (1949). *J. Exp. Zool.* **111**, 175–187.

Zwilling, E. (1956). *Cold Spring Harbor Symp. Quant. Biol.* **21**, 349–354.

Zwilling, E. (1974). *Dev. Biol.* **39**, 37–48.

Zwilling, E., and Hansborough, L. A. (1956). *J. Exp. Zool.* **132**, 219–239.

INDEX

257